Glory Be to the Father

GLORIA PATRI

H. W. Greatorex

Glo-ry be to the Fa-ther, and to the Son, and to the Ho-ly Ghost; As it

was in the beginning, is now, and ever shall be, world without end. A-men, A-men.

(Second Tune)

GLORIA PATRI

Charles Meineke

Glo-ry be to the Fa-ther, and to the Son, and to the Ho-ly Ghost; As it

was in the be-gin-ning, is now, and ever shall be, world without end. A-men, A-men.

All Things Come of Thee

OFFERINGS

Arranged from Beethoven

All things come of Thee, O Lord, and of Thine own have we giv-en Thee. A-MEN.

Favorite Hymns

of

Praise

1991

Printed in U.S.A.

ISBN: 0-916642-02-X

TABERNACLE PUBLISHING COMPANY
Wheaton, Illinois 60187

I will sing unto the Lord
As long as I live:
I will sing praise to my God
While I have my being.

—*Psalm 104:33*

Favorite Hymns of Praise

When Morning Gilds the Skies

FROM THE GERMAN
TR. BY EDWARD CASWALL

JOSEPH BARNBY

1. When morn-ing gilds the skies, My heart a-wak-ing cries:
2. When sleep her balm de-nies, My si-lent spir-it sighs:
3. Does sad-ness fill my mind, A sol-ace here I find:
4. In heav'n's e-ter-nal bliss The love-liest strain is this:
5. Be this, while life is mine, My can-ti-cle di-vine,

May Je-sus Christ be praised; A-like at work and prayer . .
May Je-sus Christ be praised; When e-vil thoughts mo-lest, . . .
May Je-sus Christ be praised; Or fades my earth-ly bliss, . .
May Je-sus Christ be praised; The pow'rs of dark-ness fear, . . .
May Je-sus Christ be praised; Be this th' e-ter-nal song, . .

To Je-sus I re-pair: . . May Je-sus Christ be praised.
With this I shield my breast: . May Je-sus Christ be praised.
My com-fort still is this: . . May Je-sus Christ be praised.
When this sweet chant they hear: . May Je-sus Christ be praised.
Thro' all the a-ges on: . . . May Je-sus Christ be praised.

2   Holy, Holy, Holy

REGINALD HEBER   JOHN B. DYKES

1. Ho-ly, Ho-ly, Ho-ly, Lord God Al-might-y! Ear-ly in the
2. Ho-ly, Ho-ly, Ho-ly! All the saints a-dore Thee, Cast-ing down their
3. Ho-ly, Ho-ly, Ho-ly! Tho' the dark-ness hide Thee, Tho' the eye of
4. Ho-ly, Ho-ly, Ho-ly! Lord God Al-might-y! All Thy works shall

morn - ing our song shall rise to Thee; Ho - ly, Ho - ly, Ho - ly!
gold-en crowns a-round the glass-y sea; Cher-u-bim and ser-a-phim
sin - ful man Thy glo - ry may not see, On-ly Thou art ho - ly;
praise Thy name, in earth, and sky, and sea; Ho - ly, Ho - ly, Ho - ly!

Mer-ci-ful and Might-y! God in Three Per-sons, bless-ed Trin-i - ty!
fall-ing down be-fore Thee, Which wert, and art, and ev - er-more shalt be.
there is none be-side Thee Per-fect in pow'r, in love, and pu - ri - ty.
Mer-ci-ful and Might-y! God in Three Per-sons, bless-ed Trin-i - ty!

3   Breathe on Me, Breath of God

EDWIN HATCH   ROBERT JACKSON

1. Breathe on me, Breath of God, Fill me with life a-new, That I may
2. Breathe on me, Breath of God, Un-til my heart is pure, Un-til with
3. Breathe on me, Breath of God, Till I am whol-ly Thine, Un-til this
4. Breathe on me, Breath of God, So shall I nev-er die, But live with

Breathe on Me, Breath of God

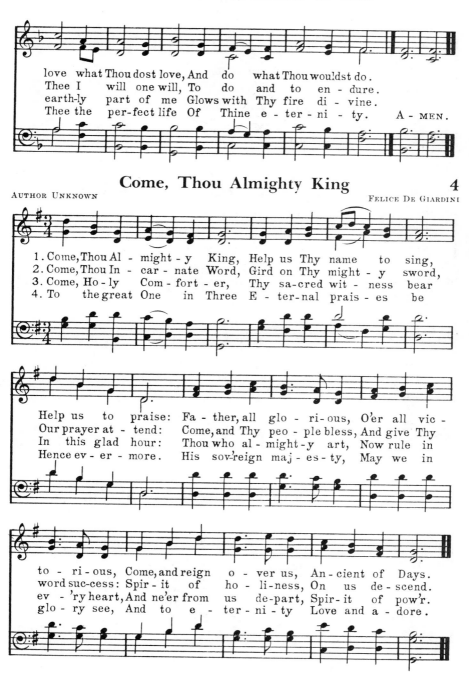

love what Thou dost love, And do what Thou wouldst do.
Thee I will one will, To do and to en - dure.
earth-ly part of me Glows with Thy fire di - vine.
Thee the per-fect life Of Thine e - ter - ni - ty. A - MEN.

Come, Thou Almighty King   4

AUTHOR UNKNOWN

FELICE DE GIARDINI

1. Come, Thou Al - might-y King, Help us Thy name to sing,
2. Come, Thou In - car - nate Word, Gird on Thy might - y sword,
3. Come, Ho - ly Com - fort - er, Thy sa-cred wit - ness bear
4. To the great One in Three E - ter-nal prais - es be

Help us to praise: Fa - ther, all glo - ri-ous, O'er all vic -
Our prayer at - tend: Come, and Thy peo - ple bless, And give Thy
In this glad hour: Thou who al - might-y art, Now rule in
Hence ev - er - more. His sov-reign maj - es - ty, May we in

to - ri-ous, Come, and reign o - ver us, An - cient of Days.
word suc-cess: Spir - it of ho - li-ness, On us de - scend.
ev - 'ry heart, And ne'er from us de-part, Spir - it of pow'r.
glo - ry see, And to e - ter-ni - ty Love and a - dore.

5 Fairest Lord Jesus

FROM THE GERMAN, 17TH CENTURY
4TH VERSE TR. JOSEPH A. SEISS

SILESIAN FOLK SONG
ARR. BY RICHARD S. WILLIS

1. Fair - est Lord Je - sus! Ru - ler of all na - ture!
2. Fair are the mead - ows, Fair - er still the wood - lands,
3. Fair is the sun - shine, Fair - er still the moon - light,
4. Beau - ti - ful Sav - ior! Lord of all the na - tions!

O Thou of God and man the Son! Thee will I cher - ish,
Robed in the bloom - ing garb of spring; Je - sus is fair - er,
And all the twin - kling star - ry host; Je - sus shines bright - er,
Son of God and Son of Man! Glo - ry and hon - or.

Thee will I hon - or, Thou, my soul's glo-ry, joy, and crown!
Je - sus is pur - er, Who makes the woe-ful heart to sing!
Je - sus shines pur - er, Than all the an-gels heav'n can boast!
Praise, a - dor - a - tion, Now and for - ev - er - more be Thine! A-MEN.

6 O, for a Faith That Will Not Shrink

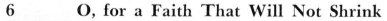

WILLIAM H. BATHURST

JOHN B. DYKES

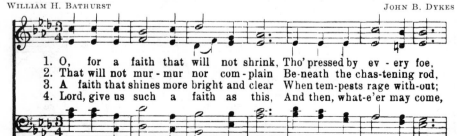

1. O, for a faith that will not shrink, Tho' pressed by ev - ery foe,
2. That will not mur - mur nor com - plain Be - neath the chas-tening rod,
3. A faith that shines more bright and clear When tem-pests rage with-out;
4. Lord, give us such a faith as this, And then, what-e'er may come,

O, for a Faith That Will Not Shrink

That will not trem-ble on the brink Of an-y earth-ly woe!—
But, in the hour of grief or pain, Will lean up-on its God;—
That when in dan-ger knows no fear, In dark-ness feels no doubt.—
We'll taste, e'en here, the hal-lowed bliss Of an e-ter-nal home.

Rejoice, Ye Pure in Heart

EDWARD H. PLUMPTRE

ARTHUR M. MESSITER

1. Re - joice, ye pure in heart, Re - joice, give thanks, and sing:
2. With all the an - gel choirs, With all the saints on earth,
3. Still lift your stand - ard high, Still march in firm ar - ray;
4. Yes, on through life's long path, Still chant - ing as ye go;
5. Then on, ye pure in heart, Re - joice, give thanks, and sing;

Your fes - tal ban - ner wave on high, The cross of Christ your King.
Pour out the strains of joy and bliss, True rap - ture, no - blest mirth!
As war - riors through the dark - ness toil Till dawns the gold - en day.
From youth to age, by night and day, In glad - ness and in woe.
Your fes - tal ban - ner wave on high, The cross of Christ your King.

REFRAIN

Re - joice, re - joice, Re - joice, give thanks, and sing! A-MEN.
Re - joice, re - joice,

All Hail the Power of Jesus' Name
(CORONATION)

EDWARD PERRONET
ALT. BY JOHN RIPPON

OLIVER HOLDEN

1. All hail the pow'r of Je - sus' name! Let an - gels pros - trate fall;
2. Ye cho - sen seed of Is - rael's race, Ye ran - somed from the fall,
3. Let ev - 'ry kin - dred, ev - 'ry tribe On this ter - res - trial ball,
4. O that with yon - der sa - cred throng We at His feet may fall!

Bring forth the roy - al di - a - dem, And crown Him Lord of all,
Hail Him who saves you by His grace, And crown Him Lord of all,
To Him all maj - es - ty as - cribe, And crown Him Lord of all,
We'll join the ev - er - last - ing song, And crown Him Lord of all,

Bring forth the roy - al di - a - dem, And crown Him Lord of all!
Hail Him who saves you by His grace, And crown Him Lord of all!
To Him all maj - es - ty as - cribe, And crown Him Lord of all!
We'll join the ev - er - last - ing song, And crown Him Lord of all!

All Hail the Power of Jesus' Name
(MILES LANE)

EDWARD PERRONET

WILLIAM SHRUBSOLE

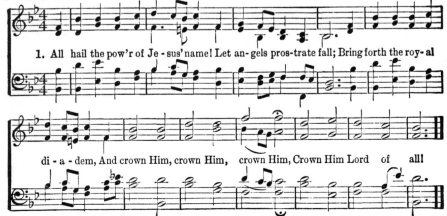

1. All hail the pow'r of Je - sus' name! Let an - gels pros - trate fall; Bring forth the roy - al

di - a - dem, And crown Him, crown Him, crown Him, Crown Him Lord of all!

All Hail the Power of Jesus' Name

(DIADEM)

Edward Perronet
Alt. by John Rippon

James Ellor

1. All hail the pow'r of Je - sus' name! Let an - gels pros-trate fall,
2. Ye cho - sen seed of Is - rael's race, Ye ran-somed from the fall,
3. Let ev - 'ry kin - dred, ev - 'ry tribe, On this ter - res - trial ball,
4. O that with yon - der sa - cred throng We at His feet may fall,

Let an - gels pros-trate fall; Bring forth the roy - al di - a - dem,
Ye ran-somed from the fall, Hail Him who saves you by His grace,
On this ter - res-trial ball, To Him all maj - es - ty as - cribe,
We at His feet may fall! We'll join the ev - er - last - ing song,

And crown . . . . Him, Crown Him,

And crown Him, crown Him, crown Him, crown Him, And crown Him Lord of
And crown . . . . Him, Crown Him,

And crown Him, crown Him, crown Him, Crown . . . .

crown Him, crown Him;

all, crown Him; And crown Him Lord of all!
crown . . . . . . Him;

Him; And crown Him Lord of all!

11 Still, Still with Thee

HARRIET BEECHER STOWE

FELIX MENDELSSOHN-BARTHOLDY

1. Still, still with Thee, when pur-ple morn-ing break-eth, When the bird
2. A - lone with Thee, a - mid the mys-tic shad-ows, The sol-emn
3. When sinks the soul, sub-dued by toil, to slum-ber, Its clos-ing
4. So shall it be at last, in that bright morn-ing When the soul

wak-eth, and the shad-ows flee; Fair-er than morn-ing, love-lier than the
hush of na-ture new-ly born; A - lone with Thee in breath-less ad - o-
eyes look up to Thee in prayer; Sweet the re - pose be-neath Thy wings o'er-
wak-eth, and life's shad-ows flee; Oh, in that hour, fair-er than day-light

day-light, Dawns the sweet con-scious-ness, I am with Thee.
ra - tion, In the calm dew and fresh-ness of the morn.
shad-ing, But sweet-er still to wake and find Thee there.
dawning, Shall rise the glo-rious thought—I am with Thee. A-MEN.

12 All People That on Earth Do Dwell

FROM PSALM 100
ASC. TO WILLIAM KETHE

"GENEVAN PSALTER"
LOUIS BOURGEOIS

1. All peo - ple that on earth do dwell, Sing to the Lord with cheerful voice; Him
2. The Lord, ye know, is God in-deed; With-out our aid He did us make; We
3. O en-ter then His gates with praise, Ap-proach with joy His courts un-to: Praise
4. For why? the Lord our God is good, His mer - cy is for - ev - er sure; His

All People That on Earth Do Dwell

serve with fear, His praise forth tell; Come ye be - fore Him and re-joice.
are His flock, He doth us feed, And for His sheep He doth us take.
laud and bless His name al-ways, For it is seem-ly so to do.
truth at all times firm - ly stood, And shall from age to age en-dure. A-MEN.

O Worship the King

13

FROM PSALM 104
ROBERT GRANT

ADAPTED FROM J. MICHAEL HAYDN

1. O wor-ship the King, all - glo-rious a - bove, And grate-ful - ly
2. O tell of His might, and sing of His grace, Whose robe is the
3. Thy boun-ti - ful care what tongue can re - cite? It breathes in the
4. Frail chil-dren of dust, and fee - ble as frail, In Thee do we

sing His won-der-ful love; Our Shield and De-fend - er, the An-cient of
light, whose can-o - py space; His char - iots of wrath the deep thunder-clouds
air, it shines in the light, It streams from the hills, it de-scends to the
trust, nor find Thee to fail; Thy mer - cies how ten - der! how firm to the

days, Pa - vil-ioned in splen-dor, and gird - ed with praise.
form, And dark is His path on the wings of the storm.
plain, And sweet-ly dis - tills in the dew and the rain.
end! Our Mak - er, De - fend-er, Re - deem-er, and Friend. A - MEN.

14 Praise Ye the Lord, the Almighty

Joachim Neander
Tr. by Catherine Winkworth

"Stralsund Gesangbuch"
Arr. in "Praxis Pietatas Melica"

1. Praise ye the Lord, the Al-might-y, the King of cre-a-
2. Praise ye the Lord, who o'er all things so won-drous-ly reign-
3. Praise ye the Lord, who with mar-vel-ous wis-dom hath made
4. Praise ye the Lord! O let all that is in me a-dore

tion! O my soul, praise Him, for He is thy health and sal-
eth, Shel-ters thee un-der His wings, yea, so gen-tly sus-
thee! Decked thee with health, and with lov-ing hand guid-ed and
Him! All that hath life and breath, come now with prais-es be-

va-tion! All ye who hear, Now to His tem-ple draw
tain-eth! Hast thou not seen How thy de-sires e'er have
stayed thee; How oft in grief Hath not He brought thee re-
fore Him! Let the A-men Sound from His peo-ple a-

near; Join me in glad ad-o-ra-tion!
been Grant-ed in what He or-dain-eth?
lief, Spread-ing His wings for to shade thee!
gain: Glad-ly for aye we a-dore Him. A-men.

O Thou God of My Salvation

THOMAS OLIVERS

DANIEL B. TOWNER

15

1. O Thou God of my sal-va-tion, My Re-deem-er from all sin;
2. Though un-seen, I love the Sav-ior, He hath brought sal-va-tion near;
3. While the an-gel choirs are cry-ing, "Glo-ry to the great I Am,"
4. An-gels now are hov-'ring round us, Un-per-ceived a-mong the throng;

Moved by Thy di-vine com-pas-sion, Who hast died my heart to win;
Man-i-fests His pard-'ning fa-vor; And when Je-sus doth ap-pear,
I with them will still be vy-ing—Glo-ry, glo-ry to the Lamb!
Won-d'ring at the love that crowned us, Glad to sing the ho-ly song;

I will praise Thee, I will praise Thee, Where shall I Thy praise be-gin?
Soul and bod-y, soul and bod-y, Shall His glo-rious im-age bear;
Oh, how pre-cious, oh, how pre-cious Is the sound of Je-sus' name!
Hal-le-lu-jah, hal-le-lu-jah, Love and praise to Christ be-long!

I will praise Thee, I will praise Thee, Where shall I Thy praise be-gin?
Soul and bod-y, soul and bod-y, Shall His glo-rious im-age bear.
Oh, how pre-cious, oh, how pre-cious Is the sound of Je-sus' name!
Hal-le-lu-jah, hal-le-lu-jah, Love and praise to Christ be-long! A-MEN.

Blessed Be the Name

16

W. H. CLARK
REFRAIN, RALPH E. HUDSON

RALPH E. HUDSON
ARR. BY WILLIAM J. KIRKPATRICK

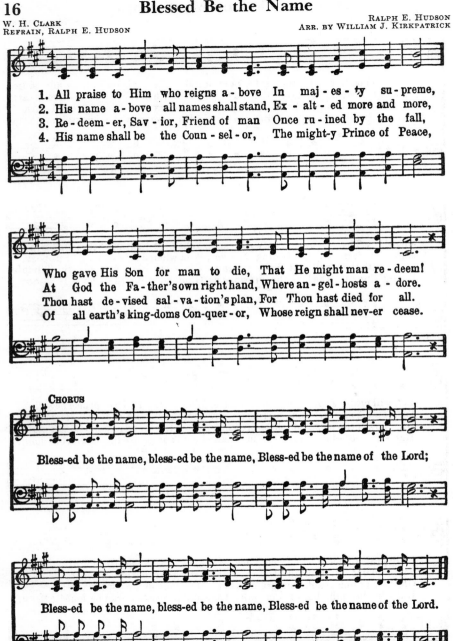

1. All praise to Him who reigns a-bove In maj-es-ty su-preme,
2. His name a-bove all names shall stand, Ex-alt-ed more and more,
3. Re-deem-er, Sav-ior, Friend of man Once ru-ined by the fall,
4. His name shall be the Coun-sel-or, The might-y Prince of Peace,

Who gave His Son for man to die, That He might man re-deem!
At God the Fa-ther's own right hand, Where an-gel-hosts a-dore.
Thou hast de-vised sal-va-tion's plan, For Thou hast died for all.
Of all earth's king-doms Con-quer-or, Whose reign shall nev-er cease.

CHORUS

Bless-ed be the name, bless-ed be the name, Bless-ed be the name of the Lord;

Bless-ed be the name, bless-ed be the name, Bless-ed be the name of the Lord.

Come, Thou Fount

Robert Robinson

John Wyeth

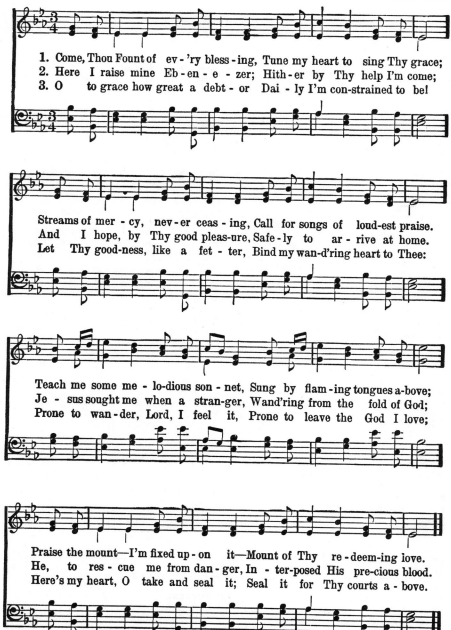

1. Come, Thou Fount of ev - 'ry bless - ing, Tune my heart to sing Thy grace;
2. Here I raise mine Eb - en - e - zer; Hith - er by Thy help I'm come;
3. O to grace how great a debt - or Dai - ly I'm con-strained to be!

Streams of mer - cy, nev - er ceas - ing, Call for songs of loud-est praise.
And I hope, by Thy good pleas-ure, Safe - ly to ar - rive at home.
Let Thy good-ness, like a fet - ter, Bind my wan-d'ring heart to Thee:

Teach me some me - lo-dious son - net, Sung by flam-ing tongues a-bove;
Je - sus sought me when a stran-ger, Wand'ring from the fold of God;
Prone to wan - der, Lord, I feel it, Prone to leave the God I love;

Praise the mount—I'm fixed up - on it—Mount of Thy re - deem-ing love.
He, to res - cue me from dan - ger, In - ter-posed His pre-cious blood.
Here's my heart, O take and seal it; Seal it for Thy courts a - bove.

18   O to Be Like Thee!

THOMAS O. CHISHOLM

WILLIAM J. KIRKPATRICK

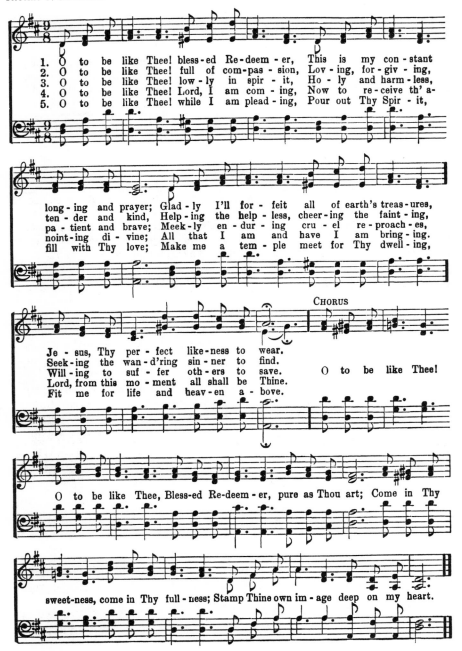

1. O to be like Thee! bless-ed Re-deem-er, This is my con-stant long-ing and prayer; Glad-ly I'll for-feit all of earth's treas-ures, Je-sus, Thy per-fect like-ness to wear.
2. O to be like Thee! full of com-pas-sion, Lov-ing, for-giv-ing, ten-der and kind, Help-ing the help-less, cheer-ing the faint-ing, Seek-ing the wan-d'ring sin-ner to find.
3. O to be like Thee! low-ly in spir-it, Ho-ly and harm-less, pa-tient and brave; Meek-ly en-dur-ing cru-el re-proach-es, Will-ing to suf-fer oth-ers to save.
4. O to be like Thee! Lord, I am com-ing, Now to re-ceive th'a-noint-ing di-vine; All that I am and have I am bring-ing. Lord, from this mo-ment all shall be Thine.
5. O to be like Thee! while I am plead-ing, Pour out Thy Spir-it, fill with Thy love; Make me a tem-ple meet for Thy dwell-ing, Fit me for life and heav-en a-bove.

CHORUS

O to be like Thee! O to be like Thee, Bless-ed Re-deem-er, pure as Thou art; Come in Thy sweet-ness, come in Thy full-ness; Stamp Thine own im-age deep on my heart.

Praise Him! Praise Him!

Fanny J. Crosby

Chester G. Allen

1. Praise Him! praise Him! Je-sus, our bless-ed Re-deem-er! Sing, O Earth, His
2. Praise Him! praise Him! Je-sus, our bless-ed Re-deem-er! For our sins He
3. Praise Him! praise Him! Je-sus, our bless-ed Re-deem-er! Heav'nly por-tals

won-der-ful love pro-claim! Hail Him! hail Him! highest archangels in glo-ry;
suffered, and bled, and died; He our Rock, our hope of e-ter-nal sal-va-tion,
loud with ho-san-nas ring! Je-sus, Sav-ior, reigneth for-ev-er and ev-er;

Strength and hon-or give to His ho-ly name! Like a shep-herd, Je-sus will
Hail Him! hail Him! Je-sus the Cru-ci-fied. Sound His Praises! Je-sus who
Crown Him! crown Him! Prophet, and Priest, and King! Christ is com-ing! o-ver the

REFRAIN

guard His children, In His arms He carries them all day long:
bore our sorrows, Love unbounded, wonderful, deep and strong: Praise Him! praise Him!
world vic-to-rious, Pow'r and glo-ry un-to the Lord be-long:

tell of His ex-cel-lent greatness; Praise Him! praise Him! ev-er in joy-ful song!

20 O Could I Speak

SAMUEL MEDLEY

WOLFGANG A. MOZART
ARR. BY LOWELL MASON

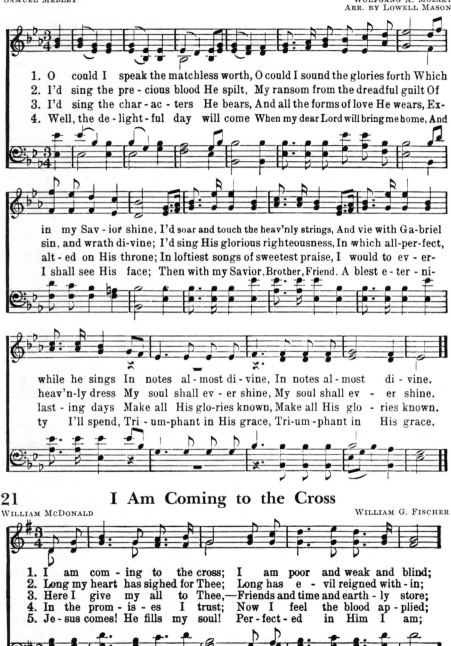

1. O could I speak the matchless worth, O could I sound the glories forth Which
2. I'd sing the pre-cious blood He spilt, My ransom from the dreadful guilt Of
3. I'd sing the char-ac-ters He bears, And all the forms of love He wears, Ex-
4. Well, the de-light-ful day will come When my dear Lord will bring me home, And

in my Sav-ior shine, I'd soar and touch the heav'nly strings, And vie with Ga-briel
sin, and wrath di-vine; I'd sing His glorious righteousness, In which all-per-fect,
alt-ed on His throne; In loftiest songs of sweetest praise, I would to ev-er-
I shall see His face; Then with my Savior, Brother, Friend, A blest e-ter-ni-

while he sings In notes al-most di-vine, In notes al-most di-vine.
heav'n-ly dress My soul shall ev-er shine, My soul shall ev-er shine.
last-ing days Make all His glo-ries known, Make all His glo-ries known.
ty I'll spend, Tri-um-phant in His grace, Tri-um-phant in His grace.

21 I Am Coming to the Cross

WILLIAM McDONALD

WILLIAM G. FISCHER

1. I am com-ing to the cross; I am poor and weak and blind;
2. Long my heart has sighed for Thee; Long has e-vil reigned with-in;
3. Here I give my all to Thee,—Friends and time and earth-ly store;
4. In the prom-is-es I trust; Now I feel the blood ap-plied;
5. Je-sus comes! He fills my soul! Per-fect-ed in Him I am;

CHO.—I am trust-ing, Lord, in Thee. Bless-ed Lamb of Cal-va-ry;

I Am Coming to the Cross

D. C. Chorus

I am count-ing all but dross; I shall full sal-va-tion find.
Je-sus sweet-ly speaks to me,— "I will cleanse you from all sin."
Soul and bod-y Thine to be,— Whol-ly Thine for-ev-er-more.
I am pros-trate in the dust; I with Christ am cru-ci-fied.
I am ev-'ry whit made whole: Glo-ry, glo-ry to the Lamb!

Hum-bly at Thy cross I bow. Save me, Je-sus, save me now.

Bring Them In

22

Alexcenah Thomas

William A. Ogden

1. Hark! 'tis the Shepherd's voice I hear, Out in the des-ert dark and drear,
2. Who'll go and help this Shepherd kind, Help Him the wand'ring ones to find?
3. Out in the des-ert hear their cry, Out on the mountains wild and high;

Call-ing the sheep who've gone a-stray Far from the Shepherd's fold a-way.
Who'll bring the lost ones to the fold, Where they'll be sheltered from the cold?
Hark! 'tis the Mas-ter speaks to thee, "Go find my sheep wher-e'er they be."

Chorus

Bring them in, bring them in, Bring them in from the fields of sin;

Bring them in, bring them in, Bring the wand'ring ones to Je-sus.

23   Joyful, Joyful, We Adore Thee

HENRY VAN DYKE

ARR. FROM LUDWIG VAN BEETHOVEN

1. Joy-ful, joy-ful, we a-dore Thee, God of glo-ry, Lord of love;
2. All Thy works with joy sur-round Thee, Earth and heav'n re-flect Thy rays,
3. Thou art giv-ing and for-giv-ing, Ev-er bless-ing, ev-er blest,
4. Mor-tals, join the might-y cho-rus Which the morn-ing stars be-gan;

Hearts un-fold like flow'rs be-fore Thee, Hail Thee as the sun a-bove.
Stars and an-gels sing a-round Thee, Cen-ter of un-bro-ken praise;
Well-spring of the joy of liv-ing, O-cean-depth of hap-py rest!
Fa-ther love is reign-ing o'er us, Broth-er-love binds man to man.

Melt the clouds of sin and sad-ness; Drive the dark of doubt a-way;
Field and for-est, vale and moun-tain, Flow-'ry mead-ow flash-ing sea,
Thou our Fa-ther, Christ our Broth-er, All who live in love are Thine:
Ev-er sing-ing, march we on-ward, Vic-tors in the midst of strife;

Giv-er of im-mor-tal glad-ness, Fill us with the light of day!
Chant-ing bird and flow-ing foun-tain, Call us to re-joice in Thee.
Teach us how to love each oth-er, Lift us to the Joy Di-vine.
Joy-ful mu-sic lifts us sun-ward In the tri-umph song of life.

From "The Poems of Henry van Dyke"; copyright 1911 by Charles Scribner's Sons, renewal 1939 by Tertius van Dyke. Reprinted by permission of the publishers

All Creatures of Our God and King

24

ST. FRANCIS OF ASSISI
TR. BY WILLIAM H. DRAPER

"GEISTLICHE KIRCHENGESANGE"

IN UNISON

1. All crea-tures of our God and King, Lift up your voice and with us
2. Thou rush-ing wind that art so strong, Ye clouds that sail in heav'n a-
3. And all ye men of ten-der heart, For-giv-ing oth-ers,take your
4. Let all things their Cre-a-tor bless, And wor-ship Him in hum-ble-
★ *Praise God from whom all bless-ings flow, Praise Him all crea-tures here be-*

sing, Al-le-lu - ia! Al-le-lu - ia! Thou burn-ing sun with gold-en
long, O praise Him! Al-le-lu - ia! Thou ris-ing morn,in praise re-
part, O sing ye! Al-le-lu - ia! Ye who long pain and sor-row
ness, O praise Him! Al-le-lu - ia! Praise,praise the Fa-ther,praise the
low, Al-le-lu - ia! Al-le-lu - ia! Praise Him a-bove, ye heav'n-ly

beam, Thou sil - ver moon with soft-er gleam! O praise Him, O
joice, Ye lights of eve-ning, find a voice! O praise Him, O
bear, Praise God and on Him cast your care! O praise Him, O
Son, And praise the Spir-it, Three in One! O praise Him, O
host, Praise Fa-ther, Son and Ho - ly Ghost, Al-le-lu - ia, Al-le-

praise Him! Al-le-lu - ia! Al-le-lu - ia! Al-le-lu - ia! A - MEN.
lu - ia!

* Sometimes called the "Keswick Doxology"

The Spacious Firmament on High

JOSEPH ADDISON

FRANZ JOSEPH HAYDN

1. The spa - cious fir - ma - ment on high, With all the blue, e-
2. Soon as the eve - ning shades pre - vail, The moon takes up the
3. What though, in sol - emn si - lence, all Move round the dark ter-

the - real sky, And spangled heavens, a shin - ing frame, Their great O-
won - drous tale; And night - ly, to the lis - tening earth, Re - peats the
res - trial ball? What though no re - al voice nor sound A - mid their

rig - i - nal pro - claim: Th'un-wea - ried sun, from day to day,
sto - ry of her birth; While all the stars that round her burn,
ra - diant orbs be found? In rea - son's ear they all re - joice,

Does his Cre - a - tor's power dis - play; And pub - lish - es to
And all the plan - ets in their turn, Con - firm the ti - dings
And ut - ter forth a glo - rious voice, For - ev - er sing - ing

ev - ery land The work of an al - might - y hand.
as they roll, And spread the truth from pole to pole.
as they shine, "The hand that made us is di - vine." A-MEN.

In My Heart There Rings a Melody

ELTON M. ROTH   ELTON M. ROTH

26

1. I have a song that Je - sus gave me, It was sent from
2. I love the Christ who died on Cal - v'ry, For He washed my
3. 'Twill be my end - less theme in glo - ry, With the an - gels

heav'n a - bove; There nev-er was a sweet - er mel - o - dy, 'Tis a
sins a - way; He put with - in my heart a mel - o - dy, And I
I will sing; 'Twill be a song with glo - rious har - mo - ny, When the

CHORUS

mel - o - dy of love.
know it's there to stay.   In my heart there rings a mel - o - dy, There
courts of heav - en ring.

rings a mel - o - dy with heav-en's har - mo - ny; In my heart there

rings a mel - o - dy; There rings a mel - o - dy of love.

27 Heavenly Sunlight

H. J. Zelley

George H. Cook

1. Walk-ing in sun-light, all of my jour-ney; O-ver the moun-tains, thro' the deep vale; Je-sus has said "I'll nev-er for-sake thee," Prom-ise di-vine that nev-er can fail.
2. Shad-ows a-round me, shad-ows a-bove me, Nev-er con-ceal my Sav-iour and Guide; He is the light, in Him is no dark-ness; Ev-er I'm walk-ing close to His side.
3. In the bright sun-light, ev-er re-joic-ing, Press-ing my way to man-sions a-bove; Sing-ing His prais-es glad-ly I'm walk-ing, Walk-ing in sun-light, sun-light of love.

CHORUS

Heav-en-ly sun-light, heav-en-ly sun-light, Flood-ing my soul with glo-ry di-vine: Hal-le-lu-jah, I am re-joic-ing, Sing-ing His prais-es, Je-sus is mine.

Ring the Bells of Heaven

WILLIAM O. CUSHING

GEORGE F. ROOT

1. Ring the bells of heav-en! there is joy to-day, For a soul re-
2. Ring the bells of heav-en! there is joy to-day, For the wan-d'rer
3. Ring the bells of heav-en! spread the feast to-day, An-gels, swell the

turn-ing from the wild; See! the Fa-ther meets him out up-on the way,
now is rec-on-ciled; Yes, a soul is res-cued from his sin-ful way,
glad tri-um-phant strain! Tell the joy-ful ti-dings, bear it far a-way!

CHORUS

Wel-com-ing His wea-ry, wan-d'ring child.
And is born a-new a ran-somed child. Glo-ry! glo-ry! how the
For a pre-cious soul is born a-gain.

an-gels sing; Glo-ry! glo-ry! how the loud harps ring! 'Tis the ran-somed

ar-my, like a might-y sea, Peal-ing forth the an-them of the free.

29 Since Jesus Came into My Heart

RUFUS H. MCDANIEL   CHARLES H. GABRIEL

1. What a won-der-ful change in my life has been wrought Since Je-sus came
2. I have ceased from my wand'ring and go-ing a-stray, Since Je-sus came
3. I'm pos-sessed of a hope that is stead-fast and sure, Since Je-sus came
4. There's a light in the val-ley of death now for me, Since Je-sus came
5. I shall go there to dwell in that Cit-y, I know, Since Je-sus came

in-to my heart! I have light in my soul for which long I had sought,
in-to my heart! And my sins, which were man-y, are all washed a-way,
in-to my heart! And no dark clouds of doubt now my path-way ob-scure,
in-to my heart! And the gates of the Cit-y be-yond I can see,
in-to my heart! And I'm hap-py, so hap-py, as on-ward I go,

CHORUS

Since Je-sus came in-to my heart! Since Je-sus came in-to my
Since Je-sus came in, came

heart, Since Je-sus came in-to my heart, Floods of joy o'er my
in-to my heart, Since Je-sus came in, came in-to my heart,

soul like the sea bil-lows roll, Since Je-sus came in-to my heart.

Sunlight

30

JUDSON W. VAN DEVENTER

WINFIELD S. WEEDEN

1. I wan-dered in the shades of night, Till Je - sus came to me,
2. Tho' clouds may gath - er in the sky, And bil - lows round me roll,
3. While walk-ing in the light of God, I sweet com-mun - ion find;
4. I cross the wide ex - tend - ed fields, I jour - ney o'er the plain,
5. Soon I shall see Him as He is, The light that came to me;

And with the sun - light of His love Bid all my dark-ness flee.
How - ev - er dark the world may be I've sun - light in my soul.
I press with ho - ly vig - or on, And leave the world be - hind.
And in the sun - light of His love I reap the gold - en grain.
Be - hold the brightness of His face. Thro'-out e - ter - ni - ty.

CHORUS

Sun - light, sun - light in my soul to - day, Sun - light, sun - light
to-day, yes,

all a - long the way: Since the Sav - ior found me,
nar - row way;

Took a-way my sin. I have had the sun-light of His love with - in.
load of sin,

31 Sunshine in the Soul

ELIZA E. HEWITT

JOHN R. SWENEY

1. There's sun-shine in my soul to-day, More glo-ri-ous and bright
2. There's mu-sic in my soul to-day, A car-ol to the King,
3. There's springtime in my soul to-day, For, when the Lord is near,
4. There's glad-ness in my soul to-day, And hope and praise and love,

Than glows in an-y earth-ly skies, For Je-sus is my light.
And Je-sus, lis-ten-ing, can hear The songs I can-not sing.
The dove of peace sings in my heart, The flow'rs of grace ap-pear.
For bless-ings which He gives me now, For joys ' laid up" a-bove.

REFRAIN

O there's sun - - - shine, bless-ed sun - - - shine,
O there's sun-shine in the soul, bless-ed sun-shine in the soul,

When the peace-ful, hap-py mo-ments roll; When
hap-py mo-ments roll;

Je-sus shows His smil-ing face, There is sun-shine in the soul.

I Will Praise Him

32

Mrs. M. J. Harris

Mrs. M. J. Harris

1. When I saw the cleansing foun-tain O - pen wide for all my sin,
2. Tho' the way seems straight and narrow, All I claimed was swept a - way;
3. Then God's fire up - on the al - tar Of my heart was set a - flame;
4. Bless - ed be the name of Je - sus! I'm so glad He took me in;
5. Glo - ry, glo - ry to the Fa - ther! Glo - ry, glo - ry to the Son!

I o - beyed the Spir - it's woo - ing, When He said, Wilt thou be clean?
My am - bi - tions, plans, and wish-es, At my feet in ash - es lay.
I shall nev - er cease to praise Him, Glo - ry, glo - ry to His name!
He's for - giv - en my trans-gres-sions, He has cleansed my heart from sin.
Glo - ry, glo - ry to the Spir - it! Glo - ry to the Three in One!

Chorus *Faster*

I will praise Him! I will praise Him! Praise the Lamb for sinners slain;
for sin-ners slain;

Give Him glo-ry, all ye peo - ple, For His blood can wash a-way each stain.

Nailed to the Cross

33

CARRIE E. BRECK

GRANT C. TULLAR

1. There was One who was will-ing to die in my stead, That a
2. He is ten-der and lov-ing and pa-tient with me, While He
3. I will cling to my Sav-ior and nev-er de-part—I will

soul so un-wor-thy might live; And the path to the cross He was
cleans-es my heart of the dross; But "there's no con-dem-na-tion"—I
joy-ful-ly jour-ney each day. With a song on my lips and a

REFRAIN

will-ing to tread, All the sins of my life to for-give.
know I am free, For my sins are all nailed to the cross. They are nailed to the cross,
song in my heart, That my sins have been tak-en a-way.

pp

They are nailed to the cross, O how much He was will-ing to bear! With what

rit.

an-guish and loss Je-sus went to the cross! But He carried my sins with Him there.

How Great Thou Art!

CARL BOBERG
TR. BY STUART K. HINE

SWEDISH FOLK MELODY
ARR. BY MANNA MUSIC, INC.

Slowly

1. O Lord my God! When I in awe-some won-der Con-sid-er
2. When through the woods and for-est glades I wan-der And hear the
3. And when I think that God, His Son not spar-ing, Sent Him to
4. When Christ shall come with-shout of ac-cla-ma-tion And take me

all the worlds Thy hands have made, I see the stars, I hear the roll-ing
birds sing sweet-ly in the trees; When I look down from loft-y moun-tain
die, I scarce can take it in;— That on the cross my bur-den glad-ly
home, what joy shall fill my heart! Then I shall bow in hum-ble ad-o-

REFRAIN

thun-der, Thy pow'r through out the un-i-verse dis-played,
gran-deur And hear the brook and feel the gen-tle breeze; Then sings my
bear-ing, He bled and died to take a-way my sin;—
ra-tion And there pro-claim, my God, how great Thou art!

soul, my Sav-ior God to Thee; How great Thou art, how great Thou art! Then sings my

soul, my Sav-ior God to Thee; How great Thou art, how great Thou art!

*Translator's original words are "works" and "mighty"

35 He Is Able to Deliver Thee

William A. Ogden

William A. Ogden

1. 'Tis the grand-est theme thro' the a-ges rung; 'Tis the grandest theme for a
2. 'Tis the grand-est theme in the earth or main; 'Tis the grandest theme for a
3. 'Tis the grand-est theme, let the ti-dings roll, To the guilt-y heart, to the

mor-tal tongue; 'Tis the grandest theme that the world e'er sung, "Our God is
mor-tal strain; 'Tis the grandest theme, tell the world a-gain, "Our God is
sin-ful soul; Look to God in faith, He will make thee whole, "Our God is

Chorus

a - ble to de-liv-er thee." He is a - - - - ble to de-liv-er thee,
a - ble, He is a - ble

He is a - - - - ble to de-liv-er thee; Tho' by sin op-prest,
a - ble, He is a - ble

Go to Him for rest; "Our God is a-ble to de-liv-er thee."

Jesus Is the Sweetest Name I Know

LELA LONG   LELA LONG

1. There have been names that I have loved to hear,   But nev-er has there
2. There is no name in earth or heav'n a-bove,   That we should give such
3. And some day I shall see Him face to face   To thank and praise Him

been a name so dear   To this heart of mine, as the name divine, The
hon-or and such love   As the blessed name, let us all acclaim, That
for His wondrous grace,   Which He gave to me, when He made me free,The

CHORUS.

pre-cious, precious name of Je-sus.
wondrous, glorious name of Je-sus.   Je-sus is the sweetest name I
bless-ed Son of God called Je-sus.

know, And He's just the same as His love-ly name, And that's the reason

rall.

why I love Him so; Oh, Je-sus is the sweet-est name I know.

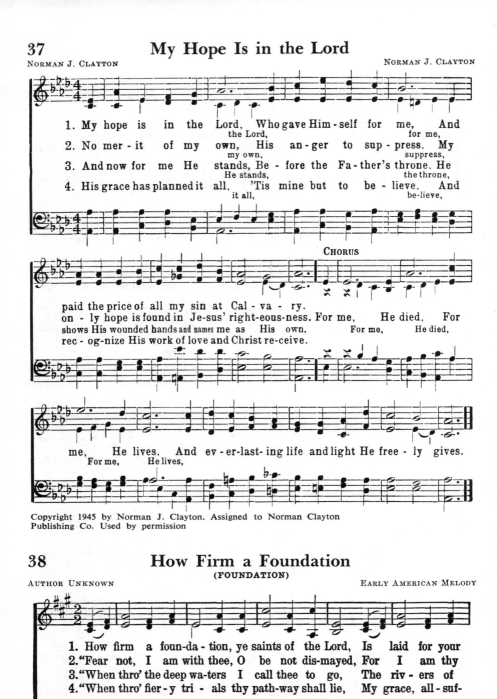

37   My Hope Is in the Lord

NORMAN J. CLAYTON   NORMAN J. CLAYTON

1. My hope is in the Lord, Who gave Him-self for me, And
   the Lord,   for me,
2. No mer-it of my own, His an-ger to sup-press. My
   my own,   suppress,
3. And now for me He stands, Be-fore the Fa-ther's throne. He
   He stands,   the throne,
4. His grace has planned it all, 'Tis mine but to be-lieve. And
   it all,   be-lieve,

CHORUS

paid the price of all my sin at Cal-va-ry.
on-ly hope is found in Je-sus' right-eous-ness. For me,   He died, For
shows His wounded hands and names me as His own.   For me,   He died,
rec-og-nize His work of love and Christ re-ceive.

me,   He lives,   And ev-er-last-ing life and light He free-ly gives.
For me,   He lives,

Copyright 1945 by Norman J. Clayton. Assigned to Norman Clayton
Publishing Co. Used by permission

38   How Firm a Foundation
(FOUNDATION)

AUTHOR UNKNOWN   EARLY AMERICAN MELODY

1. How firm a foun-da-tion, ye saints of the Lord, Is laid for your
2. "Fear not, I am with thee, O be not dis-mayed, For I am thy
3. "When thro' the deep wa-ters I call thee to go, The riv-ers of
4. "When thro' fier-y tri-als thy path-way shall lie, My grace, all-suf-

How Firm a Foundation
(FOUNDATION)

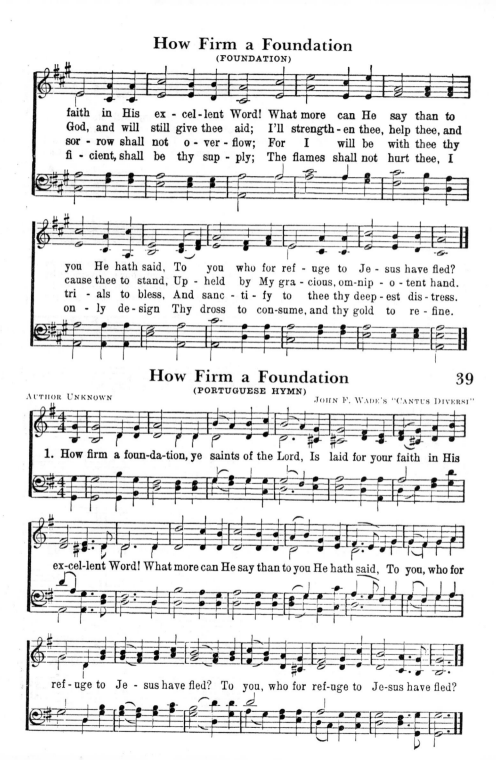

faith in His ex - cel - lent Word! What more can He say than to
God, and will still give thee aid; I'll strength-en thee, help thee, and
sor - row shall not o - ver-flow; For I will be with thee thy
fi - cient, shall be thy sup - ply; The flames shall not hurt thee, I

you He hath said, To you who for ref - uge to Je - sus have fled?
cause thee to stand, Up - held by My gra - cious, om-nip - o - tent hand.
tri - als to bless, And sanc - ti - fy to thee thy deep - est dis - tress.
on - ly de - sign Thy dross to con-sume, and thy gold to re - fine.

How Firm a Foundation
(PORTUGUESE HYMN)

AUTHOR UNKNOWN

JOHN F. WADE'S "CANTUS DIVERSI"

39

1. How firm a foun-da-tion, ye saints of the Lord, Is laid for your faith in His

ex-cel-lent Word! What more can He say than to you He hath said, To you, who for

ref-uge to Je - sus have fled? To you, who for ref-uge to Je-sus have fled?

Moment by Moment

Daniel W. Whittle

May Whittle Moody

1, Dy - ing with Je - sus, by death reckoned mine; Liv - ing with Je - sus, a
2. Nev - er a tri - al that He is not there, Nev - er a bur - den that
3. Nev - er a heart-ache, and nev - er a groan, Nev - er a tear-drop and
4. Nev - er a weak-ness that He doth not feel, Nev - er a sick-ness that

new life di-vine; Look-ing to Je-sus till glo - ry doth shine, Mo-ment by
He doth not bear, Nev - er a sor-row that He doth not share, Mo-ment by
nev - er a moan; Nev - er a dan-ger but there on the throne, Mo-ment by
He can-not heal; Mo-ment by moment, in woe or in weal, Je-sus, my

Chorus.

mo-ment, O Lord, I am Thine.
mo-ment, I'm un-der His care; Moment by mo-ment I'm kept in His love;
mo-ment He thinks of His own.
Sav - ior, a-bides with me still.

Mo-ment by mo-ment I've life from a - bove; Look-ing to Je - sus till

glo - ry doth shine; Mo-ment by mo-ment, O Lord, I am Thine.

Precious Hiding Place

41

AVIS B. CHRISTIANSEN

WENDELL P. LOVELESS

1. I was straying when Christ found me In the night so dark and cold;
2. With His nail-scarred hand He bro't me To the shel-ter of His love;
3. Tho' the night be dark a-round me, I am safe, for He is near;

Ten-der-ly His arm went round me And He bore me to His fold.
Of His grace and will He taught me, And of heav'n-ly rest a-bove.
Nev-er shall my foes con-found me, While the Sav-ior's voice I hear.

CHORUS

Pre-cious hid-ing place, Pre-cious hid-ing place, In the

shel-ter of His love; Not a doubt or fear, Since my

rit.

Lord is near, And I'm shel-tered in His love.

42 Constantly Abiding

Mrs. Will L. Murphy

Mrs. Will L. Murphy

1. There's a peace in my heart that the world nev-er gave, A peace it can
2. All the world seemed to sing of a Sav-ior and King, When peace sweetly
3. This treas-ure I have in a tem-ple of clay, While here on His

not take a - way; Tho' the tri - als of life may surround like a cloud,
came to my heart; Troubles all fled a - way and my night turned to day,
foot-stool I roam; But He's coming to take me some glo - ri - ous day,

CHORUS

I've a peace that has come there to stay!
Bless-ed Je - sus, how glorious Thou art!
O - ver there to my heav - en - ly home!

Con - - - stant-ly a-
Con-stant-ly a-bid - ing,

bid - - - ing, Je - - - sus is mine; . . . .
con - stant-ly a - bid - ing, Je - sus is mine, yes, Je - sus is mine;

Con - - - stant-ly a - bid - - - ing, rap - - ture di -
Con-stant-ly a-bid - ing, con-stant-ly a-bid-ing, rap-ture di-vine, O

Constantly Abiding

vine;   He   nev-er leaves me lone - - - ly, whis-pers,
rap-ture di-vine; He nev-er leaves   me,   nev-er leaves me lone-ly, whis-pers,

O, so kind:— "I will nev-er leave thee," Je - sus is mine.
whis-pers, O so kind:—   nev-er leave thee," Je-sus, Je-sus is mine.

My Jesus, as Thou Wilt!   43

BENJAMIN SCHMOLCK
TR. BY JANE L. BORTHWICK

CARL M. VON WEBER
ARR. BY JOSEPH P. HOLBROOK

1. My Je - sus, as Thou wilt! O may Thy will be mine; In - to Thy
2. My Je - sus, as Thou wilt! Tho' seen thro' man-y a tear, Let not my
3. My Je - sus, as Thou wilt! All shall be well for me; Each changing

hand of love I would my all re - sign. Thro' sor-row, or thro' joy,
star of hope Grow dim or dis-ap - pear. Since Thou on earth hast wept
fu - ture scene I glad-ly trust with Thee. Straight to my home a-bove

Conduct me as Thine own; And help me still to say, My Lord, Thy will be done.
And sorrowed oft a - lone, If I must weep with Thee, My Lord, Thy will be done.
I trav - el calm-ly on, And sing, in life or death, "My Lord, Thy will be done."

44 Safe in the Arms of Jesus

FANNY J. CROSBY

WILLIAM H. DOANE

1. Safe in the arms of Je - sus, Safe on His gen-tle breast, There by His
2. Safe in the arms of Je - sus, Safe from cor-rod-ing care, Safe from the
3. Je - sus, my heart's dear ref - uge, Je - sus has died for me; Firm on the

love o'er - shad - ed, Sweet-ly my soul shall rest. Hark! 'tis the voice of
world's temp-ta - tions, Sin can-not harm me there. Free from the blight of
Rock of A - ges, Ev - er my trust shall be. Here let me wait with

an - gels, Borne in a song to me,.. O - ver the fields of glo - ry,
sor - row, Free from my doubts and fears; On - ly a few more tri - als,
pa - tience, Wait till the night is o'er; Wait till I see the morn - ing

CHORUS

O - ver the jas - per sea.......
On - ly a few more tears!..... Safe in the arms of Je - sus, Safe on His
Break on the gold- en shore.....

gen- tle breast, There by His love o'er - shad- ed, Sweetly my soul shall rest.

Love Divine, All Loves Excelling

CHARLES WESLEY

JOHN ZUNDEL

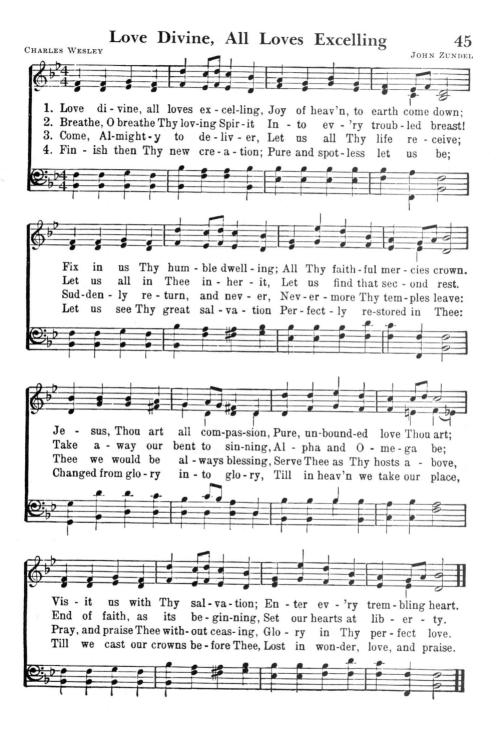

1. Love di-vine, all loves ex-cel-ling, Joy of heav'n, to earth come down;
2. Breathe, O breathe Thy lov-ing Spir-it In - to ev - 'ry troub-led breast!
3. Come, Al-might-y to de-liv-er, Let us all Thy life re - ceive;
4. Fin - ish then Thy new cre-a-tion; Pure and spot-less let us be;

Fix in us Thy hum - ble dwell-ing; All Thy faith-ful mer - cies crown.
Let us all in Thee in - her - it, Let us find that sec - ond rest.
Sud-den-ly re-turn, and nev-er, Nev-er-more Thy tem-ples leave:
Let us see Thy great sal - va - tion Per-fect-ly re-stored in Thee:

Je - sus, Thou art all com-pas-sion, Pure, un-bound-ed love Thou art;
Take a - way our bent to sin-ning, Al - pha and O - me - ga be;
Thee we would be al - ways blessing, Serve Thee as Thy hosts a - bove,
Changed from glo-ry in - to glo-ry, Till in heav'n we take our place,

Vis - it us with Thy sal-va-tion; En - ter ev - 'ry trem-bling heart.
End of faith, as its be-gin-ning, Set our hearts at lib - er - ty.
Pray, and praise Thee with-out ceas-ing, Glo - ry in Thy per-fect love.
Till we cast our crowns be-fore Thee, Lost in won-der, love, and praise.

46 Holy Spirit, Faithful Guide

MARCUS M. WELLS

MARCUS M. WELLS

1. { Ho - ly Spir - it, faith - ful Guide, Ev - er near the Chris-tian's side;
   { Gen - tly lead us by the hand, Pil - grims in a des - ert land;
2. { Ev - er pres - ent, tru - est Friend, Ev - er near Thine aid to lend,
   { Leave us not to doubt and fear, Grop-ing on in dark-ness drear;
3. { When our days of toil shall cease. Wait - ing still for sweet re - lease,
   { Noth - ing left but heav'n and prayer, Wond'ring if our names were there;

Wea - ry souls for - e'er re-joice, While they hear that sweet-est voice,
When the storms are rag - ing sore, Hearts grow faint, and hopes give o'er.
Wad - ing deep the dis - mal flood, Plead-ing naught but Je - sus' blood,

Whis-p'ring soft-ly, "Wand'rer, come! Fol - low Me, I'll guide thee home."
Whis - per soft - ly, "Wand'rer, come! Fol-low Me, I'll guide thee home."
Whis - per soft - ly, "Wand'rer, come! Fol - low Me, I'll guide thee home." A-MEN.

47 Holy Ghost, with Light Divine

ANDREW REED

LOUIS M. GOTTSCHALK
ARR. BY EDWIN P. PARKER

1. Ho - ly Ghost, with light di-vine, Shine up - on this heart of mine;
2. Ho - ly Ghost, with pow'r di-vine, Cleanse this guilt - y heart of mine;
3. Ho - ly Ghost, with joy di-vine, Cheer this sad-dened heart of mine;
4. Ho - ly Spir - it, all di-vine, Dwell with - in this heart of mine;

Holy Ghost, with Light Divine

Chase the shade of night a-way, Turn my dark-ness in-to day.
Long has sin, with-out con-trol, Held do-min-ion o'er my soul.
Bid my man-y woes de-part, Heal my wound-ed, bleed-ing heart.
Cast down ev-'ry i-dol-throne. Reign su-preme, and reign a-lone. A-MEN.

Fill Me Now

48

ELWOOD H. STOKES

JOHN R. SWENEY

1. Hov-er o'er me, Ho-ly Spir-it, Bathe my trem-bling heart and brow;
2. Thou canst fill me, gra-cious Spir-it, Though I can-not tell Thee how;
3. I am weak-ness, full of weak-ness, At Thy sa-cred feet I bow;
4. Cleanse and com-fort, bless and save me, Bathe, O bathe my heart and brow;

Fill me with Thy hal-lowed pres-ence, Come, O come and fill me now.
But I need Thee, great-ly need Thee, Come, O come and fill me now.
Blest, di-vine, e-ter-nal Spir-it, Fill with pow'r, and fill me now.
Thou art com-fort-ing and sav-ing, Thou art sweet-ly fill-ing now.

CHORUS

Fill me now, fill me now, Je-sus, come and fill me now;

Fill me with Thy hal-lowed pres-ence, Come, O come and fill me now.

49 The Comforter Has Come

FRANK BOTTOME

WILLIAM J. KIRKPATRICK

1. O spread the ti-dings 'round, wher-ev-er man is found, Wher-
2. The long, long night is past, the morn-ing breaks at last, And
3. Lo, the great King of kings, with heal-ing in His wings, To
4. O bound-less love di-vine! how shall this tongue of mine To

ev-er hu-man hearts and hu-man woes a-bound; Let ev-'ry Christian
hushed the dreadful wail and fu-ry of the blast, As o'er the gold-en
ev-'ry cap-tive soul a full de-liv'rance brings; And thro' the va-cant
wond'ring mor-tals tell the matchless grace di-vine—That I, a child of

D.S.—Ho-ly Ghost from Heav'n, The Fa-ther's promise giv'n; O spread the ti-dings

tongue pro-claim the joy-ful sound: The Com-fort-er has come!
hills the day ad-vanc-es fast! The Com-fort-er has come!
cells the song of tri-umph rings; The Com-fort-er has come!
hell, should in His im-age shine! The Com-fort-er has come!

FINE.

'round, wher-ev-er man is found— The Com-fort-er has come!

CHORUS

D. S.

The Com-fort-er has come, The Com-fort-er has come! The

Spirit of God, Descend upon My Heart

GEORGE CROLY   FREDERICK C. ATKINSON

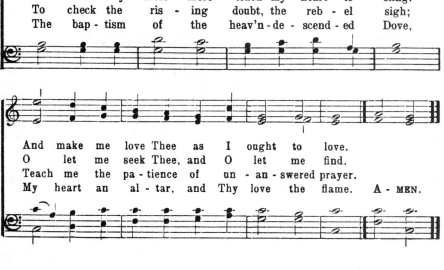

1. Spir - it of God, de - scend up - on my heart;
2. Hast Thou not bid us love Thee, God and King?
3. Teach me to feel that Thou art al - ways nigh;
4. Teach me to love Thee as Thine an - gels love,

Wean it from earth, through all its puls - es move;
All, all Thine own, soul, heart and strength and mind;
Teach me the strug - gles of the soul to bear,
One ho - ly pas - sion fill - ing all my frame;

Stoop to my weak - ness, might - y as Thou art,
I see Thy cross— there teach my heart to cling:
To check the ris - ing doubt, the reb - el sigh;
The bap - tism of the heav'n - de - scend - ed Dove,

And make me love Thee as I ought to love.
O let me seek Thee, and O let me find.
Teach me the pa - tience of un - an - swered prayer.
My heart an al - tar, and Thy love the flame. A - MEN.

51   Pass Me Not, O Gentle Savior

WILLIAM H. DOANE

1. Pass me not, O gen - tle Sav - ior, Hear my hum-ble cry; While on oth - ers
2. Let me at a throne of mer - cy Find a sweet re - lief; Kneel-ing there in
3. Trust-ing on - ly in Thy mer - it, Would I seek Thy face; Heal my wounded,
4. Thou the Spring of all my com-fort, More than life to me, Whom have I on

Chorus

Thou art call-ing, Do not pass me by.
deep con - tri - tion. Help my un - be - lief. Sav - ior, Sav - ior, Hear my humble
bro - ken spir - it, Save me by Thy grace.
earth beside Thee? Whom in Heav'n but Thee?

cry; While on oth - ers Thou art call - ing, Do not pass me by.

52   I Am Coming, Lord

LEWIS HARTSOUGH

LEWIS HARTSOUGH

1. I hear Thy welcome voice, That calls me, Lord, to Thee For cleansing in Thy
2. Tho' coming weak and vile, Thou dost my strength assure; Thou dost my vileness
3. 'Tis Je - sus calls me on To per - fect faith and love, To per-fect hope, and

Chorus

pre-cious blood That flowed on Cal - va - ry.
ful - ly cleanse, Till spot - less all and pure. I am com-ing, Lord!
peace, and trust, For earth and heav'n a - bove.

I Am Coming, Lord

Com-ing now to Thee! Wash me, cleanse me in the blood That flowed on Cal-va-ry!

Look to the Lamb of God

53

H. G. JACKSON

JAMES M. BLACK

1. If you from sin are long-ing to be free, Look to the Lamb of God;
2. When Satan tempts, and doubts and fears assail, Look to the Lamb of God;
3. Are you a-wea - ry, does the way seem long? Look to the Lamb of God;
4. Fear not when shadows on your path-way fall, Look to the Lamb of God;

He, to re-deem you, died on Cal - va - ry, Look to the Lamb of God.
You in His strength shall o-ver all pre-vail, Look to the Lamb of God.
His love will cheer and fill your heart with song, Look to the Lamb of God.
In joy or sor - row Christ is all in all, Look to the Lamb of God.

CHORUS

Look to the Lamb of God, Look to the Lamb of God,
the Lamb of God, the Lamb of God,

For He a - lone is a - ble to save you, Look to the Lamb of God.

54 I Heard the Voice of Jesus Say

Horatius Bonar

John B. Dykes

1. I heard the voice of Je - sus say, "Come un - to Me and rest;
2. I heard the voice of Je - sus say, "Be - hold, I free - ly give
3. I heard the voice of Je - sus say, "I am this dark world's Light;

Lay down, thou wea - ry one, lay down Thy head up - on My breast."
The liv - ing wa - ter; thirst - y one, Stoop down, and drink, and live."
Look un - to Me, thy morn shall rise, And all thy day be bright."

I came to Je - sus as I was, Wea - ry, and worn, and sad;
I came to Je - sus, and I drank Of that life - giv - ing stream;
I looked to Je - sus, and I found In Him my Star, my Sun;

I found in Him a rest - ing - place, And He has made me glad.
My thirst was quench'd, my soul re - vived, And now I live in Him.
And in that Light of life I'll walk, Till trav'l - ing days are done.

Let Jesus Come into Your Heart

LEILA N. MORRIS

LEILA N. MORRIS

1. If you are tired of the load of your sin, Let Je - sus come
2. If 'tis for pu - ri - ty now that you sigh, Let Je - sus come
3. If there's a tem - pest your voice can - not still, Let Je - sus come
4. If you would join the glad songs of the blest, Let Je - sus come

in - to your heart; If you de - sire a new life to be - gin,
in - to your heart; Fountains for cleans-ing are flow - ing near by,
in - to your heart; If there's a void this world nev - er can fill,
in - to your heart; If you would en - ter the man-sions of rest,

Let Je - sus come in - to your heart.

Chorus

Just now, your doubt-ings give o'er; Just now, re - ject Him no more; Just now, throw o - pen the door; Let Je - sus come in - to your heart.

56   O Jesus, Thou Art Standing

WILLIAM W. HOW

JUSTIN H. KNECHT
EDWARD HUSBAND

1. O Je-sus Thou art standing Outside the fast-closed door, In low-ly pa-tience
2. O Je-sus Thou art knocking; And lo! that hand is scarred, And thorns Thy brow en-
3. O Je-sus Thou art plead-ing In ac-cents meek and low, "I died for you, My

wait-ing To pass the thresh-old o'er: Shame on us, Chris-tian broth-ers, His Name and
cir - cle, And tears Thy face have marred; O love that pass-eth knowl-edge, So pa - tient-
chil-dren, And will ye treat me so?" O Lord, with shame and sor-row We o - pen

sign who bear, O shame, thrice shame up-on us, To keep Him standing there!
ly to wait! O sin that hath no e-qual, So fast to bar the gate!
now the door; Dear Sav-ior, en - ter, en-ter, And leave us nev-er-more! A-MEN.

57   Art Thou Weary, Art Thou Languid?

JOHN M. NEALE
BASED ON AN EARLY GREEK HYMN

HENRY W. BAKER

1. Art thou wea-ry, art thou lan-guid, Art thou sore dis-tressed?
2. Hath He marks to lead me to Him, If He be my guide?
3. Is there di - a - dem, as Mon-arch, That His brow a - dorns?
4. If I ask Him to re - ceive me, Will He say me nay?
5. Find-ing, fol-l'wing, keep-ing, strug-gling, Is He sure to bless?

Art Thou Weary, Art Thou Languid?

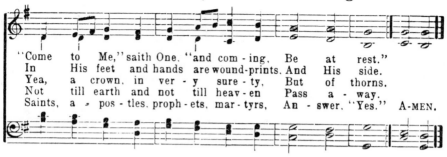

"Come to Me," saith One, "and com - ing, Be at rest."
In His feet and hands are wound-prints. And His side.
Yea, a crown, in ver - y sure - ty, But of thorns.
Not till earth and not till heav - en Pass a - way.
Saints, a - pos - tles, proph - ets, mar - tyrs, An - swer, "Yes." A-MEN.

I Gave My Life for Thee

58

Frances R. Havergal

Philip P. Bliss

1. I gave My life for thee, My pre - cious blood I shed,
2. My Fa - ther's house of light, My glo - ry - cir - cled throne,
3. I suf - fered much for thee, More than thy tongue can tell,
4. And I have brought to thee, Down from My home a - bove,

That thou might'st ran - somed be, And quick - ened from the dead;
I left for earth - ly night, For wan - d'rings sad and lone;
Of bit - t'rest ag - o - ny, To res - cue thee from hell;
Sal - va - tion full and free, My par - don and My love;

I gave, I gave My life for thee, What hast thou giv'n for Me?
I left, I left it all for thee, Hast thou left aught for Me?
I've borne, I've borne it all for thee, What hast thou borne for Me?
I bring, I bring rich gifts to thee, What hast thou brought to Me?

59 Jesus Is Calling

Fanny J. Crosby

George C. Stebbins

1. Je-sus is ten-der-ly call-ing thee home—Call-ing to-day,
2. Je-sus is call-ing the wea-ry to rest—Call-ing to-day,
3. Je-sus is wait-ing; O come to Him now—Wait-ing to-day,
4. Je-sus is plead-ing; O list to His voice: Hear Him to-day,

call-ing to-day; Why from the sun-shine of love wilt thou roam
call-ing to-day; Bring Him thy bur-den and thou shalt be blest:
wait-ing to-day; Come with thy sins; at His feet low-ly bow;
hear Him to-day; They who be-lieve on His name shall re-joice;

REFRAIN

Far-ther and far-ther a-way?
He will not turn thee a-way.
Come, and no lon-ger de-lay.
Quick-ly a-rise and a-way.

Call - - ing to-day, ...
Call-ing, call-ing to-day, to-day,

Call - - ing to-day, ...
Call-ing, call-ing to-day, to-day,

Je - - - sus is
Je-sus is ten-der-ly

call - - - ing, is ten-der-ly call-ing to-day.
call-ing to-day,

Is My Name Written There?

MARY A. KIDDER

FRANK M. DAVIS

1. Lord, I care not for rich-es, Nei-ther sil-ver nor gold; I would
2. Lord, my sins they are man-y, Like the sands of the sea, But Thy
3. Oh! that beau-ti-ful cit-y, With its man-sions of light, With its

make sure of heav-en, I would en-ter the fold. In the book of Thy
blood, O my Sav-ior, Is suf-fi-cient for me; For Thy prom-ise is
glo-ri-fied be-ings, In pure gar-ments of white; Where no e-vil thing

king-dom, With its pa-ges so fair, Tell me, Je-sus, my Sav-ior, Is my
writ-ten, In bright letters that glow, "Tho' your sins be as scar-let, I will
com-eth To de-spoil what is fair; Where the an-gels are watching, Yes, my

REFRAIN.

name writ-ten there?
make them like snow." Is my name writ-ten there, On the page white and fair?
name's written there. Yes, my name's, etc.

In the book of Thy king-dom, Is my name writ-ten there?
Yes, my name's writ-ten there.

61 Why Do You Wait?

GEORGE F. ROOT

GEORGE F. ROOT

1. Why do you wait, dear broth-er, Oh, why do you tar-ry so long?
2. What do you hope, dear broth-er, To gain by a fur-ther de-lay?
3. Do you not feel, dear broth-er, His Spir-it now striv-ing with-in?
4. Why do you wait, dear broth-er? The harvest is pass-ing a-way;

Your Sav-ior is wait-ing to give you A place in His sanc-ti-fied throng.
There's no one to save you but Je-sus, There's no other way but His way.
Oh, why not ac-cept His sal-va-tion, And throw off your burden of sin?
Your Sav-ior is long-ing to bless you, There's danger and death in de-lay.

CHORUS

Why not? why not? Why not come to Him now? now?

62 Just As I Am

CHARLOTTE ELLIOTT

WILLIAM B. BRADBURY

1. Just as I am, with-out one plea, But that Thy blood was shed for me,
2. Just as I am, and wait-ing not To rid my soul of one dark blot,
3. Just as I am, tho' tossed a-bout With many a con-flict, many a doubt,
4. Just as I am, poor, wretched, blind; Sight, riches, heal-ing of the mind,
5. Just as I am, Thou wilt re-ceive, Wilt welcome, pardon, cleanse, relieve;

Just As I Am

And that Thou bidd'st me come to Thee, O Lamb of God, I come! I come!
To Thee whose blood can cleanse each spot, O Lamb of God, I come! I come!
Fight-ings and fears with-in, with - out, O Lamb of God, I come! I come!
Yea, all I need, in Thee to find, O Lamb of God, I come! I come!
Be - cause Thy prom-ise I be-lieve, O Lamb of God, I come! I come!

Lord, I'm Coming Home 63

WILLIAM J. KIRKPATRICK   WILLIAM J. KIRKPATRICK

1. I've wan-dered far a - way from God, Now I'm com - ing home;
2. I've wast - ed man - y pre - cious years, Now I'm com - ing home;
3. I've tired of sin and stray-ing, Lord, Now I'm com - ing home;
4. My soul is sick, my heart is sore, Now I'm com - ing home;

FINE

The paths of sin too long I've trod, Lord, I'm com-ing home.
I now re - pent with bit - ter tears, Lord, I'm com-ing home.
I'll trust Thy love, be - lieve Thy word, Lord, I'm com-ing home.
My strength re - new, my hope re - store, Lord, I'm com-ing home.

D. S.—O - pen wide Thine arms of love, Lord, I'm com - ing home.

CHORUS   D. S.

Com - ing home, com - ing home, Nev - er - more to roam,

64 Springs of Living Water

JOHN W. PETERSON

JOHN W. PETERSON

1. I thirst-ed in the bar-ren land of sin and shame, And
2. How sweet the liv-ing wat-er from the hills of God, It
3. O sin-ner, won't you come to-day to Cal-va-ry, A

noth-ing sat-is-fy-ing there I found; But to the bless-ed cross of
makes me glad and hap-py all the way; Now glo-ry, grace and bless-ing
foun-tain there is flow-ing deep and wide; The Sav-iour now in-vites you

Christ one day I came, Where springs of liv-ing wat-er did a-bound.
mark the path I've trod, I'm shout-ing "Hal-le-lu-jah" ev-'ry day.
to the wat-er free, Where thirst-ing spir-its can be sat-is-fied.

CHORUS

Drink-ing at the springs of liv-ing wa-ter, Hap-py now am
Hap - py

I, My soul they sat-is-fy; Drink-ing at the
now am I, My soul they sat-is-fy; I'm

Springs of Living Water

springs of liv-ing wa - ter, O won-der-ful and boun-ti - ful sup - ply.

All That Thrills My Soul 65

THORO HARRIS

THORO HARRIS

1. Who can cheer the heart like Je - sus, By His pres-ence all di - vine?
2. Love of Christ so free - ly giv - en, Grace of God be-yond de - gree,
3. What a won - der - ful re - demp - tion! Nev - er can a mor - tal know
4. Ev - 'ry need His hand sup - ply - ing, Ev - 'ry good in Him I see;
5. By the crys - tal flow - ing riv - er With the ran-somed I will sing,

True and ten - der, pure and pre - cious, O how blest to call Him mine!
Mer - cy high - er than the heav - en, Deep - er than the deep - est sea.
How my sin, tho' red like crim - son, Can be whit - er than the snow.
On His strength di - vine re - ly - ing, He is all in all to me.
And for - ev - er and for - ev - er Praise and glo - ri - fy the King.

REFRAIN

All that thrills my soul is Je - sus, He is more than life to me (to me);

And the fair - est of ten thou-sand In my bless-ed Lord I see.

66 'Twas a Glad Day When Jesus Found Me

ALBERT S. REITZ

ALBERT S. REITZ

1. I was lost in sin when Je - sus found me, But He res - cued me, all
2. O the bells of heav- en now are ring-ing, For I hear their tones with-
3. O the joy when we shall meet in glo - ry, In the man-sions of my

glo - ry to His name! And the cords of world - ly pleas - ure bound me,
in my ran-somed soul; And my heart is filled with joy - ful sing-ing
Father's home a - bove; And thro' end-less a - ges tell the sto - ry

CHORUS

Till He saved me from sin and shame.
Since the Sav - ior hath made me whole. 'Twas a glad day when Je - sus
Of the Sav - ior's re - deem-ing love.

found me, When His strong arms were thrown around me; When my sins He buried

in the deep-est sea, And my soul He filled with joy and vic - to - ry, 'Twas a

'Twas a Glad Day When Jesus Found Me

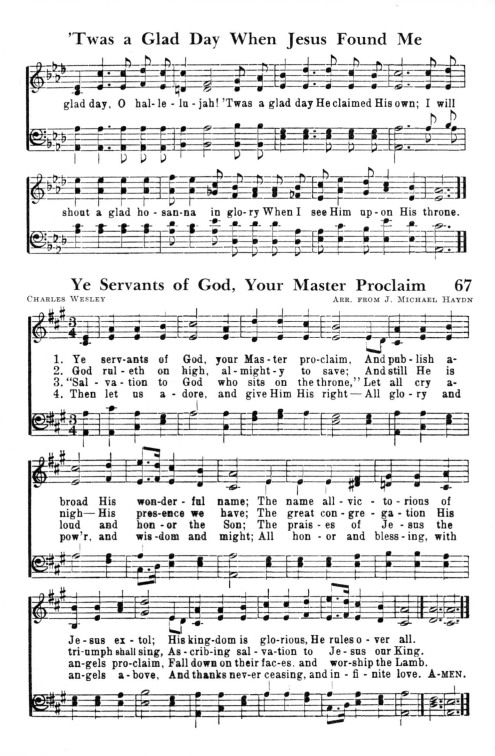

glad day, O hal-le-lu-jah! 'Twas a glad day He claimed His own; I will

shout a glad ho-san-na in glo-ry When I see Him up-on His throne.

Ye Servants of God, Your Master Proclaim   67

CHARLES WESLEY

ARR. FROM J. MICHAEL HAYDN

1. Ye serv-ants of God, your Mas-ter pro-claim, And pub-lish a-
2. God rul-eth on high, al-might-y to save; And still He is
3. "Sal-va-tion to God who sits on the throne," Let all cry a-
4. Then let us a-dore, and give Him His right— All glo-ry and

broad His won-der-ful name; The name all-vic-to-rious of
nigh—His pres-ence we have; The great con-gre-ga-tion His
loud and hon-or the Son; The prais-es of Je-sus the
pow'r, and wis-dom and might; All hon-or and bless-ing, with

Je-sus ex-tol; His king-dom is glo-rious, He rules o-ver all.
tri-umph shall sing, As-crib-ing sal-va-tion to Je-sus our King.
an-gels pro-claim, Fall down on their fac-es, and wor-ship the Lamb.
an-gels a-bove, And thanks nev-er ceasing, and in-fi-nite love. A-MEN.

68 Let Him In

JONATHAN B. ATCHINSON

EDWIN O. EXCELL

1. There's a Stran-ger at the door, Let Him in;
2. O - pen now to Him your heart, Let Him in;
3. Hear you now His lov - ing voice? Let Him in;
4. Now ad - mit the heav'n-ly Guest, Let Him in;

Let the Sav-ior in, Let the Sav-ior in;

He has been there oft be - fore, Let Him in;
If you wait He will de - part, Let Him in;
Now, oh, now make Him your choice, Let Him in;
He will make for you a feast, Let Him in;

Let the Sav-ior in, Let the Sav-ior in;

Let Him in, ere He is gone, Let Him in, the Ho - ly One, Je - sus
Let Him in, He is your Friend, He your soul will sure de - fend, He will
He is stand-ing at your door, Joy to you He will re - store, And His
He will speak your sins for-giv'n, And when earth ties all are riv'n, He will

Christ, the Fa - ther's Son, Let Him in.
keep you to the end, Let Him in.
name you will a - dore, Let Him in.
take you home to heav'n, Let Him in.

Let the Sav-ior in, Let the Sav-ior in.

You May Have the Joy-bells

69

J. Edward Ruark

William J. Kirkpatrick

1. You may have the joy-bells ring-ing in your heart, And a peace that
2. Love of Je-sus in its full-ness you may know, And this love to
3. You will meet with tri-als as you jour-ney home; Grace suf-fi-cient
4. Let your life speak well of Je-sus ev-'ry day; Own His right to

from you nev-er will de-part; Walk the straight and nar-row way,
those a-round you sweet-ly show; Words of kind-ness al-ways say,
He will give to o-ver-come; Tho' un-seen by mor-tal eye,
ev-'ry serv-ice you can pay; Sin-ners you can help to win

Live for Je-sus ev-'ry day, He will keep the joy-bells ringing in your heart.
Deeds of mer-cy do each day, Then He'll keep the joy-bells ringing in your heart.
He is with you ev-er nigh, And He'll keep the joy-bells ringing in your heart.
If your life is pure and clean, And you keep the joy-bells ringing in your heart.

Chorus   D. S.—*He will keep the joy-bells ring-ing in your heart.*

Joy - - - bells ring-ing in your heart, Joy - - - - bells
Ring-ing in your heart, You may have the joy-bells

D. S.

ringing in your heart; Take the Sav-ior here below With you ev'rywhere you go;

70 There's a New Song in My Heart

JOHN W. PETERSON

JOHN W. PETERSON

1. Once my life was filled with dis-cord, Sad-ness reigned with-in,
2. What a won-drous trans-for - ma-tion In my life was wrought,
3. Some day I will go to Heav-en Where the an-gels sing,
4. I shall nev - er cease in prais-ing Je - sus Christ my Lord,

For my heart was heav-y - lad - en With a weight of sin.
When I trust - ed Christ as Sav-ior And His par - don sought.
And I'll join their hap - py cho - rus Prais-ing Christ the King.
For the won - der - ful sal - va - tion That He did ac - cord.

CHORUS
MEN

Faster

There's a new song in my heart Since the Sav-ior set me free;

WOMEN

ALL

There's a new song in my heart— 'Tis a heav'n-ly har-mo-ny! All my

sins are washed a-way In the blood of Cal-va - ry; O what

There's a New Song in My Heart

peace and joy Noth-ing can de-stroy, There's a new song in my heart.

Some Day!
(BEAUTIFUL ISLE OF SOMEWHERE)

71

JESSIE B. POUNDS, 1
AVIS B. CHRISTIANSEN, 2, 3, REF.

J. S. FEARIS

1. Some-where the sun is shin - ing, Some-where the song-birds dwell;
2. Soon will earth's night be o - ver, Soon will the morn-ing dawn;
3. There a-mid Heav-en's beau - ties They shall be-hold His face,

Hush, then, thy sad re - pin - ing, God lives, and all is well.
Soon will the Christ of Glo - ry Call His re-deemed ones home.
And through e-ter - nal a - ges Sing of His won-drous grace.

REFRAIN

Some day! Some day! We shall be - hold His glo - ry!

Com-ing a-gain, ev - er-more to reign, All will be won-drous glo - ry!

72 Safely Through Another Week

JOHN NEWTON

LOWELL MASON

1. Safe - ly through an - oth - er week God has brought us on our way;
2. While we pray for par-d'ning grace, Thro' the dear Re-deem-er's name,
3. Here we come Thy name to praise, Let us feel Thy pres-ence near;
4. May Thy gos-pel's joy - ful sound Con-quer sin-ners, com-fort saints;

Let us now a bless-ing seek, Wait-ing in His courts to - day;
Show Thy rec - on - cil - ed face; Take a - way our sin and shame:
May Thy glo - ry meet our eyes, While we in Thy house ap - pear:
Make the fruits of grace a - bound, Bring re - lief for all com-plaints:

Day of all the week the best, Em-blem of e - ter - nal rest: Day of
From our world-ly cares set free, May we rest this day in Thee: From our
Here af - ford us, Lord, a taste Of our ev - er - last-ing feast: Here af-
Thus may all our Sab-baths prove, Till we join the Church a - bove: Thus may

all the week the best, Em - blem of e - ter - nal rest.
world-ly cares set free, May we rest this day in Thee.
ford us, Lord, a taste Of our ev - er - last-ing feast.
all our Sab-baths prove, Till we join the Church a - bove. A - MEN.

It Is Well with My Soul

HORATIO G. SPAFFORD

PHILIP P. BLISS

1. When peace, like a riv-er, at-tend-eth my way, When sor-rows like
2. Though Sa-tan should buf-fet, tho' tri-als should come, Let this blest as-
3. My sin— oh, the bliss of this glo-ri-ous tho't—My sin—not in
4. And, Lord, haste the day when the faith shall be sight, The clouds be rolled

sea-bil-lows roll; What-ev-er my lot, Thou hast taught me to say,
sur-ance con-trol, That Christ has re-gard-ed my help-less es-tate,
part, but the whole, Is nailed to the cross and I bear it no more,
back as a scroll, The trump shall re-sound and the Lord shall de-scend,

CHORUS

It is well, it is well with my soul.
And hath shed His own blood for my soul. It is well..... with my
Praise the Lord, praise the Lord, O my soul!
"E-ven so"—it is well with my soul. It is well

soul,...... It is well, it is well with my soul.
with my soul,

74 O Love That Wilt Not Let Me Go

GEORGE MATHESON

ALBERT L. PEACE

1. O Love that wilt not let me go, I rest my wea-ry
2. O Light that fol-low'st all my way, I yield my flick-'ring
3. O Joy that seek-est me thro' pain, I can-not close my
4. O Cross that lift-est up my head, I dare not ask to

soul on Thee; I give Thee back the life I owe, That
torch to Thee; My heart re-stores its bor-rowed ray, That
heart to Thee; I trace the rain-bow thro' the rain, And
hide from Thee; I lay in dust life's glo-ry dead, And

in Thine o-cean depths its flow May rich-er, full-er be.
in Thy sun-shine's glow its day May bright-er, fair-er be.
feel the prom-ise is not vain That morn shall tear-less be.
from the ground there blossoms red Life that shall end-less be.

75 Jesus Shall Reign

ISAAC WATTS

JOHN HATTON

1. Je-sus shall reign wher-e'er the sun Does his suc-ces-sive jour-neys run;
2. From north to south the prin-ces meet To pay their hom-age at His feet;
3. To Him shall end-less prayer be made, And end-less prais-es crown His head;
4. Peo-ple and realms of ev-'ry tongue Dwell on His love with sweetest song,

Jesus Shall Reign

His kingdom spread from shore to shore, Till moons shall wax and wane no more.
While west-ern em-pires own their Lord, And sav-age tribes at-tend His word.
His name like sweet perfume shall rise With ev-'ry morn-ing sac - ri - fice.
And in-fant voic - es shall pro-claim Their ear-ly bless-ings on His name.

Lead On, O King Eternal

76

ERNEST W. SHURTLEFF

HENRY SMART

1. Lead on, O King E - ter-nal, The day of march has come; Henceforth in fields of
2. Lead on, O King E - ter-nal, Till sin's fierce war shall cease, And ho-li-ness shall
3. Lead on, O King E - ter-nal, We fol-low, not with fears; For gladness breaks like

con-quest Thy tents shall be our home. Thro' days of prep-a - ra - tion Thy
whis - per The sweet A - men of peace; For not with swords loud clashing, Nor
morn - ing Where'er Thy face ap-pears; Thy cross is lift - ed o'er us; We

grace has made us strong, And now, O King E - ter - nal, We lift our bat-tle song.
roll of stir-ring drums; With deeds of love and mercy, The heav'nly kingdom comes.
jour - ney in its light: The crown awaits the conquest; Lead on, O God of might.

77 Crown Him with Many Crowns

MATTHEW BRIDGES AND
GODFREY THRING

GEORGE J. ELVEY

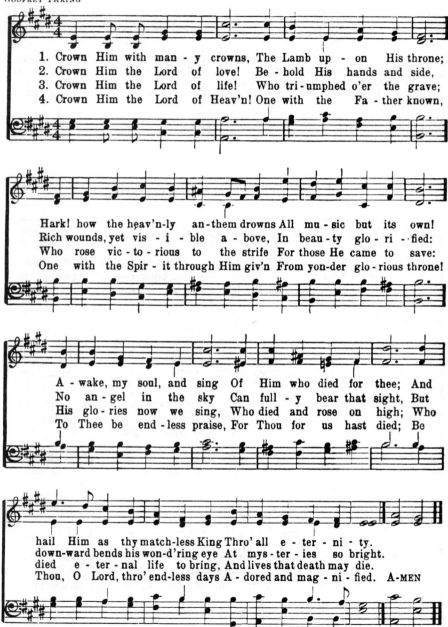

1. Crown Him with man - y crowns, The Lamb up - on His throne;
2. Crown Him the Lord of love! Be - hold His hands and side,
3. Crown Him the Lord of life! Who tri-umphed o'er the grave;
4. Crown Him the Lord of Heav'n! One with the Fa - ther known,

Hark! how the heav'n-ly an-them drowns All mu - sic but its own!
Rich wounds, yet vis - i - ble a - bove, In beau-ty glo - ri - fied:
Who rose vic - to - rious to the strife For those He came to save:
One with the Spir - it through Him giv'n From yon-der glo - rious throne!

A - wake, my soul, and sing Of Him who died for thee; And
No an - gel in the sky Can full - y bear that sight, But
His glo - ries now we sing, Who died and rose on high; Who
To Thee be end - less praise, For Thou for us hast died; Be

hail Him as thy match-less King Thro' all e - ter - ni - ty.
down-ward bends his won-d'ring eye At mys - ter - ies so bright.
died e - ter - nal life to bring, And lives that death may die.
Thou, O Lord, thro' end-less days A - dored and mag - ni - fied. A-MEN

O Day of Rest and Gladness

78

CHRISTOPHER WORDSWORTH

OLD GERMAN MELODY
ARR. BY LOWELL MASON

1. O day of rest and glad-ness, O day of joy and light,
2. On thee, at the cre-a-tion, The light first had its birth;
3. To-day on wear-y na-tions The heav'n-ly man-na falls;
4. New gra-ces ev-er gain-ing From this our day of rest,

O balm of care and sad-ness, Most beau-ti-ful, most bright;
On thee, for our sal-va-tion, Christ rose from depths of earth.
To ho-ly con-vo-ca-tions The sil-ver trump-et calls,
We reach the rest re-main-ing To spir-its of the blest.

On thee, the high and low-ly, Bend-ing be-fore the throne, Sing,
On thee our Lord vic-to-rious The Spir-it sent from Heav'n; And
Where gos-pel light is glow-ing With pure and ra-diant beams, And
To Ho-ly Ghost be prais-es, To Fa-ther and to Son; The

Ho-ly, Ho-ly, Ho-ly, To the great Three in One.
thus on thee most glo-rious A tri-ple light was given.
liv-ing wa-ter flow-ing With soul-re-fresh-ing streams.
Church her voice up-rais-es To Thee, blest Three in One. A-MEN.

79 Tell Me the Old, Old Story

A. CATHERINE HANKEY

WILLIAM H. DOANE

1. Tell me the Old, Old Sto-ry, Of un-seen things a-bove, Of Je-sus
2. Tell me the sto-ry slow-ly, That I may take it in— That won-der-
3. Tell me the sto-ry soft-ly, With ear-nest tones and grave; Re-mem-ber
4. Tell me the same old sto-ry, When you have cause to fear That this world's

and His glo-ry, Of Je-sus and His love; Tell me the sto-ry
ful re-demp-tion, God's rem-e-dy for sin; Tell me the sto-ry
I'm the sin-ner Whom Je-sus came to save; Tell me the sto-ry
emp-ty glo-ry Is cost-ing me too dear; Yes, and when that world's

sim-ply, As to a lit-tle child, For I am weak and wea-ry,
oft-en, For I for-get so soon, The "ear-ly dew" of morn-ing,
al-ways, If you would real-ly be, In an-y time of troub-le,
glo-ry Is dawn-ing on my soul, Tell me the Old, Old Sto-ry:

CHORUS

And help-less and de-filed.
Has passed a-way at noon. Tell me the Old, Old Sto-ry, Tell me the
A com-fort-er to me.
"Christ Je-sus makes thee whole."

Old, Old Sto-ry, Tell me the Old, Old Sto-ry Of Je-sus and His love.

We Three Kings of Orient Are

JOHN H. HOPKINS

JOHN H. HOPKINS

80

1. We three kings of O - ri - ent are, Bear-ing gifts we trav-erse a-far
2. Born a King on Beth-le-hem's plain, Gold I bring to crown Him a-gain,
3. Frank-in-cense to of - fer have I, In - cense owns a De - i -ty nigh;
4. Myrrh is mine; its bit - ter per-fume Breathes a life of gath-er-ing gloom;
5. Glo - rious now be - hold Him a - rise, King and God and Sac - ri - fice;

Field and foun - tain, moor and moun-tain, Fol - low-ing yon - der star.
King for - ev - er, ceas-ing nev - er O - ver us all to reign.
Prayer and prais - ing, all men rais - ing, Wor-ship Him, God on high.
Sor-rowing, sigh-ing, bleed-ing, dy - ing, Sealed in the stone-cold tomb.
Al - le - lu - ia, Al - le - lu - ia! Peals through the earth and skies.

REFRAIN *a tempo*

O star of won - der, star of night, Star with loy - al beau - ty bright,

West-ward lead-ing, still pro-ceed-ing, Guide us to thy per - fect light.

81 Hark! the Herald Angels Sing

CHARLES WESLEY

FELIX MENDELSSOHN-BARTHOLDY
ARR. BY WILLIAM H. CUMMINGS

1. Hark! the her - ald an - gels sing, "Glo - ry to the new-born King;
2. Christ, by high-est Heav'n a - dored, Christ, the ev - er - last - ing Lord:
3. Hail the Heav'n-born Prince of Peace! Hail the Sun of right-eous-ness!
4. Come, De - sire of na - tions, come! Fix in us Thy hum - ble home:

Peace on earth, and mer - cy mild; God and sin - ners rec - on - ciled."
Late in time be - hold Him come, Off - spring of a vir - gin's womb.
Light and life to all He brings, Ris'n with heal - ing in His wings:
Rise, the wom-an's con-qu'ring seed, Bruise in us the ser - pent's head;

Joy - ful, all ye na - tions, rise, Join the tri - umph of the skies;
Veiled in flesh the God - head see, Hail th' in-car - nate De - i - ty!
Mild He lays His glo - ry by, Born that man no more may die;
Ad - am's like - ness now ef - face, Stamp Thine im - age in its place:

With an - gel - ic hosts pro - claim, "Christ is born in Beth - le - hem."
Pleased as man with men to ap-pear, Je - sus our Im-man - uel here.
Born to raise the sons of earth; Born to give them sec - ond birth.
Sec - ond Ad - am from a - bove, Re - in - state us in Thy love.

Hark! the Herald Angels Sing

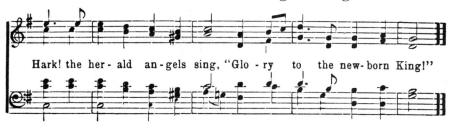

Hark! the her-ald an-gels sing, "Glo - ry   to   the new-born King!"

O Little Town of Bethlehem

82

PHILLIPS BROOKS

LEWIS H. REDNER

1. O lit-tle town of Beth-le-hem, How still we see thee lie! A-bove thy deep and
2. For Christ is born of Ma - ry; And gath-ered all a-bove, While mortals sleep, the
3. How si-lent-ly, how si-lent-ly The wondrous Gift is giv'n! So God im-parts to
4. O ho - ly Child of Beth-le-hem, De-scend to us, we pray; Cast out our sin and

dreamless sleep The si - lent stars go by; Yet in thy dark streets shin-eth The
an - gels keep Their watch of wond'ring love. O morn-ing stars, to - geth - er Pro-
hu-man hearts The bless-ings of His Heav'n. No ear may hear His com - ing; But
en - ter in, Be born in us to - day. We hear the Christmas an - gels The

ev - er-last-ing Light; The hopes and fears of all the years Are met in thee to - night.
claim the ho - ly birth, And prais-es sing to God the King, And peace to men on earth.
in this world of sin, Where meek souls will receive Him still, The dear Christ enters in.
great glad tidings tell,—O come to us, a-bide with us, Our Lord Em-man-u - el.

83 O Come, All Ye Faithful

LATIN HYMN
TR. BY FREDERICK OAKELEY

JOHN F. WADE'S "CANTUS DIVERSI"

1. O come, all ye faith-ful, joy-ful and tri-um-phant,
2. Sing, choirs of an-gels, sing in ex-ul-ta-tion,
3. Yea, Lord, we greet Thee, born this hap-py morn-ing,

O come ye, O come ye to Beth-le-hem;
O sing, all ye bright hosts of heav'n a-bove;
Je-sus, to Thee be all glo-ry giv'n;

Come and be-hold Him born the King of an-gels;
Glo-ry to God, all glo-ry in the high-est;
Word of the Fa-ther, now in flesh ap-pear-ing;

REFRAIN

O come, let us a-dore Him, O come, let us a-dore Him,

O come, let us a-dore Him, Christ, the Lord. A-MEN.

It Came upon the Midnight Clear 84

EDMUND H. SEARS

RICHARD S. WILLIS

1. It came up - on the mid-night clear, That glo-rious song of old,
2. Still thro' the clo - ven skies they come, With peace-ful wings un - furled,
3. And ye, be - neath life's crushing load, Whose forms are bend-ing low,
4. For lo, the days are has-t'ning on, By proph-et bards fore-told,

From an - gels bend-ing near the earth To touch their harps of gold:
And still their heav'n-ly mu - sic floats O'er all the wea - ry world:
Who toil a - long the climb-ing way With pain - ful steps and slow,
When with the ev - er - cir - cling years Comes round the age of gold;

"Peace on the earth, good-will to men, From heav'n's all-gracious King:" The
A - bove its sad and low - ly plains They bend on hov-'ring wing: And
Look now! for glad and gold - en hours Come swift-ly on the wing; O
When peace shall o - ver all the earth Its an-cient splen-dors fling. And

world in sol - emn still-ness lay To hear the an - gels sing.
ev - er o'er its Ba - bel sounds The bless - ed an - gels sing.
rest be - side the wea - ry road, And hear the an - gels sing.
the whole world give back the song Which now the an - gels sing. A-MEN.

85   There's a Song in the Air

JOSIAH G. HOLLAND

KARL P. HARRINGTON

Andante con moto

1. There's a song in the air! There's a star in the sky! There's a moth-er's deep
2. There's a tu-mult of joy O'er the won-der-ful birth, For the Vir-gin's sweet
3. In the light of that star Lie the a-ges im-pearled; And that song from a-
4. We re-joice in the light, And we ech-o the song That comes down thru the

ritard.   *piu mosso*

prayer, And a ba-by's low cry! And the star rains its fire while the
boy Is the Lord of the earth. Ay! the star rains its fire while the
far Has swept o-ver the world. Ev-'ry hearth is a-flame, and the
night From the heav-en-ly throng. Ay! we shout to the love-ly e-

ritard.

beau-ti-ful sing, For the man-ger of Beth-le-hem cra-dles a King!
beau-ti-ful sing, For the man-ger of Beth-le-hem cra-dles a King!
beau-ti-ful sing In the homes of the na-tions that Je-sus is King!
van-gel they bring, And we greet in His cra-dle our Sav-ior and King!

86   While Shepherds Watched Their Flocks

NAHUM TATE

GEORGE F. HANDEL

1. While shep-herds watched their flocks by night, All seat-ed on the ground, The
2. "Fear not!" said he; for might-y dread Had seized their trou-bled mind, "Glad
3. "To you, in Dav-id's town this day, Is born of Dav-id's line, The
4. "The heav'n-ly Babe you there shall find To hu-man view dis-played, All
5. "All glo-ry be to God on high, And to the earth be peace: Good

While Shepherds Watched Their Flocks

an - gel of the Lord came down, And glo-ry shone a-round, And glo-ry shone a-round.
ti - dings of great joy I bring, To you and all man-kind, To you and all man-kind.
Sav - ior who is Christ the Lord; And this shall be the sign: And this shall be the sign:
mean-ly wrapped in swath-ing-bands, And in a man-ger laid, And in a man-ger laid.
will hence-forth from heav'n to men, Be-gin and nev-er cease, Be-gin and nev-er cease."

Silent Night! Holy Night! 87

JOSEPH MOHR   FRANZ GRUBER

1. Si - lent night, ho - ly night, All   is calm,   all   is bright
2. Si - lent night, ho - ly night, Shep-herds quake at   the sight,
3. Si - lent night, ho - ly night, Son   of God, love's pure light
4. Si - lent night, ho - ly night, Won-drous star, lend thy light;

Round yon vir - gin moth-er and child. Ho - ly in-fant so ten-der and mild,
Glo - ries stream from heav-en a - far, Heav'n ly hosts sing Al - le - lu - ia;
Ra - diant beams from thy ho-ly face, With the dawn of re - deem - ing grace,
With the an - gels let us sing, Al - le - lu - ia to our King;

Sleep in heav-en - ly   peace,   Sleep in heav-en - ly   peace.
Christ the Sav-ior is   born!   Christ the Sav-ior is   born!
Je - sus, Lord, at thy   birth,   Je - sus, Lord, at thy   birth.
Christ the Sav-ior is   born.   Christ the Sav-ior is   born.

88 Joy to the World!

FROM PSALM 98
ISAAC WATTS

ARR. FROM GEORGE F. HANDEL

1. Joy to the world! the Lord is come; Let earth re-
2. Joy to the world! the Sav - ior reigns; Let men their
3. No more let sins and sor - rows grow, Nor thorns in-
4. He rules the world with truth and grace, And makes the

ceive her King; Let ev - 'ry heart pre - pare Him room,
songs em - ploy; While fields and floods, rocks, hills and plains
fest the ground; He comes to make His bless - ings flow
na - tions prove The glo - ries of His right-eous - ness,

And heav'n and na - ture sing, And heav'n and na - ture
Re - peat the sound - ing joy, Re - peat the sound - ing
Far as the curse is found, Far as the curse is
And won - ders of His love, And won - ders of His
1. And heav'n and na - ture sing,.......... And

sing, And heav'n, and heav'n and na - ture sing.
joy, Re - peat, re - peat the sound - ing joy.
found, Far as, far as the curse is found.
love, And won - ders, and won - ders of His love.
heav'n and na - ture sing,

Thou Didst Leave Thy Throne

Emily E. S. Elliott

Timothy R. Matthews

1. Thou didst leave Thy throne And Thy king-ly crown When Thou
2. Heav-en's arch-es rang When the an-gels sang, Pro- -
3. The fox-es found rest, And the birds their nest In the
4. Thou cam-est, O Lord, With the liv-ing word That should
5. When the heav-ens shall ring, And the an-gels sing, At Thy

cam-est to earth for me; But in Beth-le-hem's home
claim-ing Thy roy-al de-gree; But of low-ly birth
shade of the for-est tree; But Thy couch was the sod,
set Thy peo-ple free; But with mock-ing scorn,
com-ing to vic-to-ry, Let Thy voice call me home,

Was there found no room For Thy ho-ly na-tiv-i-ty:
Didst Thou come to earth, And in great-est hu-mil-i-ty:
O Thou Son of God, In the des-erts of Gal-i-lee:
And with crown of thorn, They bore Thee to Cal-va-ry:
Say-ing, "Yet there is room, There is room at My side for thee;"

REFRAIN

1-4. O come to my heart, Lord Je-sus, There is room in my heart for Thee.
5. My heart shall rejoice, Lord Je-sus, When Thou comest and call-est for me.

90 The First Noel

OLD ENGLISH CAROL

TRADITIONAL MELODY FROM
W. SANDY'S "CHRISTMAS CAROLS"

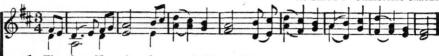

1. The first No-el the angel did say Was to certain poor shepherds in fields as they lay;
2. And by the light of that same Star, Three wise men came from country far;
3. This Star drew nigh to the northwest, O'er Beth-le-hem it took its rest.
4. Then enter-ed in those wise men three, Full rev-'rent-ly up-on their knee,

In fields where they lay keeping their sheep, On a cold winter's night that was so deep.
To seek for a King was their in-tent, And to follow the Star wherever it went.
And there it did both stop and stay, Right o-ver the place where Jesus lay.
And of-fered there in His pres-ence, Their gold, and myrrh, and frank-incense.

REFRAIN.

No-el, No-el, No-el, No-el, Born is the King of Is-ra-el.

91 I Heard the Bells on Christmas Day

HENRY W. LONGFELLOW

J. BAPTISTE CALKIN

1. I heard the bells on Christ-mas day Their old fa-mil-iar car-ols play,
2. I thought how, as the day had come, The bel-fries of all Chris-ten-dom
3. And in de-spair I bowed my head: "There is no peace on earth," I said,
4. Then pealed the bells more loud and deep: "God is not dead, nor doth He sleep;
5. Till, ring-ing, sing-ing on its way, The world revolved from night to day,

I Heard the Bells on Christmas Day

And wild and sweet the words re-peat Of peace on earth, good-will to men.
Had rolled a-long th' un-bro-ken song Of peace on earth, good-will to men.
"For hate is strong, and mocks the song Of peace on earth, good-will to men."
The wrong shall fail, the right pre-vail, With peace on earth, good-will to men:"
A voice, a chime, a chant sub-lime, Of peace on earth, good-will to men!

Angels, from the Realms of Glory 92

JAMES MONTGOMERY

HENRY SMART

1. An - gels, from the realms of glo - ry, Wing your flight o'er all the earth;
2. Shep-herds, in the field a - bid-ing, Watching o'er your flocks by night,
3. Sa - ges, leave your con-tem-pla-tions, Bright-er vi-sions beam a - far;
4. Saints, be-fore the al - tar bend-ing, Watching long in hope and fear,

Ye, who sang cre - a-tion's sto - ry, Now pro-claim Mes - si - ah's birth:
God with man is now re - sid - ing, Yon-der shines the In - fant-Light;
Seek the great De - sire of na-tions, Ye have seen His na - tal star;
Sud-den-ly the Lord, de-scend-ing, In His tem - ple shall ap - pear;

Come and wor-ship, come and wor-ship, Wor-ship Christ, the new-born King.

93 Away in a Manger

MARTIN LUTHER
MARTIN LUTHER

1. A - way in a man - ger, No crib for a bed, The lit - tle Lord
2. The cat - tle are low - ing, The poor ba - by wakes, But lit - tle Lord

Je - sus Laid down His sweet head; The stars in the sky.... Looked
Je - sus, No cry - ing He makes; I love Thee, Lord Je - sus! Look

down where He lay,—The lit - tle Lord Je - sus, A - sleep on the hay.
down from the sky, And stay by my cra - dle To watch lul - la - by.

94 Alas! and Did My Savior Bleed?

ISAAC WATTS
HUGH WILSON

1. A - las! and did my Sav - ior bleed? And did my Sov - 'reign die?
2. Was it for crimes that I have done He groaned up - on the tree?
3. Well might the sun in dark - ness hide, And shut his glo - ries in,
4. But drops of grief can ne'er re - pay The debt of love I owe;

Would He de - vote that sa - cred head For such a worm as I?
A - maz - ing pit - y! grace un-known! And love be - yond de - gree!
When Christ, the might - y Mak - er, died For man the crea - ture's sin.
Here, Lord, I give my - self to Thee,—'Tis all that I can do.

At the Cross

Isaac Watts
Ref., Ralph E. Hudson

Ralph E. Hudson

1. A - las, and did my Sav - ior bleed? And did my Sov - 'reign die?
2. Was it for crimes that I have done, He groaned up - on the tree?
3. Well might the sun in dark-ness hide, And shut his glo - ries in,
4. But drops of grief can ne'er re - pay The debt of love I owe:

Would He de - vote that sa - cred head For such a worm as I?
A - maz - ing pit - y! grace unknown! And love be - yond de - gree!
When Christ, the might-y Mak - er, died For man the crea-ture's sin.
Here, Lord, I give my - self a - way, 'Tis all that I can do!

CHORUS

At the cross, at the cross where I first saw the light, And the

bur - den of my heart rolled a - way, (rolled a-way,) It was there by faith

I re-ceived my sight, And now I am hap - py all the day!

96 Heaven Came Down and Glory Filled My Soul

John W. Peterson   John W. Peterson

1. O what a won-der-ful, won-der-ful day — Day I will nev-er for - get;
2. Born of the Spir-it with life from a-bove In-to God's fam'-ly di - vine;
3. Now I've a hope that will sure-ly en-dure Aft-er the pass-ing of time;

Af-ter I'd wan-dered in dark-ness a-way, Je - sus my Sav-ior I met.
Jus-ti-fied ful-ly thru Cal-va-ry's love, O what a stand-ing is mine!
I have a fu-ture in heav-en for sure, There in those man-sions sub-lime.

O what a ten-der, com-pas-sion-ate friend, He met the need of my heart;
And the trans-ac-tion so quick-ly was made, When as a sin-ner I came,
And it's be-cause of that won-der-ful day When at the cross I be - lieved;

Shad-ows dis-pel-ling, with joy I am tell-ing, He made all the dark-ness de - part!
Took of the of-fer of grace He did prof-fer, He saved me, O praise His dear name!
Rich-es e-ter-nal and bless-ings su-per-nal From His pre-cious hand I re - ceived.

CHORUS

Heav-en came down and glo-ry filled my soul,
filled my soul,

Heaven Came Down and Glory Filled My Soul

When at the cross the Sav-ior made me whole;
made me whole; My
sins were washed a - way And my night was turned to day —
Heav-en came down and glo-ry filled my soul!
filled my soul!

Thy Holy Spirit, Lord, Alone 97

HENRIETTA E. BLAIR

WILLIAM J. KIRKPATRICK

1. Thy Ho - ly Spir - it, Lord, a - lone Can turn our hearts from sin; His
2. Thy Ho - ly Spir - it, Lord, a - lone Can deep-er love in - spire; His
3. Thy Ho - ly Spir - it, Lord, can bring The gifts we seek in pray'r; His
4. Thy Ho - ly Spir - it, Lord, can give The grace we need this hour; And

pow'r a - lone can sanc - ti - fy And keep us pure with - in.
pow'r a - lone with - in our souls Can light the sa - cred fire.
voice can words of com-fort speak, And still each wave of care.
while we wait, O Spir - it, come In sanc - ti - fy - ing pow'r.

Be Still, My Soul

FROM PSALM 46
KATHARINA VON SCHLEGEL
TR. BY JANE L. BORTHWICK

JEAN SIBELIUS

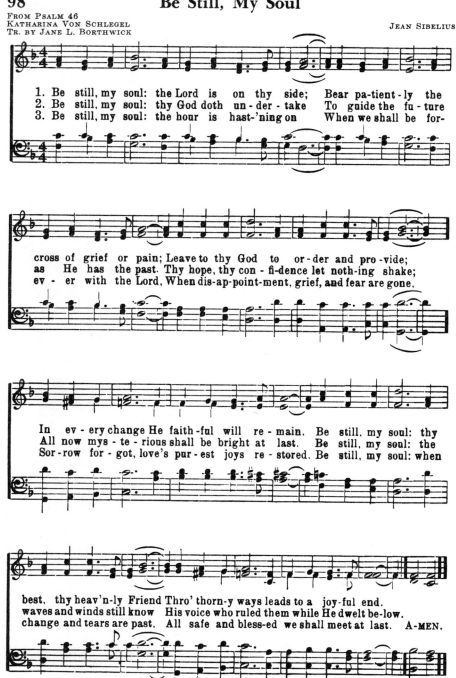

1. Be still, my soul: the Lord is on thy side; Bear pa-tient-ly the
2. Be still, my soul: thy God doth un-der-take To guide the fu-ture
3. Be still, my soul: the hour is hast-'ning on When we shall be for-

cross of grief or pain; Leave to thy God to or-der and pro-vide;
as He has the past. Thy hope, thy con-fi-dence let noth-ing shake;
ev-er with the Lord, When dis-ap-point-ment, grief, and fear are gone,

In ev-ery change He faith-ful will re-main. Be still, my soul: thy
All now mys-te-rious shall be bright at last. Be still, my soul: the
Sor-row for-got, love's pur-est joys re-stored. Be still, my soul: when

best, thy heav'n-ly Friend Thro' thorn-y ways leads to a joy-ful end.
waves and winds still know His voice who ruled them while He dwelt be-low.
change and tears are past. All safe and bless-ed we shall meet at last. A-MEN.

Sweet Peace, the Gift of God's Love

Peter P. Bilhorn   Peter P. Bilhorn

1. There comes to my heart one sweet strain, (sweet strain.) A
2. Thro' Christ on the cross peace was made, (was made.) My
3. When Je - sus as Lord I had crowned, (had crowned,) My
4. In Je - sus for peace I a - bide, (a - bide.) And

glad and a joy - ous re - frain; (re - frain;) I sing it a -
debt by His death was all paid; (all paid;) No oth - er foun -
heart with this peace did a - bound; (a - bound;) In Him the rich
as I keep close to His side, (His side,) There's noth - ing but

gain and a - gain, Sweet peace, the gift of God's love.
da - tion is laid For peace, the gift of God's love.
bless - ing I found, Sweet peace, the gift of God's love.
peace doth be - tide, Sweet peace, the gift of God's love.

CHORUS

Peace, peace, sweet peace! Won - der - ful gift from a - bove! (a - bove!)

cres.

Oh, won - der - ful, won - der - ful peace! Sweet peace, the gift of God's love!

100   Wonderful Peace

W. D. CORNELL, ALT.

W. G. COOPER

1. Far a-way in the depths of my spir-it to-night Rolls a
2. What a treas-ure I have in this won-der-ful peace, Bur-ied
3. I am rest-ing to-night in this won-der-ful peace, Rest-ing
4. And me-thinks when I rise to that Cit-y of peace, Where the
5. Ah! soul, are you here with-out com-fort or rest, March-ing

mel-o-dy sweet-er than psalm; In ce-les-tial-like strains it un-
deep in the heart of my soul; So se-cure that no pow-er can
sweet-ly in Je-sus' con-trol; For I'm kept from all dan-ger by
Au-thor of peace I shall see, That one strain of the song which the
down the rough pathway of time? Make Je-sus your friend ere the

ceas-ing-ly falls O'er my soul like an in-fi-nite calm.
mine it a-way, While the years of e-ter-ni-ty roll.
night and by day, And His glo-ry is flood-ing my soul.
ran-somed will sing, In that heav-en-ly king-dom shall be:
shad-ows grow dark; Oh, ac-cept this sweet peace so sub-lime.

CHORUS

Peace! peace! won-der-ful peace, Com-ing down from the Fa-ther a-bove; Sweep

o-ver my spir-it for-ev-er, I pray, In fath-om-less bil-lows of love.

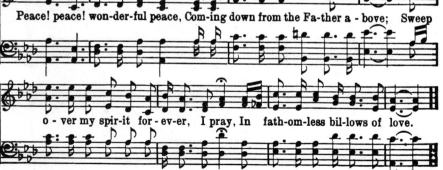

Wonderful Peace

Haldor Lillenas

Haldor Lillenas

1. Com - ing to Je - sus, my Sav - ior, I found Won - der - ful peace,
2. Peace like a riv - er, so deep and so broad, Won - der - ful peace,
3. Peace like a ho - ly and in - fi - nite calm, Won - der - ful peace,
4. Gone is the bat - tle that once raged with - in, Won - der - ful peace,

won - der - ful peace; Storms in their fu - ry may rage all a -
won - der - ful peace; Rest - ing my soul on the bos - om of
won - der - ful peace; Like to the strains of an e - ven - ing
won - der - ful peace; Je - sus has saved me and cleansed me from

REFRAIN

round, I have peace, sweet peace.
God, I have peace, sweet peace.
psalm, I have peace, sweet peace.
sin, I have peace, sweet peace. Peace, peace, won - der - ful peace,

Peace, peace, glo - ri - ous peace; Since my Re - deem - er has

ran - somed my soul, I have peace, sweet peace.......
won - der - ful peace.

102   Master, the Tempest Is Raging

MARY A. BAKER

HORATIUS R. PALME
ARR. BY FRED JACK

1. Mas - ter, the tem - pest is rag - ing! The bil - lows are toss - ing high!
2. Mas - ter, with an - guish of spir - it I bow in my grief to - day;
3. Mas - ter, the ter - ror is o - ver, The el - e-ments sweet - ly rest;

The sky is o'ershadowed with blackness, No shel - ter or help is nigh;
The depths of my sad heart are trou - bled; O wak - en and save, I pray!
Earth's sun in the calm lake is mir - rored, And heav - en's with - in my breast.

Solo   *Parts*

(*Hum*)
"Car - est Thou not that we per - ish?" How canst Thou lie a - sleep,
Tor - rents of sin and of an - guish Sweep o'er my sink - ing soul!
Lin - ger, O bless - ed Re - deem - er, Leave me a - lone no more;
(*Hum*)

When each moment so mad - ly is threat'ning A grave in the an - gry deep?
And I per - ish! I per - ish, dear Mas - ter; O has - ten, and take con - trol!
And with joy I shall make the blest har - bor, And rest on the bliss - ful shore.

Master, the Tempest Is Raging

103   Like a River Glorious

FRANCES R. HAVERGAL

JAMES MOUNTAIN

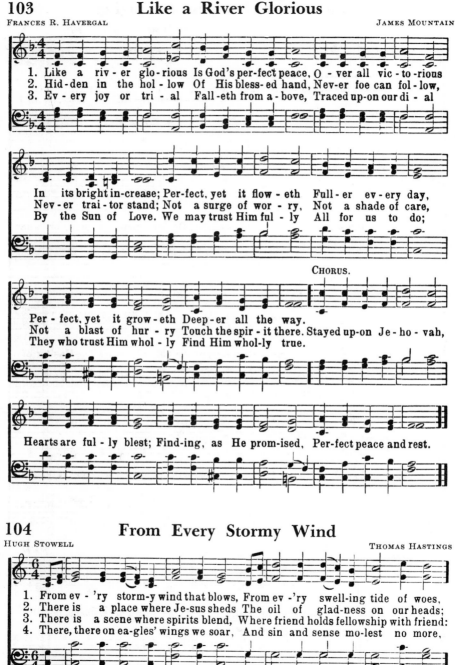

1. Like a riv-er glo-rious Is God's per-fect peace, O - ver all vic-to-rious
2. Hid-den in the hol-low Of His bless-ed hand, Nev-er foe can fol-low,
3. Ev-ery joy or tri-al Fall-eth from a-bove, Traced up-on our di-al

In its bright in-crease; Per-fect, yet it flow-eth Full-er ev-ery day,
Nev-er trai-tor stand; Not a surge of wor-ry, Not a shade of care,
By the Sun of Love. We may trust Him ful-ly All for us to do;

CHORUS.

Per-fect, yet it grow-eth Deep-er all the way.
Not a blast of hur-ry Touch the spir-it there. Stayed up-on Je-ho-vah,
They who trust Him whol-ly Find Him whol-ly true.

Hearts are ful-ly blest; Find-ing, as He prom-ised, Per-fect peace and rest.

104   From Every Stormy Wind

HUGH STOWELL

THOMAS HASTINGS

1. From ev-'ry storm-y wind that blows, From ev-'ry swell-ing tide of woes,
2. There is a place where Je-sus sheds The oil of glad-ness on our heads;
3. There is a scene where spirits blend, Where friend holds fellowship with friend:
4. There, there on ea-gles' wings we soar, And sin and sense mo-lest no more,

From Every Stormy Wind

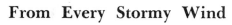

There is a calm, a sure re-treat: 'Tis found be-neath the mer-cy seat.
A place than all be-sides more sweet: It is the blood-bought mer-cy seat.
Tho' sun-dered far, by faith they meet A-round one com-mon mer-cy seat.
And heav'n comes down our souls to greet, When glo-ry crowns the mer-cy seat.

O Thou in Whose Presence   105

JOSEPH SWAIN

FREEMAN LEWIS

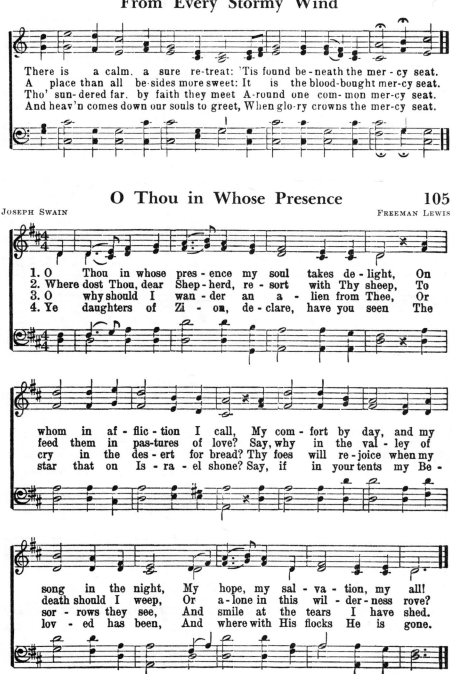

1. O Thou in whose pres-ence my soul takes de-light, On
2. Where dost Thou, dear Shep-herd, re-sort with Thy sheep, To
3. O why should I wan-der an a-lien from Thee, Or
4. Ye daughters of Zi-on, de-clare, have you seen The

whom in af-flic-tion I call, My com-fort by day, and my
feed them in pas-tures of love? Say, why in the val-ley of
cry in the des-ert for bread? Thy foes will re-joice when my
star that on Is-ra-el shone? Say, if in your tents my Be-

song in the night, My hope, my sal-va-tion, my all!
death should I weep, Or a-lone in this wil-der-ness rove?
sor-rows they see, And smile at the tears I have shed.
lov-ed has been, And where with His flocks He is gone.

106 I'd Rather Have Jesus

Rhea F. Miller

George Beverly Shea

1. I'd rath-er have Je-sus than sil-ver or gold, I'd rath-er be
2. I'd rath-er have Je-sus than men's ap-plause, I'd rath-er be
3. He's fair-er than lil-ies of rar-est bloom, He's sweet-er than

His than have rich-es un-told; I'd rath-er have Je-sus than
faith-ful to His dear cause; I'd rath-er have Je-sus than
hon-ey from out the comb; He's all that my hun-ger-ing

hous-es or lands, I'd rath-er be led by His nail-pierced hand
world-wide fame, I'd rath-er be true to His ho-ly name
spir-it needs, I'd rath-er have Je-sus and let Him lead

Than to be the king of a vast do-main Or be held in sin's dread sway;

I'd rath-er have Je-sus than an-y-thing This world af-fords to-day.

And Can It Be That I Should Gain?

CHARLES WESLEY

THOMAS CAMPBELL

1. And can it be that I should gain An in-ter-est in the Sav-iour's blood? Died He for me, who caused His pain? For me, who Him to death pur-sued? A-maz-ing love! how can it be That Thou, my God, shouldst die for me?

2. He left His Fa-ther's throne a-bove, So free, so in-fi-nite His grace; Emp-tied Him-self of all but love, And bled for A-dam's help-less race; 'Tis mer-cy all, im-mense and free; For, O my God, it found out me.

3. Long my im-pris-oned spir-it lay Fast bound in sin and na-ture's night; Thine eye dif-fused a quick-'ning ray, I woke, the dun-geon flamed with light; My chains fell off, my heart was free; I rose, went forth, and fol-lowed Thee.

REFRAIN

A-maz-ing love! how can it be That Thou, my God, shouldst die for me.

A-maz-ing love! How can it be That Thou, my God,

108 Blessed Quietness

Manie P. Ferguson

W. S. Marshall
Arr. by James M. Kirk

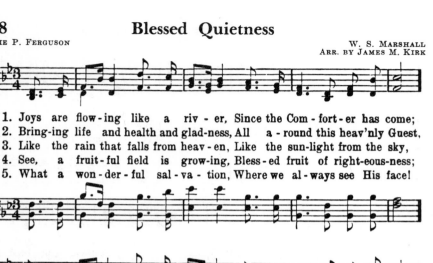

1. Joys are flow-ing like a riv - er, Since the Com - fort-er has come;
2. Bring-ing life and health and glad-ness, All a - round this heav'nly Guest,
3. Like the rain that falls from heav - en, Like the sun-light from the sky,
4. See, a fruit-ful field is grow-ing, Bless-ed fruit of right-eous-ness;
5. What a won-der-ful sal-va - tion, Where we al-ways see His face!

He a - bides with us for - ev - er, Makes the trust - ing heart His home.
Ban-ished un - be - lief and sad-ness, Changed our wea - ri - ness to rest.
So the Ho - ly Ghost is giv - en, Com - ing on us from on high.
And the streams of life are flow-ing In the lone - ly wil - der-ness.
What a per - fect hab - i - ta - tion, What a qui - et rest-ing place!

REFRAIN

Bless-ed qui - et-ness, ho - ly qui - et-ness, What as-sur-ance in my soul!

rit.

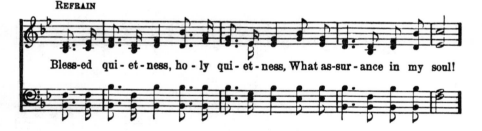

On the storm-y sea, He speaks peace to me, How the bil-lows cease to roll!

I Am Praying for You

S. O'Malley Cluff

Ira D. Sankey

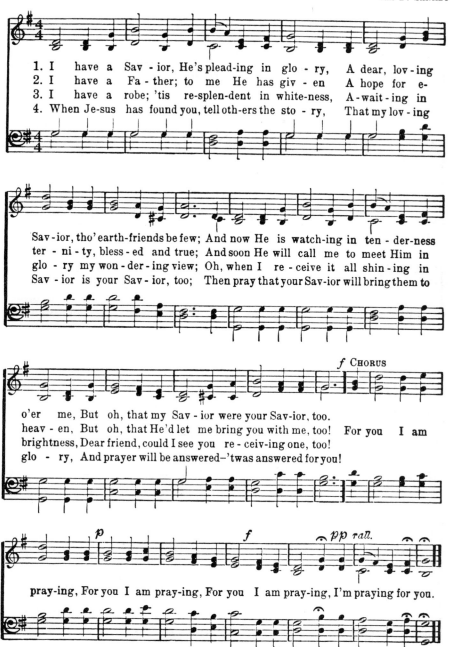

1. I have a Sav - ior, He's plead-ing in glo - ry, A dear, lov - ing
2. I have a Fa - ther; to me He has giv - en A hope for e -
3. I have a robe; 'tis re-splen-dent in white-ness, A - wait - ing in
4. When Je-sus has found you, tell oth-ers the sto - ry, That my lov - ing

Sav-ior, tho' earth-friends be few; And now He is watch-ing in ten - der-ness
ter - ni - ty, bless - ed and true; And soon He will call me to meet Him in
glo - ry my won - der-ing view; Oh, when I re - ceive it all shin - ing in
Sav - ior is your Sav - ior, too; Then pray that your Sav-ior will bring them to

o'er me, But oh, that my Sav - ior were your Sav-ior, too.
heav - en, But oh, that He'd let me bring you with me, too! For you I am
brightness, Dear friend, could I see you re - ceiv-ing one, too!
glo - ry, And prayer will be answered—'twas answered for you!

f CHORUS

p ... *f* ... *pp rall.*

pray-ing, For you I am pray-ing, For you I am pray-ing, I'm praying for you.

110 Sweet Hour of Prayer

WILLIAM W. WALFORD

WILLIAM B. BRADBURY

1. Sweet hour of prayer! sweet hour of prayer! That calls me from a world of care,
2. Sweet hour of prayer! sweet hour of prayer! Thy wings shall my pe-ti-tion bear
3. Sweet hour of prayer! sweet hour of prayer! May I thy con-so-la-tion share,

And bids me at my Fa-ther's throne Make all my wants and wish-es known;
To Him whose truth and faith-ful-ness En-gage the wait-ing soul to bless;
Till, from Mount Pisgah's loft-y height, I view my home, and take my flight:

In sea-sons of dis-tress and grief, My soul has oft-en found re-lief,
And since He bids me seek His face, Be-lieve His word and trust His grace,
This robe of flesh I'll drop, and rise To seize the ev-er-last-ing prize;

And oft es-caped the tempter's snare By thy re-turn, sweet hour of prayer.
I'll cast on Him my ev-'ry care, And wait for thee, sweet hour of prayer.
And shout, while passing thro' the air, Farewell, farewell, sweet hour of prayer.

111 Jesus, and Shall It Ever Be?

JOSEPH GRIGG
ALT. BY BENJAMIN FRANCIS

HENRY K. OLIVER

1. Je-sus, and shall it ev-er be, A mor-tal man a-shamed of Thee?
2. A-shamed of Je-sus! that dear Friend On Whom my hopes of heav'n depend!
3. A-shamed of Je-sus! yes, I may, When I've no guilt to wash a-way;
4. Till then—nor is my boast-ing vain— Till then I boast a Sav-ior slain;

Jesus, and Shall It Ever Be?

A-shamed of Thee, Whom angels praise Whose glories shine thro' endless days?
No; when I blush, be this my shame, That I no more re-vere His name.
No tears to wipe, no good to crave, No fears to quell, no soul to save.
And O, may this my glo - ry be, That Christ is not a-shamed of me. A-MEN.

Lord, I Have Shut the Door   112

WILLIAM M. RUNYAN

WILLIAM M. RUNYAN

1. Lord, I have shut the door, Speak now the word Which in the
2. Lord, I have shut the door, Here do I bow; Speak, for my
3. In this blest qui - et - ness Clam - or - ings cease; Here in Thy
4. Lord, I have shut the door, Strength-en my heart; Yon - der a—

din and throng Could not be heard; Hushed now my in - ner heart,
soul at - tent Turns to Thee now; Re - buke Thou what is vain,
pres-ence dwells In - fi - nite peace; Yon - der, the strife and cry,
waits the task— I share a part. On - ly through grace be-stowed

Whis - per Thy will, While I have come a - part, While all is still.
Coun - sel my soul, Thy ho - ly will re - veal, My will con - trol.
Yon - der, the sin: Lord, I have shut the door, Thou art with - in.
May I be true; Here, while a - lone with Thee, My strength re - new.

113   I Must Tell Jesus

ELISHA A. HOFFMAN   ELISHA A. HOFFMAN

1. I must tell Jesus all of my tri - als; I can-not bear these
2. I must tell Jesus all of my troub-les; He is a kind, com-
3. Tempted and tried I need a great Sav - ior, One who can help my
4. O how the world to e - vil al - lures me! O how my heart is

bur - dens a - lone; In my dis-tress He kind-ly will help me;
pas - sion-ate Friend; If I but ask Him, He will de - liv - er,
bur - dens to bear; I must tell Je - sus, I must tell Je - sus;
tempt-ed to sin! I must tell Je - sus, and He will help me

He ev - er loves and cares for His own.
Make of my troub-les quick-ly an end.
He all my cares and sor-rows will share.
O - ver the world the vic-t'ry to win.

CHORUS

I must tell Je - sus! I must tell Je - sus! I can-not bear my bur-dens a - lone; I must tell Je - sus! I must tell Je - sus! Je-sus can help me, Je-sus a - lone.

Revive Thy Work

ALFRED MIDLANE

JAMES McGRANAHAN

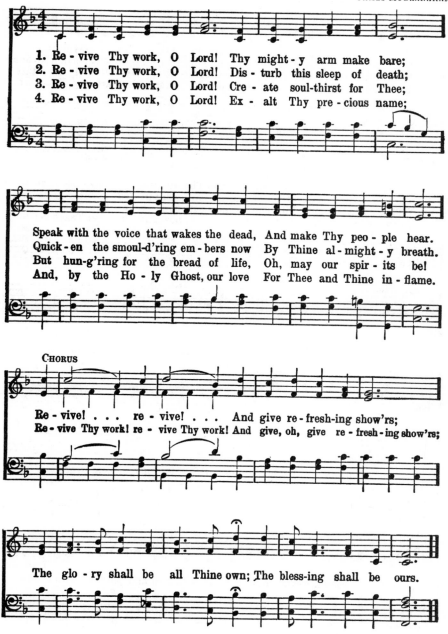

1. Re - vive Thy work, O Lord! Thy might - y arm make bare;
2. Re - vive Thy work, O Lord! Dis - turb this sleep of death;
3. Re - vive Thy work, O Lord! Cre - ate soul-thirst for Thee;
4. Re - vive Thy work, O Lord! Ex - alt Thy pre - cious name;

Speak with the voice that wakes the dead, And make Thy peo - ple hear.
Quick - en the smoul-d'ring em - bers now By Thine al - might - y breath.
But hun-g'ring for the bread of life, Oh, may our spir - its be!
And, by the Ho - ly Ghost, our love For Thee and Thine in - flame.

CHORUS

Re - vive! ... re - vive! ... And give re - fresh-ing show'rs;
Re - vive Thy work! re - vive Thy work! And give, oh, give re - fresh-ing show'rs;

The glo - ry shall be all Thine own; The bless-ing shall be ours.

115 Teach Me to Pray

ALBERT S. REITZ

ALBERT S. REITZ

1. Teach me to pray, Lord, teach me to pray; This is my heart-cry,
2. Pow - er in prayer, Lord, pow - er in prayer, Here 'mid earth's sin and
3. My weakened will, Lord, Thou canst re - new; My sin - ful na - ture
4. Teach me to pray, Lord, teach me to pray; Thou art my Pat - tern,

day un - to day; I long to know Thy will and Thy way; Teach me to
sor - row and care; Men lost and dy - ing, souls in des - pair: O give me
Thou canst sub-due; Fill me just now with pow - er a - new. Pow - er to
day un - to day; Thou art my Sure - ty, now and for aye; Teach me to

CHORUS

pray, Lord, teach me to pray.
pow - er, pow - er in prayer! Liv - ing in Thee, Lord, and Thou in
pray and pow - er to do!
pray, Lord, teach me to pray.

me; Con - stant a - bid - ing, this is my plea; Grant me Thy

pow - er, boundless and free: Pow - er with men and pow - er with Thee.

Copyright 1925 by A. S. Reitz. Renewal 1953 Broadman Press. Used by permission

Tell It to Jesus

JEREMIAH E. RANKIN

EDMUND S. LORENZ

1. Are you wea-ry, are you heav-y-heart-ed? Tell it to Je-sus,
2. Do the tears flow down your cheeks un-bid-den? Tell it to Je-sus,
3. Do you fear the gath-'ring clouds of sor-row? Tell it to Je-sus,
4. Are you troub-led at the thought of dy-ing? Tell it to Je-sus,

Tell it to Je-sus; Are you griev-ing o-ver joys de-part-ed?
Tell it to Je-sus; Have you sins that to men's eyes are hid-den?
Tell it to Je-sus; Are you anx-ious what shall be to-mor-row?
Tell it to Je-sus; For Christ's com-ing King-dom are you sigh-ing?

CHORUS

Tell it to Je-sus a-lone. Tell it to Je-sus, tell it to Je-sus,

He is a friend that's well known; You've no oth-er

such a friend or broth-er, Tell it to Je-sus a-lone.

117 The Beautiful Garden of Prayer

ELEANOR A. SCHROLL

JAMES H. FILLMORE

1. There's a gar-den where Je-sus is wait-ing, There's a place that is
2. There's a gar-den where Je-sus is wait-ing, And I go with my
3. There's a gar-den where Je-sus is wait-ing, And He bids you to

won-drous-ly fair; For it glows with the light of His pres-ence, 'Tis the
bur-den and care, Just to learn from His lips words of com-fort In the
come meet Him there; Just to bow, and re-ceive a new bless-ing, In the

beau-ti-ful gar-den of prayer.

REFRAIN

O the beau-ti-ful gar-den, the gar-den of prayer, O the beau-ti-ful gar-den of prayer; There my Sav-ior a-waits, and He o-pens the gates To the beau-ti-ful gar-den of prayer.

'Tis the Blessed Hour of Prayer

FANNY J. CROSBY

WILLIAM H. DOANE

1. 'Tis the bless-ed hour of prayer, when our hearts low-ly bend,
2. 'Tis the bless-ed hour of prayer, when the Sav-iour draws near,
3. 'Tis the bless-ed hour of prayer, when the tempt-ed and tried
4. At the bless-ed hour of prayer, trust-ing Him we be-lieve

And we gath-er to Je-sus, our Sav-iour and Friend; If we
With a ten-der com-pas-sion His chil-dren to hear; When He
To the Sav-iour who loves them their sor-row con-fide; With a
That the bless-ings we're need-ing we'll sure-ly re-ceive; In the

come to Him in faith, His pro-tec-tion to share, What a balm for the
tells us we may cast at His feet ev-ery care, What a balm for the
sym-pa-thiz-ing heart He re-moves ev-ery care; What a balm for the
full-ness of this trust we shall lose ev-ery care; What a balm for the

CHORUS

wea-ry! O how sweet to be there! Bless-ed hour of prayer, Bless-ed

hour of prayer; What a balm for the wea-ry! O how sweet to be there!

119 Did You Think to Pray?

MRS. M. A. KIDDER   W. O. PERKINS

1. Ere you left your room this morning, Did you think to pray? In the name of
2. When you met with great temp-ta-tion, Did you think to pray? By His dy - ing
3. When your heart was filled with an-ger, Did you think to pray? Did you plead for
4. When sore tri - als came up - on you, Did you think to pray? When your soul was

Christ our Sav - ior, Did you sue for lov-ing fa - vor, As a shield to - day?
love and mer - it, Did you claim the Ho-ly Spir - it As your guide and stay?
grace, my broth-er, That you might forgive an-oth - er Who had crossed your way?
bowed in sor - row, Balm of Gil-ead did you bor - row, At the gates of day?

D. S.—*So in sor-row and in glad - ness, Don't for-get to pray.*

CHORUS   D. S.

Oh, how pray-ing rests the wea - ry! Prayer will change the night to day;

120 Work, for the Night Is Coming

ANNA L. WALKER   LOWELL MASON

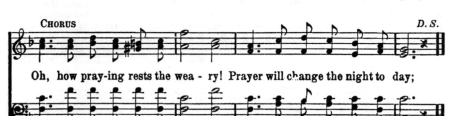

1. Work, for the night is com-ing, Work thro' the morning hours; Work while the dew is
2. Work, for the night is com-ing, Work thro' the sun-ny noon; Fill brightest hours with
3. Work, for the night is com-ing, Un - der the sun - set skies; While their bright tints are

Work, for the Night Is Coming

spark-ling; Work, 'mid springing flow'rs. Work, when the day grows bright-er,
la - bor, Rest comes sure and soon. Give ev - 'ry fly - ing min - ute
glow-ing, Work, for day-light flies. Work till the last beam fad - eth,

Work in the glow-ing sun; Work, for the night is coming, When man's work is done.
Something to keep in store; Work, for the night is coming, When man works no more.
Fad-eth to shine no more; Work, while the night is dark'ning, When man's work is o'er.

Praise Ye the Father

AUTHOR UNKNOWN

FRIEDRICH F. FLEMMING

121

1. Praise ye the Fa - ther! for His lov - ing kind-ness, Ten - der - ly
2. Praise ye the Sav - iour! great is His com - pas - sion, Gra - cious - ly
3. Praise ye the Spir - it! Com-fort - er of Is - rael, Sent of the

cares He for His err - ing chil-dren; Praise Him, ye an - gels,
cares He for His cho - sen peo - ple; Young men and maid - ens,
Fa - ther and the Son to bless us; Praise ye the Fa - ther,

praise Him in the heav-ens, Praise ye Je - ho - vah!
ye old men and chil-dren, Praise ye the Sav - iour!
Son and Ho - ly Spir - it, Praise ye the Tri - une God! A-MEN.

122 Unto the Hills

JOHN D. S. CAMPBELL
FROM PSALM 121

CHARLES H. PURDAY

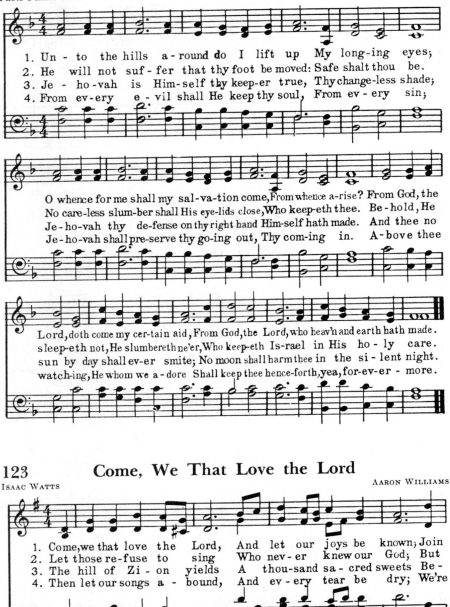

1. Un - to the hills a - round do I lift up My long-ing eyes;
2. He will not suf - fer that thy foot be moved: Safe shalt thou be.
3. Je - ho-vah is Him-self thy keep-er true, Thy change-less shade;
4. From ev - ery e - vil shall He keep thy soul, From ev - ery sin;

O whence for me shall my sal-va-tion come, From whence a-rise? From God, the
No care-less slum-ber shall His eye-lids close, Who keep-eth thee. Be-hold, He
Je - ho-vah thy de-fense on thy right hand Him-self hath made. And thee no
Je - ho-vah shall pre-serve thy go-ing out, Thy com-ing in. A-bove thee

Lord, doth come my cer-tain aid, From God, the Lord, who heav'n and earth hath made.
sleep-eth not, He slumbereth ne'er, Who keep-eth Is-rael in His ho - ly care.
sun by day shall ev-er smite; No moon shall harm thee in the si - lent night.
watch-ing, He whom we a-dore Shall keep thee hence-forth, yea, for-ev-er - more.

123 Come, We That Love the Lord

ISAAC WATTS

AARON WILLIAMS

1. Come, we that love the Lord, And let our joys be known; Join
2. Let those re-fuse to sing Who nev-er knew our God; But
3. The hill of Zi - on yields A thou-sand sa - cred sweets Be-
4. Then let our songs a - bound, And ev - ery tear be dry; We're

Come, We That Love the Lord

in a song with sweet ac-cord, And thus sur-round the throne.
chil-dren of the heaven-ly King May speak their joys a-broad.
fore we reach the heaven-ly fields, Or walk the gold-en streets.
march-ing thro' Em-man-uel's ground To fair-er worlds on high. A-MEN.

Teach Me Thy Will, O Lord   124

KATHERINE A. GRIMES

WILLIAM M. RUNYAN

1. Teach me Thy will, O Lord, Teach me Thy way; Teach me to
2. Teach me Thy won-drous grace, Bound-less and free; Lord, let Thy
3. Teach me by pain Thy power, Teach me by love; Teach me to
4. Teach Thou my lips to sing, My heart to praise; Be Thou my

know Thy word, Teach me to pray. What-e'er seems best to Thee, That be my
bless-ed face Shine up-on me. Heal Thou sin's ev-ery smart, Dwell Thou with-
know, each hour, Thou art a-bove. Teach me as seem-eth best In Thee to
Lord and King Through all my days. Teach Thou my soul to cry, "Be Thou, dear

ear-nest plea; So that Thou draw-est me Clos-er each day.
in my heart; Grant that I nev-er part, Sav-iour, from Thee.
find sweet rest; Lean-ing up-on Thy breast, All doubt re-move.
Sav-iour, nigh, Teach me to live, to die, Saved by Thy grace." A-MEN.

125 Sweet Will of God

Leila N. Morris

Leila N. Morris

DUET

1. My stub-born will at last hath yield-ed; I would be Thine, and
2. I'm tired of sin, foot-sore and wea-ry, The dark-some path hath
3. Thy pre-cious will, O con-qu'ring Sav-ior, Doth now em-brace and
4. Shut in with Thee, O Lord, for - ev - er, My way-ward feet no

Thine a - lone; And this the prayer my lips are bring-ing,
drear-y grown, But now a light has ris'n to cheer me;
com - pass me; All dis-cords hushed, my peace a riv - er,
more to roam; What pow'r from Thee my soul can sev - er?

rit. **CHORUS**

"Lord, let in me Thy will be done." Sweet will of God, still
I find in Thee my Star, my Sun.
My soul a pris-oned bird set free.
The cen-ter of God's will my home.

fold me clos-er, Till I am whol-ly lost in Thee; Sweet will of

God, still fold me clos-er, Till I am whol-ly lost in Thee.

We're Marching to Zion

ISAAC WATTS

ROBERT LOWRY

Spirited

1. Come, we that love the Lord, And let our joys be known, Join
2. Let those re - fuse to sing Who nev - er knew our God; But
3. The hill of Zi - on yields A thou - sand sa - cred sweets Be-
4. Then let our songs a - bound, And ev - 'ry tear be dry; We're

in a song with sweet ac - cord, Join in a song with sweet ac - cord, And
chil-dren of the heav'n-ly King, But chil-dren of the heav'n-ly King, May
fore we reach the heav'n-ly fields, Be - fore we reach the heav'n-ly fields, Or
marching thro' Immanuel's ground, We're marching thro' Immanuel's ground, To

thus sur - - round the throne, And thus sur-round the throne.
speak their joys a - broad, May speak their joys a - broad.
walk the gold - en streets, Or walk the gold - en streets.
fair - - er worlds on high, To fair - er worlds on high.

thus sur-round the throne, And thus sur - round the throne.

CHORUS

We're march - ing to Zi - on, Beau-ti - ful, beau-ti - ful Zi - on; We're
We're march-ing on to Zi - on,

march-ing up-ward to Zi - on, The beau-ti - ful cit - y of God.
Zi - on, Zi - on,

127 To God Be the Glory

FANNY J. CROSBY

WILLIAM H. DOANE

1. To God be the glo-ry — great things He hath done, So loved He the world that He
2. O per - fect re-demp-tion, the purchase of blood! To ev - 'ry be-liev-er the
3. Great things He hath taught us, great things He hath done, And great our rejoicing thro'

gave us His Son, Who yield-ed His life an a-tone-ment for sin And o-pened the
prom-ise of God; The vil - est of-fend-er who tru-ly be-lieves, That moment from
Je - sus the Son; But pu - rer and higher and greater will be Our won-der, our

CHORUS

Life-gate that all may go in.
Je - sus a par-don receives. Praise the Lord, praise the Lord, Let the earth hear His
transport, when Jesus we see.

voice! Praise the Lord, praise the Lord, Let the peo-ple re - joice! O come to the

Fa-ther thro' Je-sus the Son, And give Him the glo-ry — great things He hath done.

Blessed Redeemer

Avis B. Christiansen

Harry D. Loes

128

1. Up Cal-vary's mountain one dreadful morn, Walked Christ my Saviour, weary and worn;
2. "Fa-ther, forgive them!" thus did He pray, E'en while His life-blood flowed fast a-way;
3. O how I love Him, Sav-iour and Friend, How can my prais-es ev - er find end!

Fac-ing for sin-ners death on the cross, That He might save them from endless loss.
Pray-ing for sin-ners while in such woe— No one but Je - sus ev - er loved so.
Thro' years un-num-bered on heaven's shore, My tongue shall praise Him for-ev-er-more.

CHORUS

Bless-ed Re-deem - er! pre-cious Re-deem - er! Seems now I
Bless-ed Re-deem-er! bless-ed Re-deem - er!

see Him on Cal-va-ry's tree; Wound-ed and bleed - ing, for sin-ners
Wound-ed and bleed-ing,

plead - ing— Blind and un-heed - - ing— dy-ing for me!
for sin-ners plead-ing— Blind and un-heed - ing—

129 Arise, My Soul, Arise!

CHARLES WESLEY

LEWIS EDSON

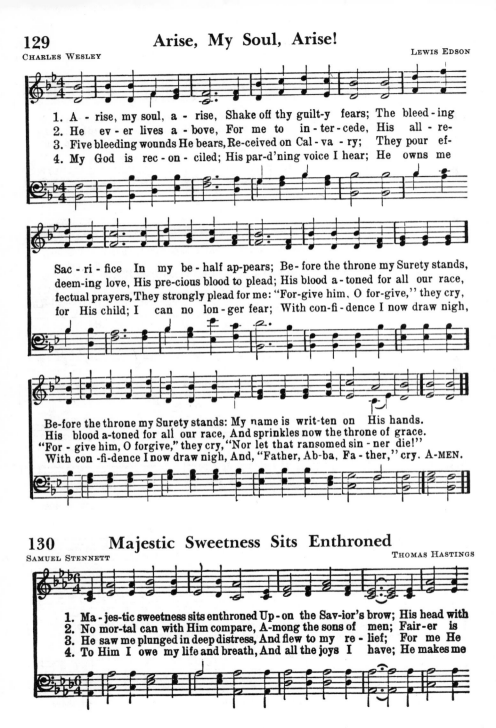

1. A - rise, my soul, a - rise, Shake off thy guilt-y fears; The bleed-ing
2. He ev - er lives a - bove, For me to in - ter-cede, His all - re-
3. Five bleeding wounds He bears, Re-ceived on Cal - va - ry; They pour ef-
4. My God is rec - on - ciled; His par-d'ning voice I hear; He owns me

Sac - ri - fice In my be - half ap-pears; Be - fore the throne my Surety stands,
deem-ing love, His pre-cious blood to plead; His blood a - toned for all our race,
fectual prayers, They strongly plead for me: "For-give him, O for-give," they cry,
for His child; I can no lon - ger fear; With con-fi - dence I now draw nigh,

Be - fore the throne my Surety stands: My name is writ-ten on His hands.
His blood a-toned for all our race, And sprinkles now the throne of grace.
"For - give him, O forgive," they cry, "Nor let that ransomed sin - ner die!"
With con -fi-dence I now draw nigh, And, "Father, Ab-ba, Fa - ther," cry. A-MEN.

130 Majestic Sweetness Sits Enthroned

SAMUEL STENNETT

THOMAS HASTINGS

1. Ma - jes-tic sweetness sits enthroned Up-on the Sav-ior's brow; His head with
2. No mor-tal can with Him compare, A-mong the sons of men; Fair-er is
3. He saw me plunged in deep distress, And flew to my re - lief; For me He
4. To Him I owe my life and breath, And all the joys I have; He makes me

Majestic Sweetness Sits Enthroned

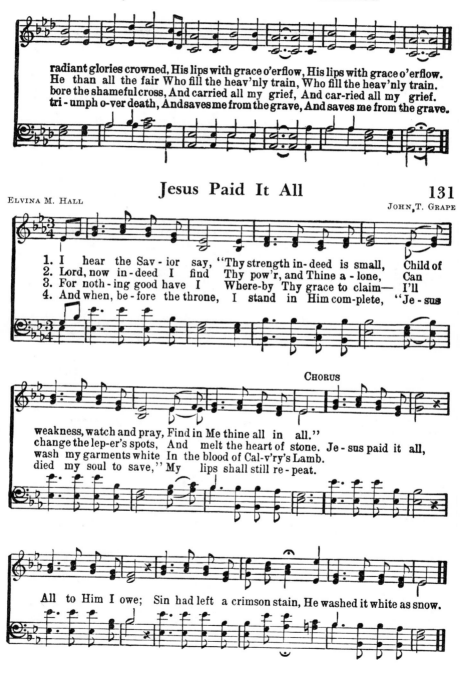

radiant glories crowned, His lips with grace o'erflow, His lips with grace o'erflow.
He than all the fair Who fill the heav'nly train, Who fill the heav'nly train.
bore the shameful cross, And carried all my grief, And car-ried all my grief.
tri - umph o-ver death, And saves me from the grave, And saves me from the grave.

Jesus Paid It All

131

ELVINA M. HALL

JOHN T. GRAPE

1. I hear the Sav - ior say, "Thy strength in-deed is small, Child of
2. Lord, now in-deed I find Thy pow'r, and Thine a - lone, Can
3. For noth-ing good have I Where-by Thy grace to claim— I'll
4. And when, be-fore the throne, I stand in Him com-plete, "Je - sus

CHORUS

weakness, watch and pray, Find in Me thine all in all."
change the lep-er's spots, And melt the heart of stone. Je-sus paid it all,
wash my garments white In the blood of Cal-v'ry's Lamb.
died my soul to save," My lips shall still re-peat.

All to Him I owe; Sin had left a crimson stain, He washed it white as snow.

Hallelujah for the Cross!

HORATIUS BONAR, ARR.   JAMES MCGRANAHAN

1. The cross it stand-eth fast, Hal-le-lu-jah, hal-le-lu-jah! De-fy-ing
2. It is the old cross still, Hal-le-lu-jah, hal-le-lu-jah! Its tri-umph
3. 'Twas here the debt was paid, Hal-le-lu-jah, hal-le-lu-jah! Our sins on

ev-ery blast, Hal-le-lu-jah, hal-le-lu-jah! The winds of hell have blown, The
let us tell, Hal-le-lu-jah, hal-le-lu-jah! The grace of God here shone Thro'
Je-sus laid, Hal-le-lu-jah, hal-le-lu-jah! So round the cross we sing Of

cres.

world its hate hath shown, Yet it is not over-thrown, Hal-le-lu-jah for the cross!
Christ the bless-ed Son, Who did for sin a-tone, Hal-le-lu-jah for the cross!
Christ our of-fer-ing, Of Christ our liv-ing King, Hal-le-lu-jah for the cross!

OBBLIGATO DUET SOP. (or TEN.) and ALTO

Hal-le-lu-jah,   hal-le-lu-jah,   Hal-le-

SOPRANO & ALTO*

CHORUS mp   Hal-le-lu-jah,   hal-le-lu-jah, Hal-le-

TENOR & BASS

*If desired, the Soprano and Alto may sing the upper staff, omitting the middle staff.

Hallelujah for the Cross!

lu - jah for the cross! Hal - le - lu - jah,

lu - jah for the cross, hal - le - lu-jah for the cross! Hal - le - lu - jah,

hal - le - lu - jah, It shall nev - er suf - fer loss!

hal - le - lu - jah, It shall nev - er suf - fer, nev - er suf - fer loss!

FULL CHORUS

*Hal - le - lu - jah, hal - le - lu - jah, Hal - le - lu - jah for the cross!

cres. ff

Hal - le - lu - jah, hal - le - lu - jah, It shall nev - er suf - fer loss!

*For a final ending, all the voices may sing the melody in unison through the last eight measures—the instrument playing the harmony.

133 I Will Sing the Wondrous Story

Francis H. Rowley

Peter P. Bilhorn

1. I will sing the won-drous sto-ry Of the Christ who died for me,
2. I was lost, but Je-sus found me, Found the sheep that went a-stray,
3. I was bruised, but Je-sus healed me; Faint was I from many a fall;
4. Days of dark-ness still come o'er me, Sor-row's paths I oft-en tread,
5. He will keep me till the riv-er Rolls its wa-ters at my feet;

How He left His home in glo-ry For the cross of Cal-va-ry.
Threw His lov-ing arms a-round me, Drew me back in-to His way.
Sight was gone, and fears possessed me, But He freed me from them all.
But the Sav-ior still is with me; By His hand I'm safe-ly led.
Then He'll bear me safe-ly o-ver, Where the loved ones I shall meet.

CHORUS

Yes, I'll sing . . . . the won-drous sto - - - ry Of the
Yes, I'll sing the won-drous sto-ry

Christ . . . . who died for me, ... Sing it with . . . . the saints in
Of the Christ who died for me, Sing it with

glo - - ry, Gath-ered by . . . . . . the crys-tal sea . . . .
the saints in glo-ry, Gath-ered by the crys-tal sea.

Love Led Him to Calvary

134

GEORGE O. WEBSTER

CHARLES H. GABRIEL

1. Love led the Sav-ior, in days long a-go, Down to earth's dark-ness, its
2. Love, for a man-ger, a-ban-doned a throne, Seek-ing the sin-ful, the
3. See-ing the soul in its in-fi-nite worth, Stoop-ing, in love, to the
4. Long-ing, in pit-y, the lost ones to save, Brav-ing the Gar-den, the

sin and its woe; Seek-ing the lost ones, His mer-cy to show,
sad and the lone; Yearn-ing to win them and make them His own,
low-li-est birth, Seek-ing the lost in the by-ways of earth,
Cross and the Grave, Seek-ing this on-ly, the sin-ful to save,

CHORUS *faster*

Love led Him to Cal-va-ry. Love led Him to Cal-va-ry,

Love led Him to Cal-va-ry; Seek-ing the lost, at the

ut-ter-most cost, Love led Him to Cal-va-ry.

135 It Took a Miracle

JOHN W. PETERSON

JOHN W. PETERSON

1. My Fa-ther is om-nip-o-tent, And that you can't de-ny;
2. Tho here His glo-ry has been shown, We still can't ful-ly see
3. The Bi-ble tells us of His pow'r And wis-dom all way thru,

A God of might and mir-a-cles—'Tis writ-ten in the sky.
The won-ders of His might, His throne—'Twill take e-ter-ni-ty.
And ev-'ry lit-tle bird and flow'r Are tes-ti-mo-nies too.

CHORUS

It took a mir-a-cle to put the stars in place, It took a

mir-a-cle to hang the world in space; But when He saved my soul,

Cleansed and made me whole, It took a mir-a-cle of love and grace!

My Sins Are Blotted Out, I Know! 136

MERRILL DUNLOP

MERRILL DUNLOP

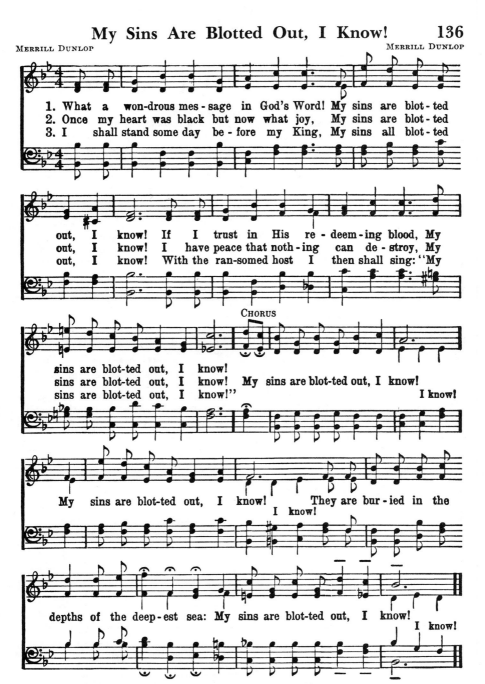

1. What a won-drous mes-sage in God's Word! My sins are blot-ted out, I know! If I trust in His re-deem-ing blood, My sins are blot-ted out, I know!
2. Once my heart was black but now what joy, My sins are blot-ted out, I know! I have peace that noth-ing can de-stroy, My sins are blot-ted out, I know!
3. I shall stand some day be-fore my King, My sins all blot-ted out, I know! With the ran-somed host I then shall sing: "My sins are blot-ted out, I know!"

CHORUS

My sins are blot-ted out, I know! My sins are blot-ted out, I know! I know! They are bur-ied in the depths of the deep-est sea: My sins are blot-ted out, I know! I know!

137 Nor Silver Nor Gold

JAMES M. GRAY

DANIEL B. TOWNER

1. Nor sil - ver nor gold hath ob-tained my re-demp-tion, Nor rich - es of
2. Nor sil - ver nor gold hath ob-tained my re-demp-tion, The guilt on my
3. Nor sil - ver nor gold hath ob-tained my re-demp-tion, The ho - ly com-
4. Nor sil - ver nor gold hath ob-tained my re-demp-tion, The way in - to

earth could have saved my poor soul; The blood of the cross is my
con-science too heav - y had grown; The blood of the cross is my
mand-ment for - bade me draw near; The blood of the cross is my
heav - en could not thus be bought; The blood of the cross is my

on - ly foun - da-tion, The death of my Sav - ior now mak - eth me whole.
on - ly foun - da-tion, The death of my Sav - ior could on - ly a - tone.
on - ly foun - da-tion, The death of my Sav - ior re - mov - eth my fear.
on - ly foun - da-tion, The death of my Sav - ior re - demp-tion hath wrought

CHORUS

I am re - deemed, ... but not with sil - ver;
I am re-deemed, I am re-deemed, but not with sil - ver;

I am bought, . but not with gold; Bought with a
I am bought, I am bought, but not with gold;

Nor Silver Nor Gold

price...... the blood of Je - sus, Pre-cious price of love un-told.
Bought with a price— the precious blood of Je-sus,

Nothing but the Blood

138

ROBERT LOWRY

ROBERT LOWRY

1. What can wash a - way my sin? Noth-ing but the blood of Je - sus;
2. For my par - don this I see— Noth-ing but the blood of Je - sus;
3. Noth - ing can for sin a - tone— Noth-ing but the blood of Je - sus;
4. This is all my hope and peace— Noth-ing but the blood of Je - sus;

What can make me whole a - gain? Noth-ing but the blood of Je - sus.
For my cleans-ing, this my plea—Noth-ing but the blood of Je - sus.
Naught of good that I have done—Noth-ing but the blood of Je - sus.
This is all my right-eous - ness—Noth-ing but the blood of Je - sus.

REFRAIN

Oh! pre - cious is the flow That makes me white as snow;

No oth - er fount I know, Noth-ing but the blood of Je - sus.

139

Once for All

PHILIP P. BLISS

PHILIP P. BLISS

1. Free from the law, O hap-py con-di-tion, Je-sus hath bled, and there is re-mis-sion; Cursed by the law and bruised by the fall, Grace hath redeemed us once for all.

2. Now are we free—there's no con-dem-na-tion, Je-sus pro-vides a per-fect sal-va-tion; "Come un-to Me," O hear His sweet call, Come, and He saves us once for all.

3. "Chil-dren of God," O glo-ri-ous call-ing, Sure-ly His grace will keep us from fall-ing; Pass-ing from death to life at His call, Bless-ed sal-va-tion once for all.

CHORUS

Once for all, O sin-ner, re-ceive it, Once for all, O broth-er, be-lieve it; Cling to the Cross, the bur-den will fall, Christ hath re-deemed us once for all.

Redeemed

FANNY J. CROSBY

WILLIAM J. KIRKPATRICK

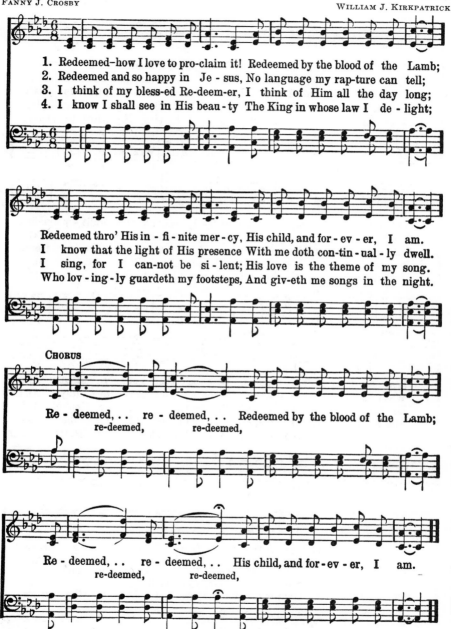

1. Redeemed–how I love to pro-claim it! Redeemed by the blood of the Lamb;
2. Redeemed and so happy in Je - sus, No language my rap-ture can tell;
3. I think of my bless-ed Re-deem-er, I think of Him all the day long;
4. I know I shall see in His beau - ty The King in whose law I de - light;

Redeemed thro' His in - fi - nite mer - cy, His child, and for - ev - er, I am.
I know that the light of His presence With me doth con-tin - ual - ly dwell.
I sing, for I can-not be si - lent; His love is the theme of my song.
Who lov - ing - ly guardeth my footsteps, And giv-eth me songs in the night.

CHORUS

Re - deemed, .. re - deemed, .. Redeemed by the blood of the Lamb;
re-deemed, re-deemed,

Re - deemed, .. re - deemed, .. His child, and for - ev - er, I am.
re-deemed, re-deemed,

141 There Is a Fountain

WILLIAM COWPER   EARLY AMERICAN MELODY

1. There is a foun-tain filled with blood Drawn from Im-man-uel's veins;
2. The dy-ing thief re-joiced to see That foun-tain in his day;
3. Dear dy-ing Lamb, Thy pre-cious blood Shall nev-er lose its pow'r,
4. E'er since, by faith, I saw the stream Thy flow-ing wounds sup-ply,
5. Then in a no-bler, sweet-er song, I'll sing Thy pow'r to save,

And sin-ners, plunged be-neath that flood, Lose all their guilt-y stains:
And there may I, though vile as he, Wash all my sins a-way:
Till all the ran-somed Church of God Be saved, to sin no more:
Re-deem-ing love has been my theme, And shall be till I die:
When this poor lisp-ing, stamm'ring tongue Lies si-lent in the grave:

Lose all their guilt-y stains, Lose all their guilt-y stains; And
Wash all my sins a-way, Wash all my sins a-way; And
Be saved, to sin no more, Be saved, to sin no more; Till
And shall be till I die, And shall be till I die; Re-
Lies si-lent in the grave, Lies si-lent in the grave; When

sin-ners, plunged be-neath that flood, Lose all their guilt-y stains.
there may I, though vile as he, Wash all my sins a-way.
all the ran-somed Church of God Be saved, to sin no more.
deem-ing love has been my theme, And shall be till I die.
this poor lisp-ing, stam-m'ring tongue Lies si-lent in the grave.

142 Though Your Sins Be As Scarlet

Fanny J. Crosby

William H. Doane

DUET *Gently*

1. "Tho' your sins be as scar-let, They shall be as white as snow;
2. Hear the voice that en-treats you, O re-turn ye un-to God!
3. He'll for-give your trans-gres-sions, And re-mem-ber them no more;

Tho' your sins be as scar-let, They shall be as white as snow;
Hear the voice that en-treats you, O re-turn ye un-to God!
He'll for-give your trans-gres-sions, And re-mem-ber them no more;

QUARTET

Tho' they be red . . . . like crim-son, They shall be as wool!"
He is of great . . . com-pas-sion, And of won-drous love;
"Look un-to Me, . . . ye peo-ple," Saith the Lord your God!

1. Tho' they be red

DUET *p*   QUARTET *f*

"Tho' your sins be as scar-let, Tho' your sins be as scar-let,
Hear the voice that en-treats you, Hear the voice that en-treats you,
He'll for-give your trans-gres-sions, He'll for-give your trans-gres-sions,

p rit.

They shall be as white as snow, They shall be as white as snow."
O re-turn ye un-to God! O re-turn ye un-to God!
And re-mem-ber them no more, And re-mem-ber them no more.

143 When Love Shines In

MRS. FRANK A. BRECK

WILLIAM J. KIRKPATRICK

1. Je - sus comes with pow'r to gladden, When love shines in, Ev - 'ry life that
2. How the world will grow with beauty, When love shines in, And the heart re-
3. Dark-est sor - row will grow brighter, When love shines in, And the heav-iest
4. We may have un - fad - ing splendor, When love shines in, And a friend-ship

woe can sad-den, When love shines in. Love will teach us how to pray,
joice in du - ty, When love shines in. Tri - als may be sanc - ti - fied,
bur - den light-er, When love shines in. 'Tis the glo - ry that will throw
true and ten - der, When love shines in. When earth vic-t'ries shall be won,

Love will drive the gloom away, Turn our darkness in - to day, When love shines in.
And the soul in peace a-bide, Life will all be glo-ri-fied, When love shines in.
Light to show us where to go; O, the heart shall blessing know, When love shines in.
And our life in Heav'n begun, There will be no need of sun, When love shines in.

CHORUS

When love shines in,....... When love shines in,...
When love shines in,........
When love shines in, When love shines in, When love shines in,....

How the heart is tuned to sing-ing, When love.. shines in;......
When love shines in;......

When Love Shines In

When love shines in,...... When love shines in,..

When love shines in,........

When love shines in, When love shines in,

When love shines in,...

Joy and peace to oth - ers bring-ing, When love shines in...

When love, when love shines in....

Only Trust Him

JOHN H. STOCKTON

144

JOHN H. STOCKTON

1. Come, ev - 'ry soul by sin op-pressed, There's mer - cy with the Lord,
2. For Je - sus shed His pre-cious blood, Rich bless-ings to be - stow;
3. Yes, Je - sus is the Truth, the Way, That leads you in - to rest:
4. Come, then, and join this ho - ly band, And on to glo - ry go,

And He will sure - ly give you rest By trust-ing in His word.
Plunge now in - to the crim - son flood That wash - es white as snow.
Be - lieve in Him with-out de - lay, And you are ful - ly blest.
To dwell in that ce - les - tial land, Where joys im - mor - tal flow.

{ On - ly trust Him, on-ly trust Him, On - ly trust Him now. }
{ He will save you, He will save you, He will (*Omit* . . . . .) } save you now.

145 Whiter Than Snow

JAMES NICHOLSON

WILLIAM G. FISCHER

1. Lord Je-sus, I long to be per-fect-ly whole; I want Thee for-ev-er to
2. Lord Je-sus, look down from Thy throne in the skies, And help me to make a com-
3. Lord Je-sus, for this I most hum-bly en-treat, I wait, bless-ed Lord, at Thy
4. Lord Je-sus, Thou seest I pa-tient-ly wait, Come now, and with-in me a

live in my soul, Break down ev-'ry i-dol, cast out ev-'ry foe;
plete sac-ri-fice; I give up my-self, and what-ev-er I know,
cru-ci-fied feet; By faith, for my cleans-ing, I see Thy blood flow,
new heart cre-ate; To those who have sought Thee, Thou nev-er saidst "No,"

CHORUS.

Now wash me, and I shall be whit-er than snow. Whit-er than snow, yes,

whit-er than snow; Now wash me, and I shall be whit-er than snow.

Wonderful Story of Love

J. M. DRIVER   J. M. DRIVER

1. Won-der-ful sto-ry of love; Tell it to me a-gain; Won-der-ful
2. Won-der-ful sto-ry of love; Tho' you are far a-way; Won-der-ful
3. Won-der-ful sto-ry of love; Je-sus pro-vides a rest; Won-der-ful

sto-ry of love; Wake the im-mor-tal strain! An-gels with rapture announce it,
sto-ry of love; Still He doth call to-day; Call-ing from Cal-va-ry's mountain,
sto-ry of love; For all the pure and blest, Rest in those mansions a-bove us,

Shepherds with won-der re-ceive it; Sin-ner, O won't you be-lieve it?
Down from the crys-tal bright foun-tain, E'en from the dawn of cre-a-tion,
With those who've gone on be-fore us, Sing-ing the rap-tur-ous cho-rus,

CHORUS

Won-der-ful sto-ry of love. Won - der - ful! Won - der-
Won-der-ful sto-ry of love; Won-der-ful sto-ry of

ful! Won - der - ful! Won-der-ful sto-ry of love!
love; Won-der-ful sto-ry of love;

147 Ye Must Be Born Again

William T. Sleeper

George C. Stebbins

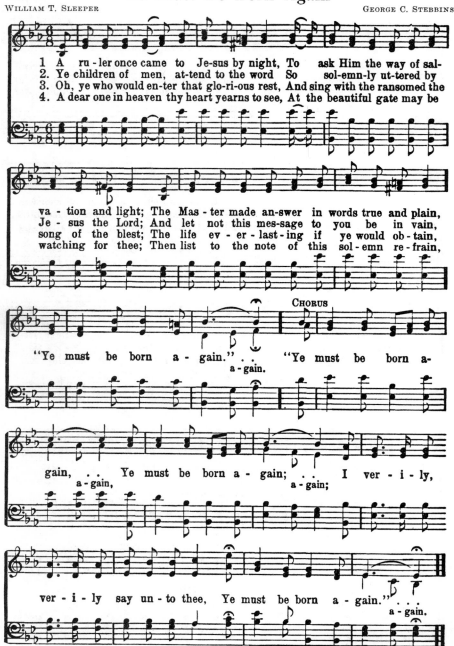

1. A ru-ler once came to Je-sus by night, To ask Him the way of sal-
2. Ye children of men, at-tend to the word So sol-emn-ly ut-tered by
3. Oh, ye who would en-ter that glo-ri-ous rest, And sing with the ransomed the
4. A dear one in heaven thy heart yearns to see, At the beautiful gate may be

va - tion and light; The Mas - ter made an-swer in words true and plain,
Je - sus the Lord; And let not this mes-sage to you be in vain,
song of the blest; The life ev - er - last-ing if ye would ob - tain,
watching for thee; Then list to the note of this sol - emn re - frain,

Chorus

"Ye must be born a - gain."... a-gain. "Ye must be born a-

gain,... a-gain, Ye must be born a - gain;... a-gain; I ver - i - ly,

ver - i - ly say un - to thee, Ye must be born a - gain."... a-gain.

Great Is Thy Faithfulness

Thomas O. Chisholm

William M. Runyan

1. "Great is Thy faith-ful-ness," O God my Fa-ther, There is no shad-ow of
2. Sum-mer and win-ter, and spring-time and harvest, Sun, moon and stars in their
3. Par-don for sin and a peace that en-dur-eth, Thy own dear presence to

turn-ing with Thee; Thou chang-est not, Thy com-pas-sions, they fail not;
cours-es a-bove, Join with all na-ture in man-i-fold wit-ness,
cheer and to guide; Strength for to-day and bright hope for to-mor-row,

CHORUS

As Thou hast been Thou for-ev-er wilt be.
To Thy great faith-ful-ness, mer-cy and love. "Great is Thy faith-ful-ness!
Blessings all mine, with ten thou-sand be-side!

Great is Thy faithfulness!" Morning by morning new mercies I see; All I have

need-ed Thy hand hath provided—"Great is Thy faithfulness," Lord, un-to me!

rall.

149 Why Do I Sing About Jesus?

ALBERT A. KETCHUM   ALBERT A. KETCHUM

1. Deep in my heart there's a glad-ness, Je-sus has saved me from sin! Praise to His name, what a Sav-iour! Cleans-ing with-out and with-in.
2. On-ly a glimpse of His good-ness, That was suf-fi-cient for me; On-ly one look at the Sav-iour, Then was my spir-it set free.
3. He is the fair-est of fair ones, He is the Lil-y, the Rose; Riv-ers of mer-cy sur-round Him, Grace, love and pit-y He shows.

REFRAIN

Why do I sing a-bout Je-sus? Why is He pre-cious to me? He is my Lord and my Sav-iour, Dy-ing, He set me free! (set me free!)

He Took My Sins Away

MRS. M. J. HARRIS   MRS. M. J. HARRIS

1. I came to Je-sus, wea-ry, worn, and sad. He took my sins a-way, He
2. The load of sin was more than I could bear. He took them all a-way, He
3. No con-dem-na-tion have I in my heart. He took my sins a-way, He
4. If you will come to Je-sus Christ to-day, He'll take your sins a-way, He'll

took my sins a-way, And now His love has made my heart so glad. He
took them all a-way, And now on Him I roll my ev-'ry care. He
took my sins a-way, His per-fect peace He did to me im-part. He
take your sins a-way, And keep you hap-py in His love each day. He'll

CHORUS

took my sins a - way.
took my sins a - way.
took my sins a - way.
take your sins a - way.

He took my sins a-way, He

took my sins a-way, And keeps me sing-ing ev-'ry day!

I'm so glad He took my sins a-way. He took my sins a - way.

151 Wonderful, Wonderful Jesus

ANNA B. RUSSELL

ERNEST O. SELLERS

1. There is nev-er a day so drear-y, There is nev-er a
2. There is nev-er a cross so heav-y, There is nev-er a
3. There is nev-er a care or bur-den, There is nev-er a
4. There is nev-er a guilt-y sin-ner, There is nev-er a

night so long (so long), But the soul that is trust-ing Je - sus Will
weight of woe (of woe), But that Je - sus will help to car - ry Be-
grief or loss (or loss), But that Je - sus in love will light - en When
wan-d'ring one (not one), But that God can in mer - cy par - don Thro'

CHORUS.

some-where find a song (a song).
cause He lov - eth so (loves so). Won - der-ful, won-der - ful Je - sus,
car - ried to the cross (the cross).
Je - sus Christ, His Son (His Son).

In the heart He im-plant-eth a song: . . . . A song of de-liv-'rance, of

He plant-eth a song,

cour-age, of strength, In the heart He im-plant-eth a song (a song).

Jesus, Lover of My Soul

CHARLES WESLEY

SIMEON B. MARSH

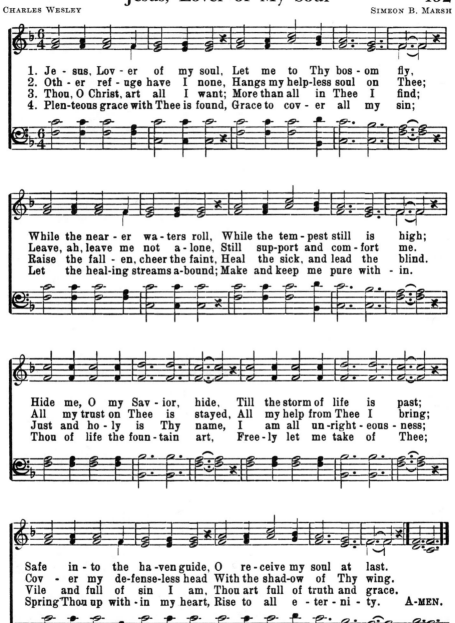

1. Je - sus, Lov - er of my soul, Let me to Thy bos - om fly,
2. Oth - er ref - uge have I none, Hangs my help-less soul on Thee;
3. Thou, O Christ, art all I want; More than all in Thee I find;
4. Plen-teous grace with Thee is found, Grace to cov - er all my sin;

While the near - er wa - ters roll, While the tem - pest still is high;
Leave, ah, leave me not a - lone, Still sup-port and com - fort me.
Raise the fall - en, cheer the faint, Heal the sick, and lead the blind.
Let the heal-ing streams a-bound; Make and keep me pure with - in.

Hide me, O my Sav - ior, hide, Till the storm of life is past;
All my trust on Thee is stayed, All my help from Thee I bring;
Just and ho - ly is Thy name, I am all un -right - eous - ness;
Thou of life the foun - tain art, Free - ly let me take of Thee;

Safe in - to the ha - ven guide, O re - ceive my soul at last.
Cov - er my de-fense-less head With the shad - ow of Thy wing.
Vile and full of sin I am, Thou art full of truth and grace.
Spring Thou up with - in my heart, Rise to all e - ter - ni - ty. A-MEN.

153

Only Jesus

AVIS B. CHRISTIANSEN

LANCE B. LATHAM

1. I've found a ref-uge from life's care in Je-sus, I am
2. I've found a pre-cious joy in know-ing Je-sus, Nev-er
3. I've found a bless-ed hope di-vine in Je-sus, 'Tis a

hid - ing in His love di - vine; He ful-ly un-der-stands my
dreamed of in this world of woe; No clouds, how-ev-er dark, can
Day Star ev-er shin-ing bright; It fills my earth-ly way with

soul's deep long - ing, And He whis-pers soft-ly, "Thou art mine."
dim the ra - diance Of the heav'n-ly light He doth be - stow.
heav'n-ly glo - ry, And it turns life's dark-ness in - to light.

REFRAIN

On - ly Je - sus! On - ly Je - sus! On - ly He can sat - is - fy;

Ev-'ry bur - den be-comes a bless-ing, When I know my Lord is nigh.

Our Great Savior

J. WILBUR CHAPMAN

ROWLAND W. PRICHARD
ARR. BY ROBERT HARKNESS

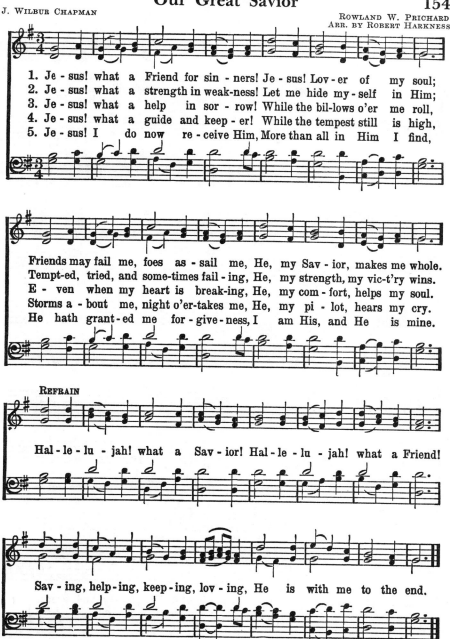

1. Je - sus! what a Friend for sin - ners! Je - sus! Lov - er of my soul;
2. Je - sus! what a strength in weak-ness! Let me hide my-self in Him;
3. Je - sus! what a help in sor - row! While the bil-lows o'er me roll,
4. Je - sus! what a guide and keep - er! While the tempest still is high,
5. Je - sus! I do now re - ceive Him, More than all in Him I find,

Friends may fail me, foes as - sail me, He, my Sav - ior, makes me whole.
Tempt-ed, tried, and some-times fail - ing, He, my strength, my vic-t'ry wins.
E - ven when my heart is break-ing, He, my com - fort, helps my soul.
Storms a - bout me, night o'er-takes me, He, my pi - lot, hears my cry.
He hath grant-ed me for - give - ness, I am His, and He is mine.

REFRAIN

Hal - le - lu - jah! what a Sav - ior! Hal - le - lu - jah! what a Friend!

Sav - ing, help-ing, keep-ing, lov - ing, He is with me to the end.

155 The Heavenly Vision

HELEN H. LEMMEL

HELEN H. LEMMEL

With expression

1. O soul, are you wea-ry and troub-led? No light in the
2. Thro' death in-to life ev-er-last-ing He passed, and we
3. His word shall not fail you—He prom-ised; Be-lieve Him, and

dark-ness you see? There's light for a look at the Sav-ior,
fol-low Him there; O-ver us sin no more hath do-min-ion—
all will be well: Then go to a world that is dy-ing,

REFRAIN

And life more a-bun-dant and free!
For more than con-qu'rors we are!
His per-fect sal-va-tion to tell!

Turn your eyes up-on Je-

sus, Look full in His won-der-ful face; .... And the things of

p

earth will grow strange-ly dim In the light of His glo-ry and grace.

The Light of the World Is Jesus

156

Philip P. Bliss

Philip P. Bliss

1. The whole world was lost in the dark-ness of sin; The Light of the world is Je-sus; Like sun-shine at noon-day His glo-ry shone in,
2. No dark-ness have we who in Je-sus a-bide, The Light of the world is Je-sus; We walk in the Light when we fol-low our Guide,
3. Ye dwell-ers in dark-ness with sin-blind-ed eyes, The Light of the world is Je-sus; Go, wash at His bid-ding, and light will a-rise,
4. No need of the sun-light in heav-en, we're told, The Light of the world is Je-sus; The Lamb is the Light in the Cit-y of Gold,

CHORUS

The Light of the world is Je-sus. Come to the Light, 'tis shin-ing for thee; Sweet-ly the Light has dawned up-on me; Once I was blind, but now I can see; The Light of the world is Je-sus.

157   The Lily of the Valley

CHARLES W. FRY   ARR. FROM WILLIAM S. HAYS

1. I have found a friend in Je-sus, He's ev-ery-thing to me, He's the
2. He all my griefs has tak-en, and all my sor-rows borne; In temp-
3. He will nev-er, nev-er leave me, nor yet for-sake me here, While I

fair-est of ten thou-sand to my soul; The Lil-y of the Val-ley,
ta-tion He's my strong and mighty tower; I have all for Him for-sak-en,
live by faith and do His bless-ed will; A wall of fire a-bout me,

D. S.—*Lil-y of the Val-ley,*

FINE.

in Him a-lone I see All I need to cleanse and make me ful-ly whole.
and all my i-dols torn From my heart, and now He keeps me by His power.
I've noth-ing now to fear, With His man-na He my hun-gry soul shall fill.

the Bright and Morn-ing Star, He's the fair-est of ten thou-sand to my soul.

In sor-row He's my com-fort, in trou-ble He's my stay,
Though all the world for-sake me, and Sa-tan tempt me sore,
Then sweep-ing up to glo-ry to see His bless-ed face,

D. S.

He tells me ev-ery care on Him to roll: He's the
Through Je-sus I shall safe-ly reach the goal: He's the
Where riv-ers of de-light shall ev-er roll: He's the

Hallelujah, What a Savior!

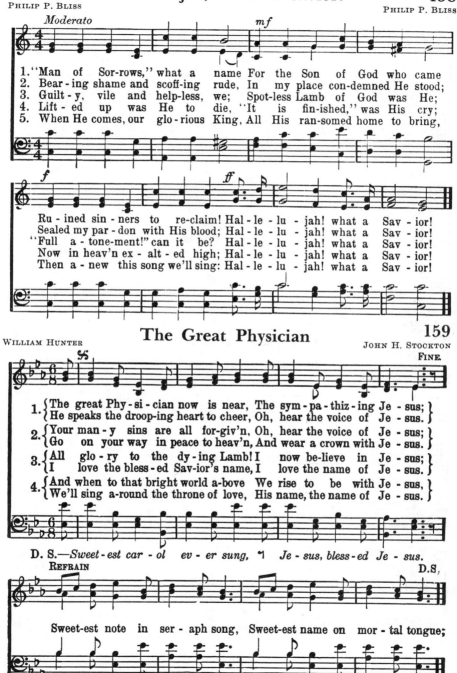

158

Philip P. Bliss

Philip P. Bliss

Moderato

1. "Man of Sor-rows," what a name For the Son of God who came
2. Bear-ing shame and scoff-ing rude, In my place con-demned He stood;
3. Guilt-y, vile and help-less, we; Spot-less Lamb of God was He;
4. Lift-ed up was He to die, "It is fin-ished," was His cry;
5. When He comes, our glo-rious King, All His ran-somed home to bring,

Ru-ined sin-ners to re-claim! Hal-le-lu-jah! what a Sav-ior!
Sealed my par-don with His blood; Hal-le-lu-jah! what a Sav-ior!
"Full a-tone-ment!" can it be? Hal-le-lu-jah! what a Sav-ior!
Now in heav'n ex-alt-ed high; Hal-le-lu-jah! what a Sav-ior!
Then a-new this song we'll sing: Hal-le-lu-jah! what a Sav-ior!

The Great Physician

159

William Hunter

John H. Stockton

Fine.

1. The great Phy-si-cian now is near, The sym-pa-thiz-ing Je-sus;
   He speaks the droop-ing heart to cheer, Oh, hear the voice of Je-sus.
2. Your man-y sins are all for-giv'n, Oh, hear the voice of Je-sus;
   Go on your way in peace to heav'n, And wear a crown with Je-sus.
3. All glo-ry to the dy-ing Lamb! I now be-lieve in Je-sus;
   I love the bless-ed Sav-ior's name, I love the name of Je-sus.
4. And when to that bright world a-bove We rise to be with Je-sus,
   We'll sing a-round the throne of love, His name, the name of Je-sus.

D. S.—*Sweet-est car-ol ev-er sung,* Je-sus, bless-ed Je-sus.

Refrain

D.S.

Sweet-est note in ser-aph song, Sweet-est name on mor-tal tongue;

160 The Name of Jesus

W. C. MARTIN

EDMUND S. LORENZ

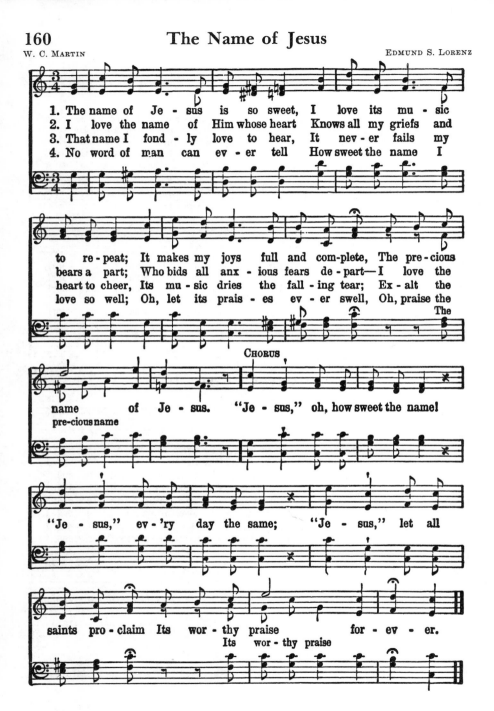

1. The name of Je - sus is so sweet, I love its mu - sic
2. I love the name of Him whose heart Knows all my griefs and
3. That name I fond - ly love to hear, It nev - er fails my
4. No word of man can ev - er tell How sweet the name I

to re - peat; It makes my joys full and com-plete, The pre - cious
bears a part; Who bids all anx - ious fears de - part— I love the
heart to cheer, Its mu - sic dries the fall - ing tear; Ex - alt the
love so well; Oh, let its prais - es ev - er swell, Oh, praise the The

CHORUS

name of Je - sus. "Je - sus," oh, how sweet the name!
pre - cious name

"Je - sus," ev - 'ry day the same; "Je - sus," let all

saints pro - claim Its wor - thy praise for - ev - er.
Its wor - thy praise

The Unveiled Christ

161

N. B. Herrell

N. B. Herrell

1. Once our bless-ed Christ of beau - ty Was veiled off from hu-man view;
2. Now He is with God the Fa - ther, In - ter-ced-ing there for you;
3. Ho - ly an-gels bow be - fore Him, Men of earth give prais-es due;
4. Thro'-out time and end-less a - ges, Heights and depths of love so true;

But thro' suff'ring, death and sor - row He has rent the veil in two.
For He is the might-y con-qu'ror Since He rent the veil in two.
For He is the well-be - lov - ed Since He rent the veil in two.
He a - lone can be the giv - er Since He rent the veil in two.

Chorus

O be-hold the Man of Sor - rows, O be-hold Him in plain view;

Lo! He is the might-y con - qu'ror, Since He rent the veil in two.

Lo! He is the might-y con - qu'ror, Since He rent the veil in two.

162 The Stranger of Galilee

LEILA N. MORRIS   LEILA N. MORRIS

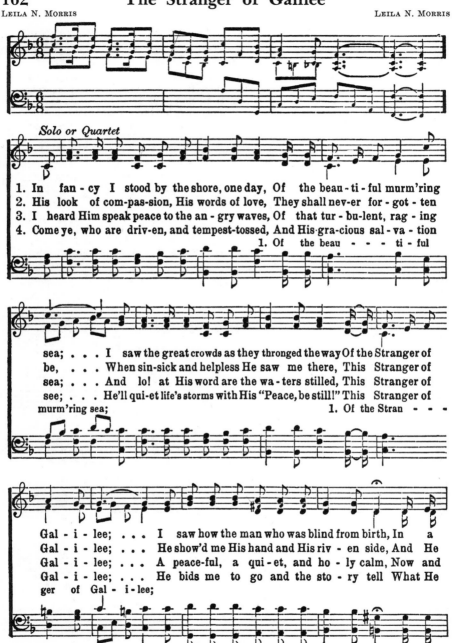

Solo or Quartet

1. In fan-cy I stood by the shore, one day, Of the beau-ti-ful murm'ring
2. His look of com-pas-sion, His words of love, They shall nev-er for-got-ten
3. I heard Him speak peace to the an-gry waves, Of that tur-bu-lent, rag-ing
4. Come ye, who are driv-en, and tempest-tossed, And His gra-cious sal-va-tion

1. Of the beau - - - ti-ful

sea; ... I saw the great crowds as they thronged the way Of the Stranger of
be, ... When sin-sick and helpless He saw me there, This Stranger of
sea; ... And lo! at His word are the wa-ters stilled, This Stranger of
see; ... He'll qui-et life's storms with His "Peace, be still!" This Stranger of

murm'ring sea;

1. Of the Stran - - -

Gal-i-lee; ... I saw how the man who was blind from birth, In a
Gal-i-lee; ... He show'd me His hand and His riv-en side, And He
Gal-i-lee; ... A peace-ful, a qui-et, and ho-ly calm, Now and
Gal-i-lee; ... He bids me to go and the sto-ry tell What He

ger of Gal-i-lee;

The Stranger of Galilee

mo-ment was made to see; . . . The lame was made whole by the matchless skill
whispered "It was for thee!" . . My bur-den fell off at the pierc-ed feet
ev - er a-bides with me; . . . He hold-eth my life in His might-y hands,
ev - er to you will be, . . . If on-ly you let Him with you a-bide,
1. mo - - ment was made to see;

Of the Stranger of Gal - i - lee.
Of the Stranger of Gal - i - lee. And I felt I could love Him for-
This Stranger of Gal - i - lee.
This Stranger of Gal - i - lee. (4 v.) Oh, my friend, won't you love Him for-

ev - - - er, So gra-cious and ten-der was He! I
ev - - - er? So gra-cious and ten-der was He! . . . . Ac-
ev - er and ev - er, so ten-der was He!

claimed Him that day as my Sav - ior, This Stranger of Gal - i - lee.
cept Him to-day as your Sav - ior, This Stranger of Gal - i - lee.
Lord and my Sav-ior,

163

Christ Is King

CHARLES R. SCOVILLE

DE LOSS SMITH

1. Come, friends sing, of the faith that's so dear to me, . . .
2. Cru - ci - fied, thus He suf-fered and bled for me, . . .
3. At His feet, on old Ol - i - vet's Hill they say, . . .

Re - vealed thro' God's Son, in Gal - i - lee; He brought
Death and the grave won sin's vic - to - ry; Then the
Cloud char - iots halt - ed, took Christ a - way; Then the

peace on earth and good will to the sons of men,
sky grew dark and the tem-ple veil rent in twain,
an - gels came and to wond'ring dis - ci - ples said

Go tell it to the world, her King reigns a - - gain.
Rocks rent, and an - gels came, for He lived a - - gain.
He'll come, and earth and sea shall yield up their dead.

Christ Is King

CHORUS *Unison*

I am so hap-py in Je - sus, Cap-tiv-i-ty's Cap-tor is

He; .... An-gels re-joice when a soul's saved, Some day we

like Him shall be, ... Sor-row and joy have the same Lord,

cres.

Val - ley of shad-ows shall sing; ... Death has its life, its door

Harmony

o-pens in heav-en e - ter-nal-ly, Christ is King ....

164 He Lives

ALFRED H. ACKLEY

ALFRED H. ACKLEY

1. I serve a ris-en Sav-ior, He's in the world to-day; I know that He is
2. In all the world a-round me I see His lov-ing care, And tho' my heart grows
3. Re-joice, rejoice, O Christian, lift up your voice and sing E-ter-nal hal-le-

liv-ing, what-ev-er men may say; I see His hand of mer-cy, I
wea-ry I nev-er will de-spair; I know that He is lead-ing thro'
lu-jahs to Je-sus Christ the King! The Hope of all who seek Him, the

hear His voice of cheer, And just the time I need Him He's al-ways near.
all the storm-y blast, The day of His ap-pear-ing will come at last.
Help of all who find, None oth-er is so lov-ing, so good and kind.

REFRAIN *Spirited*

He lives, He lives, Christ Je-sus lives to-day! He walks with me and
He lives, He lives,

talks with me a-long life's nar-row way. He lives, He lives, sal-
He lives, He lives,

He Lives

rit. ff

va - tion to im - part! You ask me how I know He lives? He lives within my heart.

Jesus Never Fails

165

ARTHUR A. LUTHER

ARTHUR A. LUTHER

1. Earth-ly friends may prove un - true, Doubts and fears as - sail;
2. Tho' the sky be dark and drear, Fierce and strong the gale,
3. In life's dark and bit - ter hour Love will still pre - vail;

One still loves and cares for you: Je - sus nev - er fails.
Just re - mem - ber He is near, And He will not fail. *nev - er fails.*
Trust His ev - er - last-ing pow'r, Je - sus will not fail. *will not fail.*
will not fail.

CHORUS

Je - sus nev - er fails, Je - sus nev - er fails;

Heav'n and earth may pass a - way But Je - sus nev - er fails.

166 The Love of God

FREDERICK M. LEHMAN

FREDERICK M. LEHMAN
ARR. BY CLAUDIA L. MAYS

1. The love of God is great-er far Than tongue or pen can ev-er tell;
2. When hoar-y time shall pass a-way, And earth-ly thrones and king-doms fall;
3. Could we with ink the o-cean fill, And were the skies of parch-ment made,

It goes be-yond the high-est star, And reach-es to the low-est hell;
When men who here re-fuse to pray, On rocks and hills and moun-tains call;
Were ev-'ry stalk on earth a quill, And ev-'ry man a scribe by trade;

The guilt-y pair, bowed down with care, God gave His Son to win;
God's love, so sure, shall still en-dure, All meas-ure-less and strong;
To write the love of God a-bove Would drain the o-cean dry;

His err-ing child He rec-on-ciled, And par-doned from his sin.
Re-deem-ing grace to Ad-am's race—The saints' and an-gels' song.
Nor could the scroll con-tain the whole, Tho' stretched from sky to sky.

CHORUS

Oh love of God, how rich and pure! How meas-ure-less and strong!

The Love of God

It shall for - ev - er - more en - dure, The saints' and an - gels' song.

I Long to Glorify Thee

167

RALPH MANCHEE

HERMAN VOSS

1. Christ my Lord gave all for me, That from sin I might be free,
2. Christ my Lord a - rose and lives, O - ver all the vic-t'ry gives,
3. Christ my Lord will come one day, Take me home with Him to stay,

Now in me He lives a - gain; Glo - ry to His pre-cious Name.
Now in Him I live a - new, Praise His Name, I know 'tis true.
Then a-new His praise I'll sing; Reign with Him my Lord and King.

CHORUS

I long to glo-ri-fy Thee, dear Lord, I long to glo-ri-fy Thee. on-ly Thee.

In all I do, in all I say, I long to glo-ri-fy Thee. on-ly Thee.

168 Depth of Mercy! Can There Be

CHARLES WESLEY

WILLIAM B. BRADBURY

1. Depth of mer - cy! can there be   Mer - cy still re - served for me?
2. I   have long with - stood His grace,   Long pro-voked Him to   His face,
3. Now in-cline me   to   re - pent;   Let me now my   sins   la - ment;
4. There for me my   Sav-iour stands,   Hold - ing forth His   wounded hands;

Can my God His wrath for-bear—   Me,   the chief of   sin-ners spare?
Would not hearken to   His calls,   Grieved Him by a   thousand falls.
Now my foul re - volt ·de-plore,   Weep,be-lieve,and sin   no more.
God is love! I know, I   feel,   Je - sus weeps and loves me still. A - MEN.

169 Jesus, Thy Blood and Righteousness

NICOLAUS L. ZINZENDORF
TR. BY JOHN WESLEY

WILLIAM GARDINER'S "SACRED MELODIES"

1. Je - sus, Thy blood and right-eous-ness My beau-ty are, my   glo - rious dress;
2. Bold shall I stand in   Thy great day, For who aught to   my   charge shall lay?
3. Lord, I   be-lieve Thy pre-cious blood,Which,at the mer - cy - seat   of God,
4. Lord, I   be-lieve were sin - ners more Than sands up-on the   o - cean shore,

'Midst flaming worlds,in these ar-rayed,With joy shall I   lift   up my head.
Ful - ly ab-solved through these I am, From sin and fear,from guilt and shame.
For - ev - er doth for sin-ners plead,For me, e'en for my   soul was shed.
Thou hast for   all   a   ran-som paid,For all   a   full a-tone-ment paid. A-MEN.

Christ Returneth

H. L. TURNER

JAMES McGRANAHAN

1. It may be at morn, when the day is a-wak-ing, When sunlight thro'
2. It may be at mid-day, it may be at twi-light, It may be, per-
3. While its hosts cry Hosanna, from heaven de-scend-ing, With glo-ri-fied
4. Oh, joy! oh, de-light! should we go with-out dy-ing, No sick-ness, no

dark-ness and shad-ow is break-ing, That Je-sus will come in the
chance, that the black-ness of mid-night Will burst in-to light in the
saints and the an-gels at-tend-ing, With grace on His brow, like a
sad-ness, no dread and no cry-ing, Caught up thro' the clouds with our

full-ness of glo-ry, To re-ceive from the world "His own."
blaze of His glo-ry, When Je-sus re-ceives "His own."
ha-lo of glo-ry, Will Je-sus re-ceive "His own."
Lord in-to glo-ry, When Je-sus re-ceives "His own."

CHORUS

O Lord Je-sus, how long, how long Ere we shout the glad song, Christ re-

rit.

turn-eth! Hal-le-lu-jah! hal-le-lu-jah! A-men. Hal-le-lu-jah! A-men.

171 He Is Coming Again

MABEL JOHNSTON CAMP MABEL JOHNSTON CAMP

1. Lift up your heads, Pil-grims a-wea-ry, See day's ap-proach Now
2. Dark was the night, Sin warred a-gainst us; Heav-y the load Of
3. O bless-ed hope! O bliss-ful prom-ise! Fill-ing our hearts With
4. E - ven so, come, Pre-cious Lord Je - sus; Cre - a - tion waits Re-

crim-son the sky; Night shad-ows flee, And your Be - lov - ed, A-
sor - row we bore; But now we see Signs of His com - ing; Our
rap - ture di-vine; O day of days! Hail Thy ap - pear - ing! Thy
demp-tion to see; Caught up in clouds, Soon we shall meet Thee; O

CHORUS

wait - ed with long-ing, At last draw-eth nigh.
hearts glow with-in us, Joy's cup run-neth o'er!   He is com-ing a-
tran - scend-ent glo - ry For - ev - er shall shine.
bless - ed as - sur-ance, For - ev - er with Thee!

gain, He is com - ing a-gain, The ver - y same Je - sus, Re-

ject - ed of men; He is com-ing a - gain, He is com-ing a - gain,

He Is Coming Again

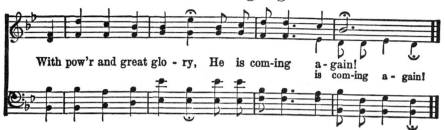

With pow'r and great glo - ry, He is com-ing a - gain!
is com-ing a - gain!

Is Thy Heart Right With God? 172

ELISHA A. HOFFMAN   ELISHA A. HOFFMAN

1. Have thy af-fec-tions been nailed to the cross? Is thy heart right with God?
2. Hast thou do-min-ion o'er self and o'er sin? Is thy heart right with God?
3. Is there no more con-dem-na-tion for sin? Is thy heart right with God?
4. Art thou now walk-ing in heaven's pure light? Is thy heart right with God?

Count-est thou all things for Je - sus but loss? Is thy heart right with God?
O - ver all e - vil with-out and with-in? Is thy heart right with God?
Does Je-sus rule in the tem-ple with-in? Is thy heart right with God?
Is thy soul wear-ing the gar-ment of white? Is thy heart right with God?

CHORUS

Is thy heart right with God, Washed in the crim - son flood,

Cleansed and made ho-ly, hum-ble and low-ly, Right in the sight of God?

Jesus Is Coming Again

JOHN W. PETERSON

JOHN W. PETERSON

1. Mar-vel-ous mes-sage we bring, Glo-ri-ous car-ol we sing,
2. For-est and flow-er ex-claim, Moun-tain and mead-ow the same,
3. Stand-ing be-fore Him at last, Tri-al and trou-ble all past,

Won-der-ful word of the King— Je-sus is com-ing a-gain! (a-gain!)
All earth and heav-en pro-claim— Je-sus is com-ing a-gain! (a-gain!)
Crowns at His feet we will cast— Je-sus is com-ing a-gain! (a-gain!)

CHORUS

Com-ing a-gain, Com-ing a-gain;

May-be morn-ing, may-be noon, May-be eve-ning and may-be soon!

Com-ing a-gain, Com-ing a-gain;

Jesus Is Coming Again

O what a won-der-ful day it will be — Je-sus is com-ing a-gain!

Have You Any Room for Jesus?

174

SOURCE UNKNOWN
ARR. BY DANIEL W. WHITTLE

C. C. WILLIAMS

1. Have you an-y room for Je - sus, He who bore your load of sin?
2. Room for pleas-ure, room for busi - ness, But for Christ the Cru-ci - fied,
3. Have you an-y room for Je - sus, As in grace He calls a - gain?
4. Room and time now give to Je - sus, Soon will pass God's day of grace;

As He knocks and asks ad-mis - sion, Sin - ner, will you let Him in?
Not a place that He can en - ter, In the heart for which He died?
O to - day is time ac - cept - ed, To-mor - row you may call in vain.
Soon thy heart left cold and si - lent, And thy Sav-ior's pleading cease.

CHORUS

Room for Je-sus, King of glo - ry! Has - ten now His word o - bey;

Swing the heart's door wide-ly o - pen, Bid Him en - ter while you may.

175 What If It Were Today?

Leila N. Morris

Leila N. Morris

1. Je - sus is com-ing to earth a-gain, What if it were to - day?
2. Sa - tan's do - min-ion will then be o'er, O that it were to - day!
3. Faith-ful and true would He find us here If He should come to - day?

Com-ing in pow-er and love to reign, What if it were to - day?
Sor - row and sigh-ing shall be no more, O that it were to - day!
Watching in glad-ness and not in fear, If He should come to - day?

Com-ing to claim His cho-sen Bride, All the re-deemed and pu - ri - fied,
Then shall the dead in Christ a - rise, Caught up to meet Him in the skies,
Signs of His com-ing mul - ti - ply, Morning light breaks in east-ern sky,

rit. *a tempo*

O - ver this whole earth scat-tered wide, What if it were to - day?
When shall these glo - ries meet our eyes? What if it were to - day?
Watch, for the time is draw-ing nigh, What if it were to - day?

Chorus

Glo - ry, glo-ry! Joy to my heart 'twill bring;.. Glo-ry, glo-ry!
Joy to my heart 'twill bring;

What If It Were Today?

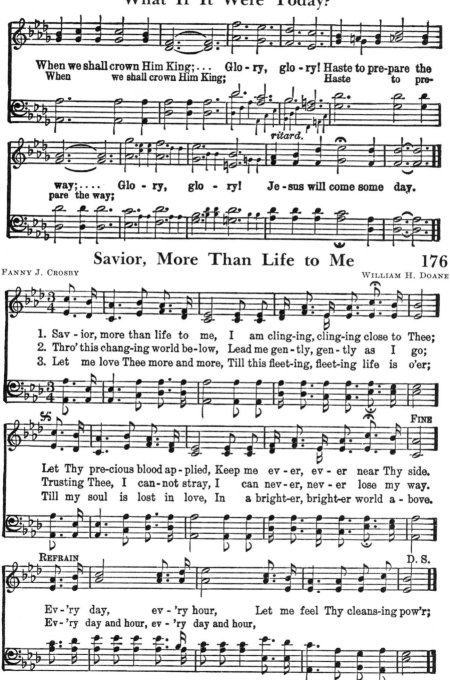

When we shall crown Him King;... Glo - ry, glo - ry! Haste to pre-pare the
When we shall crown Him King; Haste to pre-

ritard.

way;.... Glo - ry, glo - ry! Je - sus will come some day.
pare the way;

Savior, More Than Life to Me 176

FANNY J. CROSBY

WILLIAM H. DOANE

1. Sav - ior, more than life to me, I am cling-ing, cling-ing close to Thee;
2. Thro' this chang-ing world be-low, Lead me gen - tly, gen - tly as I go;
3. Let me love Thee more and more, Till this fleet-ing, fleet-ing life is o'er;

FINE

Let Thy pre-cious blood ap - plied, Keep me ev - er, ev - er near Thy side.
Trusting Thee, I can-not stray, I can nev - er, nev - er lose my way.
Till my soul is lost in love, In a bright-er, bright-er world a - bove.

REFRAIN

D. S.

Ev - 'ry day, ev - 'ry hour, Let me feel Thy cleans-ing pow'r;
Ev - 'ry day and hour, ev - 'ry day and hour,

177 God Be with You

JEREMIAH E. RANKIN   WILLIAM G. TOMER

1. God be with you till we meet a-gain; By His counsels guide, uphold you,
2. God be with you till we meet a-gain;'Neath His wings protecting hide you,
3. God be with you till we meet a-gain; When life's perils thick confound you,
4. God be with you till we meet a-gain; Keep love's banner floating o'er you;

With His sheep se-cure-ly fold you; God be with you till we meet a-gain.
Dai-ly man-na still pro-vide you; God be with you till we meet a-gain.
Put His arms un-fail-ing round you; God be with you till we meet a-gain.
Smite death's threat'ning wave before you; God be with you till we meet a-gain.

CHORUS

Till we meet,.... till we meet, Till we meet at Je-sus' feet;
Till we meet, till we meet, till we meet;

Till we meet,.... till we meet, God be with you till we meet a-gain.
Till we meet, till we meet,

In the Service of the King

ALFRED H. ACKLEY

BENTLEY D. ACKLEY

178

1. I am hap - py in the serv - ice of the King, I am
2. I am hap - py in the serv - ice of the King, I am
3. I am hap - py in the serv - ice of the King, I am
4. I am hap - py in the serv - ice of the King, I am

hap - py, oh, so hap - py; I have peace and joy that
hap - py, oh, so hap - py; Thro' the sun - shine and the
hap - py, oh, so hap - py; To His guid - ing hand for-
hap - py, oh, so hap - py; All that I pos - sess to

noth - ing else can bring, In the serv - ice of the King.
shad - ow I can sing, In the serv - ice of the King.
ev - er I will cling, In the serv - ice of the King.
Him I glad - ly bring, In the serv - ice of the King.

CHORUS

In the serv - ice of the King, Ev - 'ry tal - ent I will bring;

I have peace and joy and bless - ing In the serv - ice of the King.

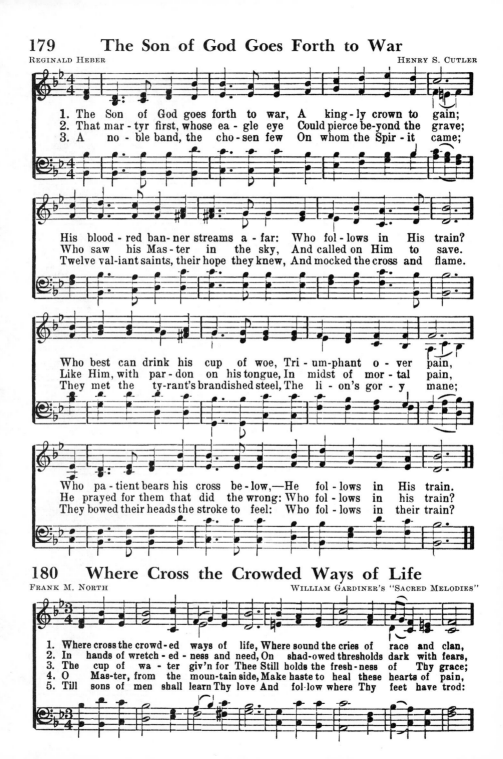

179 The Son of God Goes Forth to War

REGINALD HEBER

HENRY S. CUTLER

1. The Son of God goes forth to war, A king-ly crown to gain;
2. That mar-tyr first, whose ea-gle eye Could pierce be-yond the grave;
3. A no-ble band, the cho-sen few On whom the Spir-it came;

His blood-red ban-ner streams a-far: Who fol-lows in His train?
Who saw his Mas-ter in the sky, And called on Him to save.
Twelve val-iant saints, their hope they knew, And mocked the cross and flame.

Who best can drink his cup of woe, Tri-um-phant o-ver pain,
Like Him, with par-don on his tongue, In midst of mor-tal pain,
They met the ty-rant's brandished steel, The li-on's gor-y mane;

Who pa-tient bears his cross be-low,—He fol-lows in His train.
He prayed for them that did the wrong: Who fol-lows in his train?
They bowed their heads the stroke to feel: Who fol-lows in their train?

180 Where Cross the Crowded Ways of Life

FRANK M. NORTH

WILLIAM GARDINER'S "SACRED MELODIES"

1. Where cross the crowd-ed ways of life, Where sound the cries of race and clan,
2. In hands of wretch-ed-ness and need, On shad-owed thresholds dark with fears,
3. The cup of wa-ter giv'n for Thee Still holds the fresh-ness of Thy grace;
4. O Mas-ter, from the moun-tain side, Make haste to heal these hearts of pain,
5. Till sons of men shall learn Thy love And fol-low where Thy feet have trod:

Where Cross the Crowded Ways of Life

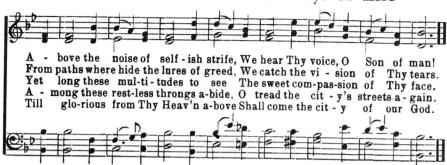

A - bove the noise of self - ish strife, We hear Thy voice, O Son of man!
From paths where hide the lures of greed, We catch the vi - sion of Thy tears.
Yet long these mul - ti - tudes to see The sweet com - pas - sion of Thy face.
A - mong these rest - less throngs a - bide, O tread the cit - y's streets a - gain.
Till glo - rious from Thy Heav'n a - bove Shall come the cit - y of our God.

Let the Lower Lights Be Burning 181

PHILIP P. BLISS

PHILIP P. BLISS

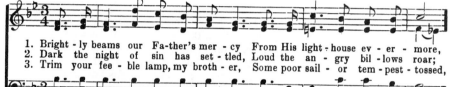

1. Bright - ly beams our Fa - ther's mer - cy From His light - house ev - er - more,
2. Dark the night of sin has set - tled, Loud the an - gry bil - lows roar;
3. Trim your fee - ble lamp, my broth - er, Some poor sail - or tem - pest - tossed,

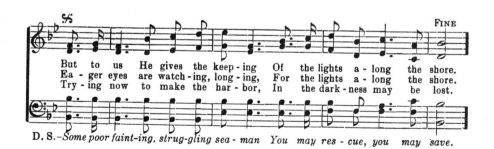

But to us He gives the keep - ing Of the lights a - long the shore.
Ea - ger eyes are watch - ing, long - ing, For the lights a - long the shore.
Try - ing now to make the har - bor, In the dark - ness may be lost.

D. S.—*Some poor faint - ing, strug - gling sea - man You may res - cue, you may save.*

CHORUS

D. S.

Let the low - er lights be burn - ing! Send a gleam a - cross the wave!

182   My Savior's Love

CHARLES H. GABRIEL   CHARLES H. GABRIEL

1. I stand a-mazed in the pres-ence Of Je-sus the Naz-a-rene,
2. For me it was in the gar-den He prayed: "Not My will, but Thine;"
3. In pit-y an-gels be-held Him, And came from the world of light
4. He took my sins and my sor-rows, He made them His ver-y own;
5. When with the ransomed in glo-ry His face I at last shall see,

And won-der how He could love me, A sin-ner, condemned, un-clean.
He had no tears for His own griefs, But sweat-drops of blood for mine.
To com-fort Him in the sor-rows He bore for my soul that night.
He bore the bur-den to Cal-v'ry, And suf-fered, and died a-lone.
'Twill be my joy thro' the a-ges To sing of His love for me.

CHORUS.

How mar-vel-ous! how won-der-ful! And my song shall ev-er be:
Oh, how mar-vel-ous! oh, how won-der-ful!

How mar-vel-ous! how won-der-ful Is my Sav-ior's love for me! A-MEN.
Oh, how mar-vel-ous! oh, how won-der-ful

It Pays to Serve Jesus

183

Frank C. Huston

Frank C. Huston

1. The serv-ice of Je-sus true pleas-ure af-fords, In Him there is
joy with-out an al-loy; 'Tis heav-en to trust Him and rest on His
words; It pays to serve Je-sus each day.

2. It pays to serve Je-sus what-e'er may be-tide, It pays to be
true what-e'er you may do; 'Tis rich-es of mer-cy in Him to a-
bide; It pays to serve Je-sus each day.

3. Tho' sometimes the shad-ows may hang o'er the way, And sor-rows may
come to beck-on us home, Our pre-cious Re-deem-er each toil will re-
pay; It pays to serve Je-sus each day.

CHORUS

It pays to serve Je-sus, it pays ev-'ry day, It pays ev-'ry step of the way; ..... Tho' the pathway to
ev-'ry step of the way;
glo-ry may sometimes be drear, You'll be hap-py each step of the way.

184 Make Me a Blessing

IRA B. WILSON

GEORGE S. SCHULER

Slowly

1. Out in the high-ways and by-ways of life, Man-y are
2. Tell the sweet sto-ry of Christ and His love, Tell of His
3. Give as 'twas giv-en to you in your need, Love as the

wea-ry and sad; . . . . Car-ry the sunshine where darkness is rife,
are wea-ry and sad;
pow'r to for-give; . . . . Oth-ers will trust Him if on-ly you prove
His pow'r to for-give;
Mas-ter loved you; . . . . Be to the help-less a help-er in-deed,
the Mas-ter loved you;

rit.

CHORUS *Men or Unison*

Mak-ing the sor-row-ing glad. . . .
True, ev-'ry mo-ment you live. . . . . Make me a bless-ing,
Un-to your mis-sion be true. . . . .

Women

Make me a bless-ing, Out of my life . . . may Je-

Out of my life

Men

rit.

Unison

Women

sus shine; . . Make me a bless-ing, O Sav-ior,

Make Me a Blessing

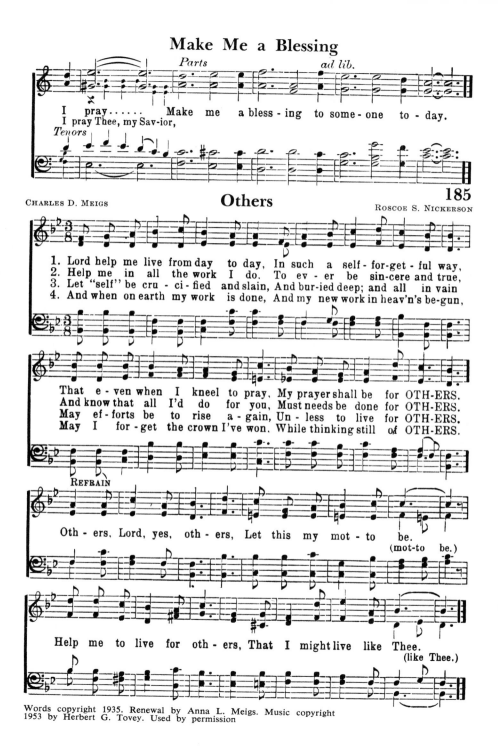

Parts   *ad lib.*

I pray...... Make me a bless-ing to some-one to-day.
I pray Thee, my Sav-ior,

Tenors

185

CHARLES D. MEIGS

Others

ROSCOE S. NICKERSON

1. Lord help me live from day to day, In such a self-for-get-ful way,
2. Help me in all the work I do, To ev-er be sin-cere and true,
3. Let "self" be cru-ci-fied and slain, And bur-ied deep; and all in vain
4. And when on earth my work is done, And my new work in heav'n's be-gun,

That e-ven when I kneel to pray, My prayer shall be for OTH-ERS.
And know that all I'd do for you, Must needs be done for OTH-ERS.
May ef-forts be to rise a-gain, Un-less to live for OTH-ERS.
May I for-get the crown I've won, While thinking still of OTH-ERS.

REFRAIN

Oth-ers, Lord, yes, oth-ers, Let this my mot-to be.
(mot-to be.)

Help me to live for oth-ers, That I might live like Thee.
(like Thee.)

186   Make Me a Channel of Blessing

HARPER G. SMYTH   HARPER G. SMYTH

1. Is your life a chan-nel of bless-ing? Is the love of God
2. Is your life a chan-nel of bless-ing? Are you bur-dened for
3. Is your life a chan-nel of bless-ing? Is it dai - ly
4. We can-not be chan-nels of bless-ing If our lives are not

flow-ing thro' you? Are you tell-ing the lost of the Sav - iour? Are you
those that are lost? Have you urged up-on those who are stray-ing, The
tell - ing for Him? Have you spo-ken the word of sal - va - tion To
free from known sin; We will bar - ri - ers be and a hin-drance To

CHORUS

read - y His serv-ice to do?
Sav-iour who died on the cross?   Make me a chan-nel of bless-ing to-day,
those who are dy-ing in sin?
those we are try-ing to win.

Make me a chan-nel of bless-ing, I pray; My life pos-sess-ing,

rit.

my serv-ice bless-ing, Make me a chan-nel of bless-ing to - day.

Will Jesus Find Us Watching?

187

FANNY J. CROSBY

WILLIAM H. DOANE

1. When Je-sus comes to re-ward His serv-ants, Wheth-er it be
2. If, at the dawn of the ear-ly morn-ing, He shall call us
3. Have we been true to the trust He left us? Do we seek to
4. Bless-ed are those whom the Lord finds watch-ing. In His glo-ry

noon or night, Faith-ful to Him will He find us watch-ing,
one by one, When to the Lord we re-store our tal-ents,
do our best? If in our hearts there is naught con-demns us,
they shall share; If He shall come at the dawn or mid-night,

rit.

With our lamps all trimmed and bright?
Will He an-swer thee—"Well done"?
We shall have a glo-rious rest.
Will He find us watch-ing there?

CHORUS

Oh, can we say we are

read-y, broth-er? Read-y for the soul's bright home? Say, will He

find you and me still watch-ing. Wait-ing, wait-ing when the Lord shall come?

188 Glory to His Name

ELISHA A. HOFFMAN

JOHN H. STOCKTON

1. Down at the cross where my Sav-ior died, Down where for cleansing from
2. I am so won-drous-ly saved from sin, Je-sus so sweet-ly a-
3. Oh, pre-cious foun-tain that saves from sin, I am so glad I have
4. Come to this foun-tain so rich and sweet; Cast thy poor soul at the

FINE

sin I cried, There to my heart was the blood ap-plied; Glo-ry to His name.
bides with-in, There at the cross where He took me in; Glo-ry to His name.
en-tered in; There Jesus saves me and keeps me clean; Glo-ry to His name.
Sav-ior's feet; Plunge in to-day, and be made com-plete; Glo-ry to His name.

D. S.—*There to my heart was the blood ap-plied; Glo-ry to His name.*

CHORUS

D. S.

Glo-ry to His name,... Glo-ry to His name;...

189 Must Jesus Bear the Cross Alone?

THOMAS SHEPHERD

GEORGE N. ALLEN

1. Must Je-sus bear the cross a-lone, And all the world go free?
2. The con-se-crat-ed cross I'll bear, Till death shall set me free,
3. Up-on the crys-tal pave-ment, down At Je-sus' pierc-ed feet,
4. O pre-cious cross! O glo-rious crown! O res-ur-rec-tion day!

Must Jesus Bear the Cross Alone?

No; there's a cross for ev-'ry one, And there's a cross for me.
And then go home my crown to wear, For there's a crown for me.
Joy-ful, I'll cast my gold-en crown, And His dear name re-peat.
Ye an-gels, from the stars come down, And bear my soul a-way.

Savior, Breathe an Evening Blessing   190

JAMES EDMESTON

GEORGE C. STEBBINS

1. Sav - ior, breathe an eve - ning bless - ing, Ere re-
2. Though de - struct - ion walk a - round us, Though the
3. Though the night be dark and drear - y, Dark - ness
4. Should swift death this night o'er - take us, And our

pose our spir - its seal: Sin and want we come con-
ar - rows past us fly; An - gel - guards from Thee sur-
can - not hide from Thee; Thou art He who, nev - er
couch be - come our tomb, May the morn in heav'n a-

fess - ing, Thou canst save and Thou canst heal.
round us, We are safe if Thou art nigh.
wea - ry, Watch - est where Thy peo - ple be.
wake us, Clad in bright and death-less bloom. A-MEN.

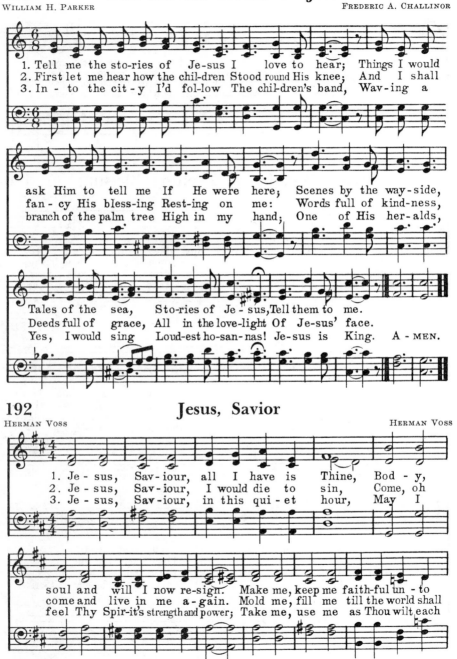

191 Tell Me the Stories of Jesus

William H. Parker

Frederic A. Challinor

1. Tell me the sto-ries of Je-sus I love to hear; Things I would ask Him to tell me If He were here; Scenes by the way-side, Tales of the sea, Sto-ries of Je-sus, Tell them to me.

2. First let me hear how the chil-dren Stood round His knee; And I shall fan-cy His bless-ing Rest-ing on me: Words full of kind-ness, Deeds full of grace, All in the love-light Of Je-sus' face.

3. In-to the cit-y I'd fol-low The chil-dren's band, Wav-ing a branch of the palm tree High in my hand; One of His her-alds, Yes, I would sing Loud-est ho-san-nas! Je-sus is King. A-men.

192 Jesus, Savior

Herman Voss

Herman Voss

1. Je-sus, Sav-iour, all I have is Thine, Bod-y, soul and will I now re-sign. Make me, keep me faith-ful un-to

2. Je-sus, Sav-iour, I would die to sin, Come, oh come and live in me a-gain. Mold me, fill me till the world shall

3. Je-sus, Sav-iour, in this qui-et hour, May I feel Thy Spir-it's strength and power; Take me, use me as Thou wilt each

Jesus, Savior

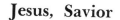

Thee,	Je - sus,	Sav - iour,	through e - ter - ni - ty.
see	Je - sus,	Sav - iour,	liv - ing now in me.
day,	Je - sus,	Sav - iour,	this I hum - bly pray.

No Other Plea

193

LIDIE H. EDMUNDS

ARR. BY WILLIAM J. KIRKPATRICK

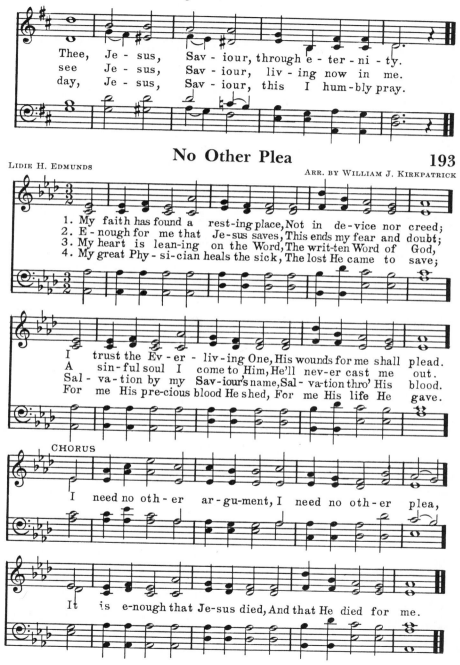

1. My faith has found a rest-ing place, Not in de-vice nor creed;
2. E - nough for me that Je-sus saves, This ends my fear and doubt;
3. My heart is lean-ing on the Word, The writ-ten Word of God,
4. My great Phy - si-cian heals the sick, The lost He came to save;

I trust the Ev - er - liv-ing One, His wounds for me shall plead.
A sin-ful soul I come to Him, He'll nev-er cast me out.
Sal - va-tion by my Sav-iour's name, Sal - va-tion thro' His blood.
For me His pre-cious blood He shed, For me His life He gave.

CHORUS

I need no oth - er ar - gu-ment, I need no oth - er plea,

It is e-nough that Je-sus died, And that He died for me.

194 Rescue the Perishing

FANNY J. CROSBY

WILLIAM H. DOANE

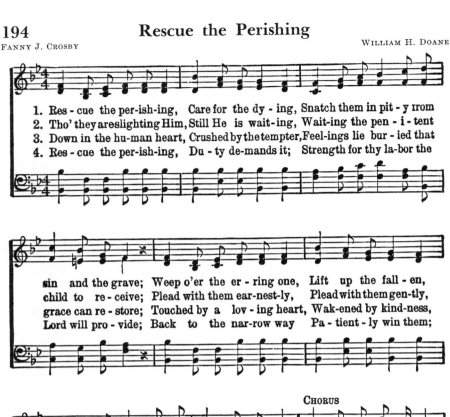

1. Res-cue the per-ish-ing, Care for the dy-ing, Snatch them in pit-y from
2. Tho' they are slighting Him, Still He is wait-ing, Wait-ing the pen-i-tent
3. Down in the hu-man heart, Crushed by the tempter, Feel-ings lie bur-ied that
4. Res-cue the per-ish-ing, Du-ty de-mands it; Strength for thy la-bor the

sin and the grave; Weep o'er the er-ring one, Lift up the fall-en,
child to re-ceive; Plead with them ear-nest-ly, Plead with them gen-tly,
grace can re-store; Touched by a lov-ing heart, Wak-ened by kind-ness,
Lord will pro-vide; Back to the nar-row way Pa-tient-ly win them;

CHORUS

Tell them of Je-sus the migh-ty to save.
He will for-give if they on-ly be-lieve. Res-cue the per-ish-ing,
Chords that are bro-ken will vi-brate once more.
Tell the poor wan-d'rer a Sav-ior has died.

Care for the dy-ing; Je-sus is mer-ci-ful, Je-sus will save.

A Passion for Souls

195

HERBERT G. TOVEY

FOSS L. FELLERS

1. Give me a pas-sion for souls, dear Lord, A pas-sion to save the lost;
2. Though there are dan-gers un-told and stern Con-front-ing me in the way,
3. How shall this pas-sion for souls be mine? Lord, make Thou the an-swer clear;

O that Thy love were by all a-dored, And wel-comed at an-y cost.
Will-ing-ly still would I go, nor turn, But trust Thee for grace each day.
Help me to throw out the old Life-Line To those who are strug-gling near.

CHORUS.

Je-sus, I long, I long to be win-ning Men who are lost, and con-stant-ly sin-ning; O may this hour be one of be-gin-ning The sto-ry of par-don to tell.

196 Help Somebody Today

CARRIE E. BRECK

CHARLES H. GABRIEL

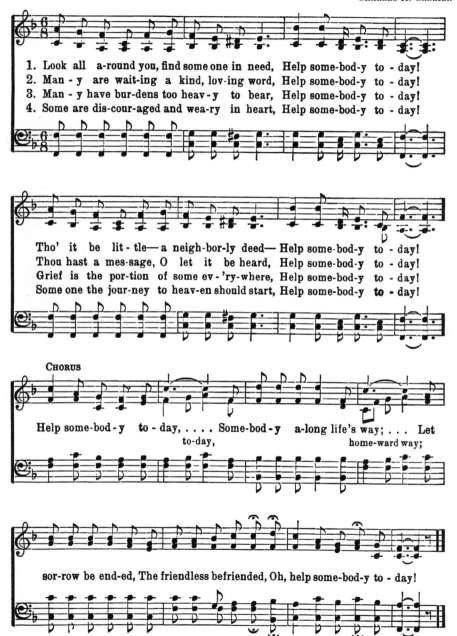

1. Look all a-round you, find some one in need, Help some-bod-y to-day!
2. Man - y are wait-ing a kind, lov-ing word, Help some-bod-y to - day!
3. Man - y have bur-dens too heav-y to bear, Help some-bod-y to - day!
4. Some are dis-cour-aged and wea-ry in heart, Help some-bod-y to - day!

Tho' it be lit - tle—a neigh-bor-ly deed— Help some-bod-y to - day!
Thou hast a mes-sage, O let it be heard, Help some-bod-y to - day!
Grief is the por-tion of some ev - 'ry-where, Help some-bod-y to - day!
Some one the jour-ney to heav-en should start, Help some-bod-y to - day!

CHORUS

Help some-bod-y to - day, ... Some-bod-y a-long life's way; ... Let
to-day,   home-ward way;

sor-row be end-ed, The friendless befriended, Oh, help some-bod-y to - day!

The Ninety and Nine

Elizabeth C. Clephane

Ira D. Sankey

1. There were ninety and nine that safe - ly lay   In the shel-ter   of the
2. "Lord,   Thou   hast here Thy nine-ty and nine; Are   they not enough for
3. But   none of the ransomed ev - er knew   How deep were the waters
4. "Lord, whence are those blood-drops all the way That mark out the mountain's
5. But   all thro' the mountains, thun-der-riv'n, And   up from the rock-y

fold,   But   one   was   out on the hills a-way,   Far   off from the
Thee?" But the Shep-herd made answer: "This of mine   Has wan-dered a-
crossed; Nor how dark was the night that the Lord passed thro' Ere He found His
track?" "They were shed for one who had gone a-stray Ere the Shepherd could
steep,   There a-rose a glad cry to the gate of heav'n, "Re - joice! I have

rit.

gates   of   gold— A - way on the moun - tains wild and bare,   A-
way   from   me, And al - tho'   the   road   be rough and steep,   I
sheep that was lost.   Out in the des - ert He heard   its   cry—
bring   him back." "Lord, whence are Thy hands so rent and torn?" "They're
found   my sheep!" And the an - gels ech-oed a - round the throne, "Re-

way from the ten-der Shepherd's care, A-way from the ten - der Shep-herd's care.
go   to the des-ert to find my sheep, I   go to the des-ert to   find my sheep."
Sick   and helpless, and ready to die;   Sick and helpless, and ready to die.
pierced to - night by many a thorn; They're pierced to-night by man-y a thorn."
joice, for the Lord brings back His own! Re-joice, for the Lord brings back His own."

198 Throw Out the Life-Line

EDWARD S. UFFORD

EDWARD S. UFFORD
ARR. BY GEORGE C. STEBBINS

1. Throw out the Life-Line a-cross the dark wave, There is a broth-er whom
2. Throw out the Life-Line with hand quick and strong: Why do you tar-ry, why
3. Throw out the Life-Line to dan-ger-fraught men, Sink-ing in an-guish where
4. Soon will the sea-son of res-cue be o'er, Soon will they drift to e-

some one should save; Some-bod-y's broth-er! oh, who then will dare To
lin-ger so long? See! he is sink-ing; oh, has-ten to-day—And
you've nev-er been: Winds of temp-ta-tion and bil-lows of woe Will
ter-ni-ty's shore, Haste then, my broth-er, no time for de-lay, But

CHORUS

throw out the Life-Line, his per-il to share?
out with the Life-Boat! a-way, then, a-way! Throw out the Life-Line!
soon hurl them out where the dark wa-ters flow.
throw out the Life-Line and save them to-day.

Throw out the Life-Line! Some-one is drift-ing a-way; Throw out the

Life-Line! Throw out the Life-Line! Some one is sink-ing to-day.

He's a Friend of Mine

199

John H. Sammis

Daniel B. Towner

1. Why should I charge my soul with care? The wealth of ev-'ry mine
2. The sil-ver moon, the gold-en sun, The count-less stars that shine,
3. He dai-ly spreads a glo-rious feast, And at His ta-ble dine
4. And when He comes in bright ar-ray, And leads the conquering line,

Be-longs to Christ, God's Son and Heir, And He's a Friend of mine.
Are His a-lone, yes, ev-'ry one, And He's a Friend of mine.
The whole cre-a-tion, man and beast, And He's a Friend of mine.
It will be glo-ry then to say, And He's a Friend of mine.

CHORUS

Yes, He's a Friend of mine, And He with me doth all things share;

Since all is Christ's, and Christ is mine, Why should I have a

care? For Je-sus is a Friend of mine....

200 A New Name in Glory

C. Austin Miles

1. I was once a sin-ner, but I came Par-don to re-ceive from my
2. I was hum-bly kneel-ing at the cross, Fear-ing naught but God's an-gry
3. In the Book 'tis writ-ten, "Saved by Grace," O the joy that came to my

Lord: This was free-ly giv-en, and I found That He al-ways kept His
frown; When the heav-ens o-pened and I saw That my name was writ-ten
soul! Now I am for-giv-en, and I know By the blood I am made

REFRAIN

word (kept His word). There's a new name writ-ten down in glo-ry,
down (writ-ten down).
whole (am made whole).

And it's mine, O yes, it's mine! And the white-robed an-gels sing the
And it's mine, yes, it's mine!

sto-ry, "A sin-ner has come home." For there's a
has come home."

A New Name in Glory

new name writ-ten down in glo-ry, And it's mine, O yes, it's mine!
And it's mine, yes, it's mine!

With my sins for-giv-en I am bound for heav-en, Nev-er-more to roam.

Come, Ye Disconsolate

201

THOMAS MOORE
ALT. BY THOMAS HASTINGS

SAMUEL WEBBE

1. Come, ye dis-con-so-late, wher-e'er ye lan-guish; Come to the
2. Joy of the des-o-late, light of the stray-ing, Hope of the
3. Here see the bread of life; see wa-ters flow-ing Forth from the

mer-cy-seat, fer-vent-ly kneel; Here bring your wound-ed hearts,
pen-i-tent, fade-less and pure, Here speaks the Com-fort-er,
throne of God, pure from a-bove; Come to the feast of love;

here tell your an-guish; Earth has no sor-row that Heav'n can-not heal.
ten-der-ly say-ing, "Earth has no sor-row that Heav'n can-not cure."
come, ev-er know-ing Earth has no sor-row but Heav'n can re-move. A-MEN.

202 All Things in Jesus

HARRY D. LOES   HARRY D. LOES

1. Friends all a-round me are try-ing. to find What the heart yearns for, by
2. Some car-ry burdens whose weight has for years Crushed them with sorrow and
3. No oth-er name thrills the joy-chords within, And thro' none else is re-
4. Je - sus is all this poor world needs to-day, Blind-ly they strive, for sin

sin un-der-mined; I have the se-cret, I know where 'tis found:
blind-ed with tears, Yet One stands read-y to help them just now,
mis-sion of sin; He knows the pain of the heart sore-ly tried,
dark-ens their way; O to draw back the grim cur-tains of night,

CHORUS

On-ly true pleas-ures in Je-sus a-bound.
If they will hum-bly in pen-i-tence bow. All that I want is in
Both need and want will by Him be sup-plied.
One glimpse of Je-sus and all will be bright!

Je - - sus, He sat-is-fies, ... joy He sup-plies;
Je-sus, in Je-sus, with the free-ly;

ad lib.

Life would be worthless without Him, All things in Je-sus I find.
without Him, without Him,

Burdens Are Lifted at Calvary

203

JOHN M. MOORE

JOHN M. MOORE

1. Days are filled with sor - row and care, Hearts are lone - ly and drear;
2. Cast your care on Je - sus to - day, Leave your wor - ry and fear;
3. Trou - bled soul, the Sav - iour can see Ev - 'ry heart-ache and tear;

Bur - dens are lift - ed at Cal - va - ry, Je - sus is ver - y near.
Bur - dens are lift - ed at Cal - va - ry, Je - sus is ver - y near.
Bur - dens are lift - ed at Cal - va - ry, Je - sus is ver - y near.

CHORUS

Bur - dens are lift - ed at Cal - va - ry, Cal - va - ry, Cal - va - ry;

Bur - dens are lift - ed at Cal - va - ry, Je - sus is ver - y near.
ver - y near.

204 Christ Receiveth Sinful Men

ERDMANN NEUMEISTER
TR. BY EMMA F. BEVAN

JAMES MCGRANAHAN

1. Sin - ners Je - sus will re - ceive; Sound this word of grace to all
2. Come, and He will give you rest; Trust Him, for His word is plain;
3. Now my heart con-demns me not, Pure be - fore the law I stand;
4. Christ re - ceiv - eth sin - ful men, E - ven me with all my sin;

Who the heav'n - ly path-way leave, All who lin - ger, all who fall.
He will take the sin - ful - est; Christ re - ceiv - eth sin - ful men.
He who cleansed me from all spot, Sat - is - fied its last de-mand.
Purged from ev - 'ry spot and stain, Heav'n with Him I en - ter in.

REFRAIN

Sing it o'er . . . . . and o'er a - gain; . . . . . Christ re-
Sing it o'er a-gain, Sing it o'er a-gain; Christ re-

ceiv - - - eth sin-ful men; . . . . . Make the mes - - - - sage
ceiv-eth sin - ful men, Christ re-ceiv-eth sin - ful men; Make the message plain,

clear and plain: . . . . . Christ re - ceiv - eth sin - ful men.
Make the mes-sage plain:

He Included Me

205

Johnson Oatman, Jr.

Hampton H. Sewell

1. I am so hap-py in Christ to-day, That I go sing-ing a-long my way;
2. Glad-ly I read, "Who-so-ev-er may Come to the fountain of life to-day;"
3. Ever God's Spirit is saying, "Come!" Hear the Bride saying, "No longer roam;"
4. "Freely come drink," words the soul to thrill! O with what joy they my heart do fill!

Yes, I'm so hap-py to know and say, "Je-sus in-clud-ed me too."
But when I read it I al-ways say, "Je-sus in-clud-ed me too."
But I am sure while they're calling home, Je-sus in-clud-ed me too.
For when He said, "Who-so-ev-er will," Je-sus in-clud-ed me too.

CHORUS.

Je-sus in-clud-ed me, Yes, He in-clud-ed me, When the Lord said "Who-so-ev-er," He in-clud-ed me; Je-sus in-clud-ed me, Yes, He in-clud-ed me, When the Lord said "Who-so-ev-er," He included me. A-MEN.

206 Dwelling in Beulah Land

C. AUSTIN MILES

C. AUSTIN MILES

1. Far a-way the noise of strife up-on my ear is fall-ing, Then I know the
2. Far be-low the storm of doubt up-on the world is beat-ing, Sons of men in
3. Let the storm-y breez-es blow, their cry can-not a-larm me; I am safe-ly
4. Viewing here the works of God, I sink in con-tem-pla-tion, Hearing now His

sins of earth be-set on ev-'ry hand: Doubt and fear and things of earth in
bat-tle long the en-e-my with-stand: Safe am I with-in the cas-tle
sheltered here, pro-tect-ed by God's hand: Here the sun is al-ways shin-ing,
bless-ed voice, I see the way He planned: Dwell-ing in the Spir-it, here I

vain to me are call-ing, None of these shall move me from Beu-lah Land.
of God's word re-treat-ing, Nothing then can reach me—'tis Beu-lah Land.
here there's naught can harm me, I am safe for-ev-er in Beu-lah Land.
learn of full sal-va-tion, Glad-ly will I tar-ry in Beu-lah Land.

CHORUS

I'm liv-ing on the moun-tain, un-der-neath a cloud-less sky, I'm
Praise God!

drink-ing at the foun-tain that never shall run dry; O yes! I'm feasting on the

Copyright 1939, renewal extended. Rodeheaver Co., owner. Used by permission

Dwelling in Beulah Land

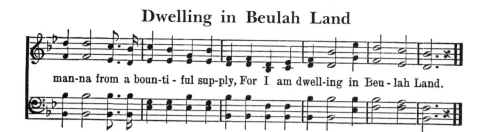

man-na from a boun-ti-ful sup-ply, For I am dwell-ing in Beu-lah Land.

Christ Liveth in Me

207

DANIEL W. WHITTLE

JAMES McGRANAHAN

1. Once far from God and dead in sin, No light my heart could see;
2. As rays of light from yon-der sun, The flow'rs of earth set free,
3. As lives the flow'r with-in the seed, As in the cone the tree,
4. With long-ing all my heart is filled, That like Him I may be,

But in God's Word the light I found, Now Christ liv-eth in me.
So life and light and love came forth From Christ liv-ing in me.
So, praise the God of truth and grace, His Spir-it dwell-eth in me.
As on the won-drous tho't I dwell That Christ liv-eth in me.

CHORUS

Christ liv-eth in me, Christ liv-eth in me,
Christ liv-eth in me, Christ liv-eth in me, Christ liv-eth in

Oh! what a sal-va-tion this, That Christ liv-eth in me.
me, Oh!

208 He Is So Precious to Me

CHARLES H. GABRIEL

CHARLES H. GABRIEL

1. So pre-cious is Je-sus, my Sav-ior, my King, His praise all the day
2. He stood at my heart's door 'mid sunshine and rain, And pa-tient-ly wait-
3. I stand on the moun-tain of bless-ing at last, No cloud in the heav-
4. I praise Him be-cause He ap-point-ed a place Where, some day, thro' faith

long with rap-ture I sing; To Him in my weak-ness for strength I can cling,
ed an en-trance to gain; What shame that so long He en-treat-ed in vain,
ens a shad-ow to cast; His smile is up-on me, the val-ley is past,
in His won-der-ful grace, I know I shall see Him—shall look on His face,

CHORUS. *Faster.*

For He is so pre-cious to me. For He is so pre-cious to me, ...
so pre-cious to me,

For He is so pre-cious to me; . . . . 'Tis Heav-en be-low
so pre-cious to me;

rit. . .

My Re-deem-er to know, For He is so pre-cious to me. A-MEN.

He Lifted Me

Charles H. Gabriel

Charles H. Gabriel

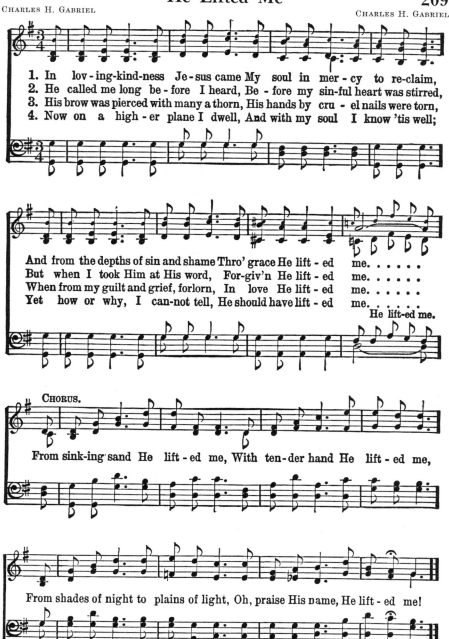

1. In lov-ing-kind-ness Je-sus came My soul in mer-cy to re-claim,
2. He called me long be-fore I heard, Be-fore my sin-ful heart was stirred,
3. His brow was pierced with many a thorn, His hands by cru - el nails were torn,
4. Now on a high - er plane I dwell, And with my soul I know 'tis well;

And from the depths of sin and shame Thro' grace He lift - ed me.
But when I took Him at His word, For-giv'n He lift - ed me.
When from my guilt and grief, forlorn, In love He lift - ed me.
Yet how or why, I can-not tell, He should have lift - ed me.

He lift-ed me.

CHORUS.

From sink-ing sand He lift - ed me, With ten-der hand He lift - ed me,

From shades of night to plains of light, Oh, praise His name, He lift - ed me!

210 A Child of the King

HARRIET E. BUELL

JOHN B. SUMMERS

1. My Fa-ther is rich in hous-es and lands, He hold-eth the
2. My Fa-ther's own Son, the Sav-ior of men, Once wan-dered on
3. I once was an out-cast stran-ger on earth, A sin-ner by
4. A tent or a cot-tage, why should I care? They're build-ing a

wealth of the world in His hands! Of ru-bies and dia-monds, of
earth as the poor-est of them; But now He is plead-ing our
choice, and an al-ien by birth; But I've been a-dopt-ed, my
pal-ace for me o-ver there; Tho' ex-iled from home, yet,

sil-ver and gold, His cof-fers are full, He has rich-es un-told.
par-don on high, That we may be His when He comes by and by.
name's writ-ten down, An heir to a man-sion, a robe, and a crown.
still I may sing: All glo-ry to God, I'm a child of the King.

REFRAIN

I'm a child of the King, A child of the King:

With Je-sus my Sav-ior I'm a child of the King.

A Shelter in the Time of Storm

211

VERNON J. CHARLESWORTH
ARR. BY IRA D. SANKEY

IRA D. SANKEY

1. The Lord's our Rock, in Him we hide, A shel-ter in the time of storm;
2. A shade by day, de-fence by night, A shel-ter in the time of storm;
3. The rag-ing storms may round us beat, A shel-ter in the time of storm;
4. O Rock di-vine, O Ref-uge dear, A shel-ter in the time of storm;

Se-cure what-ev-er ill be-tide, A shel-ter in the time of storm.
No fears a-larm, no foes af-fright, A shel-ter in the time of storm.
We'll nev-er leave our safe re-treat, A shel-ter in the time of storm.
Be Thou our help-er ev-er near, A shel-ter in the time of storm.

REFRAIN

Oh, Je-sus is a Rock in a wea-ry land, A wea-ry land, a wea-ry land;

Oh, Je-sus is a Rock in a wea-ry land, A shel-ter in the time of storm.

212 I Belong to the King

IDA L. REED

MAURICE A. CLIFTON

1. I be-long to the King, I'm a child of His love, I shall dwell in His
2. I be-long to the King, and He loves me I know, For His mer-cy and
3. I be-long to the King, and His prom-ise is sure, That we all shall be

pal-ace so fair; For He tells of its bliss in yon heav-en a-bove, And His
kindness, so free, Are un-ceas-ing-ly mine, where-so-ev-er I go, And my
gathered at last In His king-dom a-bove, by life's wa-ters so pure, When this

Chorus

chil-dren in splen-dor shall share.
ref-uge un-fail-ing is He.   I be-long to the King, I'm a
life with its tri-als is past.

child of His love, And He nev-er for-sak-eth His own; He will call me some

day to His pal-ace a-bove, I shall dwell by His glo-ri-fied throne.

I Know Whom I Have Believed

DANIEL W. WHITTLE

JAMES McGRANAHAN

1. I know not why God's won-drous grace To me He hath made known,
2. I know not how this sav-ing faith To me He did im-part,
3. I know not how the Spir-it moves, Con-vinc-ing men of sin,
4. I know not what of good or ill May be re-served for me,
5. I know not when my Lord may come, At night or noon-day fair,

Nor why un-wor-thy—Christ in love Re-deemed me for His own.
Nor how be-liev-ing in His Word Wrought peace within my heart.
Re-veal-ing Je-sus thro' the Word, Cre-at-ing faith in Him.
Of wea-ry ways or gold-en days, Be-fore His face I see.
Nor if I walk the vale with Him, Or "meet Him in the air."

CHORUS

But "I know whom I have be-liev-ed, and am per-suad-ed that He is a-ble To keep that which I've committed Un-to Him a-gainst that day."

214   I Love Him Because He First Loved Me

FRANK E. ROUSH

J. E. STURGIS

1. Christ Je-sus my Lord from heav-en came, To save me from guilt and
2. He sweat drops of blood in prayer for me, Heart-bro-ken in dark Geth-
3. Up Cal-va-ry's hill the cross He bore, And for me a crown of
4. My Lord who was slain by sin-ful man, A won-der-ful Friend to

sin and shame; His death on the cross of Cal-va-ry Brought
sem-a-ne, While an-gels from bless-ed realms of light Gave
thorns He wore; They nailed Him up-on the tree to die, Then
me has been; He rose from the tomb with vic-to-ry, And

par-don and gave me lib-er-ty.
strength to His ach-ing heart that night.
dark-ness came o-ver earth and sky.
now I love Him who first loved me.

CHORUS

I love Him be-cause He

first loved me, He first loved me, He first loved me; I love Him be-

cause He first loved me, And died on the cross of Cal-va-ry.

I Love to Tell the Story

A. CATHERINE HANKEY

WILLIAM G. FISCHER

1. I love to tell the sto - ry Of un - seen things a - bove, Of
2. I love to tell the sto - ry, More won - der - ful it seems Than
3. I love to tell the sto - ry,'Tis pleas - ant to re - peat What
4. I love to tell the sto - ry, For those who know it best Seem

Je - sus and His glo - ry, Of Je - sus and His love. I love to
all the gold - en fan - cies Of all our gold - en dreams. I love to
seems, each time I tell it, More won - der - ful - ly sweet. I love to
hun - ger - ing and thirst-ing To hear it like the rest. And when, in

tell the sto - ry, Be - cause I know 'tis true; It sat - is - fies my
tell the sto - ry, It did so much for me; And that is just the
tell the sto - ry, For some have nev - er heard The mes - sage of sal -
scenes of glo - ry, I sing the new, new song, 'Twill be the old, old

CHORUS

longings As noth - ing else can do.
rea - son I tell it now to thee.   I love to tell the sto - ry, 'Twill
va - tion From God's own ho - ly Word.
sto - ry That I have loved so long.

be my theme in glo - ry To tell the old, old sto - ry Of Jesus and His love.

216 I've Heard the King

Grant C. Tullar

Donald P. Hustad

1. I've heard the King! The King of heav-en! Nor can I e'er for-get the
2. I've heard the King! The King of glo-ry; For whom my heart's door opened
3. I've heard the King! Oh, had I missed Him, My life for-ev-er-more could
4. I've heard the King! and now I'm tell-ing To all the world the gos-pel

mu-sic of His voice. I've heard the King! His call I've answered. I've made the
wide and He came in. I've heard the King! Oh, blessed hear-ing, His voice spoke
not re-gain the loss. From heav'n He came, the world to ran-som, And this He
of un-dy-ing love, That oth-ers too may catch the mu-sic His voice can

Chorus

King of heav'n my ev-er-last-ing choice.
peace and par-don for my guilt and sin. He came to me, and with Him came a
did one day on Calv-'ry's cru-el cross.
bring, and find their way to heav'n above.

mp

bless-ing. He spoke to me, and glo-ry filled my soul; His voice I heard, so

f

charm-ing and so won-drous. I've heard the King, and hearing am made whole.

Jesus Has Lifted Me!

AVIS B. CHRISTIANSEN

HALDOR LILLENAS

1. Out of the depths to the glo-ry a-bove, I have been
2. Out of the world in-to heav-en-ly rest, In-to the
3. Out of my-self in-to Him I a-dore, There to a-

lift-ed in won-der-ful love; From ev-'ry fet-ter my
land of the ran-somed and blest; There in the glo-ry with
bide in His love ev-er-more; Thro' end-less a-ges His

spir-it is free— For Je-sus has lift-ed me! . . . .
Him I shall be— For Je-sus has lift-ed me!
glo-ry to see— My Je-sus has lift-ed me!
lift-ed me!

CHORUS

Je-sus has lift-ed me! . . . Je-sus has lift-ed me! . . .
lift-ed me! lift-ed me!

Out of the night in-to glo-ri-ous light, Yes, Je-sus has lift-ed me! . . . .
lift-ed me!

218 It's Just Like His Great Love

EDNA H. WORRELL   CLARENCE B. STROUSE

1. A Friend I have, called Je-sus, Whose love is strong and true, And nev-er
2. Sometimes the clouds of troub-le Be - dim the sky a - bove, I   can-not
3. When sorrow's clouds o'ertake me, And break up-on my head, When life seems
4. Oh,   I could sing for-ev - er Of Je - sus' love di - vine, Of all His

fails how-e'er 'tis tried, No mat-ter what I do; I've sinned a-gainst this
see my Sav-ior's face, I doubt His won-drous love; But He, from Heav-en's
worse than use - less, And I were bet-ter dead; I   take my grief to
care and ten - der-ness For this poor life of mine; His love is in and

love of His, But when I knelt to pray, Con - fess - ing all my
mer - cy - seat, Be - hold-ing my de - spair, In   pit - y bursts the
Je - sus then, Nor do I go in vain, For heav'n-ly hope He
o - ver all, And wind and waves o - bey When Je - sus whis-pers

CHORUS

guilt to Him, The sin-clouds rolled a - way.
clouds be - tween, And shows me He is there. It's just like Je-sus to
gives that cheers Like sun-shine aft - er rain.
"Peace, be still!" And rolls the clouds a - way.

It's Just Like His Great Love

roll the clouds a-way, It's just like Je-sus to keep me day by day,

It's just like Je-sus all a-long the way, It's just like His great love.

He Leadeth Me

219

JOSEPH H. GILMORE

WILLIAM B. BRADBURY

1. He lead-eth, me O bless-ed tho't! O words with heav'nly comfort fraught!
2. Sometimes 'mid scenes of deepest gloom, Sometimes where Eden's bowers bloom,
3. Lord, I would clasp Thy hand in mine, Nor ev-er mur-mur nor re-pine,
4. And when my task on earth is done, When, by Thy grace, the vic-t'ry's won,

What-e'er I do, wher-e'er I be, Still 'tis God's hand that lead-eth me.
By wa-ters still, o'er trou-bled sea,—Still 'tis His hand that lead-eth me!
Con-tent, what-ev-er lot I see, Since 'tis my God that lead-eth me!
E'en death's cold wave I will not flee, Since God thro' Jor-dan lead-eth me.

REFRAIN

He lead-eth me, He lead-eth me! By His own hand He leadeth me!
His faithful foll'wer I would be, For by His hand He(*Omit.....*)leadeth me.

220 Jesus Is All the World to Me

WILL H. THOMPSON

WILL L. THOMPSON

1. Je-sus is all the world to me, My life, my joy, my all;
2. Je-sus is all the world to me, My Friend in tri-als sore;
3. Je-sus is all the world to me, And true to Him I'll be;
4. Je-sus is all the world to me, I want no bet-ter friend;

He is my strength from day to day, With-out Him I would fall.
I go to Him for bless-ings, and He gives them o'er and o'er.
Oh, how could I this Friend de-ny, When He's so true to me?
I trust Him now, I'll trust Him when Life's fleet-ing days shall end.

When I am sad, to Him I go, No oth-er one can
He sends the sun-shine and the rain, He sends the har-vest's
Fol-low-ing Him I know I'm right, He watch-es o'er me
Beau-ti-ful life with such a Friend; Beau-ti-ful life that

cheer me so; When I am sad He makes me glad, He's my Friend.
gold-en grain; Sun-shine and rain, har-vest of grain, He's my Friend.
day and night; Fol-low-ing Him, by day and night, He's my Friend.
has no end; E-ter-nal life, e-ter-nal joy, He's my Friend.

Love Lifted Me

JAMES ROWE

HOWARD E. SMITH

1. I was sink-ing deep in sin, Far from the peaceful shore, Ver - y deep-ly
2. All my heart to Him I give, Ev - er to Him I'll cling, In His bless-ed
3. Souls in dan-ger, look a-bove, Je - sus com-plete-ly saves; He will lift you

stained with-in, Sink-ing to rise no more; But the Mas-ter of the sea
pres - ence live, Ev - er His prais-es sing. Love so might-y and so true
by His love Out of the an - gry waves. He's the Mas-ter of the sea,

Heard my despairing cry, From the wa-ters lift - ed me, Now safe am I.
Mer-its my soul's best songs; Faith-ful, lov-ing serv-ice, too, To Him be - longs.
Bil-lows His will o - bey; He your Sav-ior wants to be—Be saved to - day.

CHORUS

Love lift - ed me!.... Love lift - ed me!.... When noth-ing
e - ven me! e - ven me!

1. else could help, Love lift - ed me.
2. Love lift - ed me.

My Redeemer

PHILIP P. BLISS

JAMES McGRANAHAN

1. I will sing of my Re-deem-er, And His won-drous love to me;
2. I will tell the won-drous sto-ry, How my lost es-tate to save,
3. I will praise my dear Re-deem-er, His tri-um-phant pow'r I'll tell,
4. I will sing of my Re-deem-er, And His heav'n-ly love to me;

On the cru-el cross He suf-fered, From the curse to set me free.
In His bound-less love and mer-cy, He the ran-som free-ly gave.
How the vic-to-ry He giv-eth O-ver sin, and death, and hell.
He from death to life hath bro't me, Son of God with Him to be.

CHORUS

Sing, oh, sing . . . . of my Re-deem - er,
of my Re-deem-er, Sing, oh, sing of my Re-deem-er,

With His blood . . . . He pur-chased me, ...
He pur-chased me, With His blood He pur-chased me,

On the cross . . . . He sealed my par - don,
He sealed my par-don, On the cross He sealed my par-don,

My Redeemer

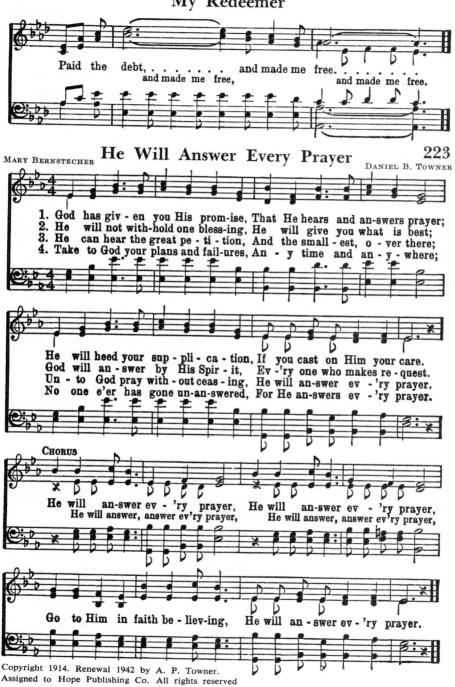

Paid the debt, ... and made me free. . . . . . .
and made me free, and made me free.

He Will Answer Every Prayer

223

MARY BERNSTECHER

DANIEL B. TOWNER

1. God has giv-en you His prom-ise, That He hears and an-swers prayer;
2. He will not with-hold one bless-ing, He will give you what is best;
3. He can hear the great pe-ti-tion, And the small-est, o-ver there;
4. Take to God your plans and fail-ures, An-y time and an-y-where;

He will heed your sup-pli-ca-tion, If you cast on Him your care.
God will an-swer by His Spir-it, Ev-'ry one who makes re-quest.
Un-to God pray with-out ceas-ing, He will an-swer ev-'ry prayer.
No one e'er has gone un-an-swered, For He an-swers ev-'ry prayer.

CHORUS

He will an-swer ev-'ry prayer, He will an-swer ev-'ry prayer,
He will answer, answer ev'ry prayer, He will answer, answer ev'ry prayer,

Go to Him in faith be-liev-ing, He will an-swer ev-'ry prayer.

No, Not One!

224 JOHNSON OATMAN, JR.   GEORGE C. HUGG

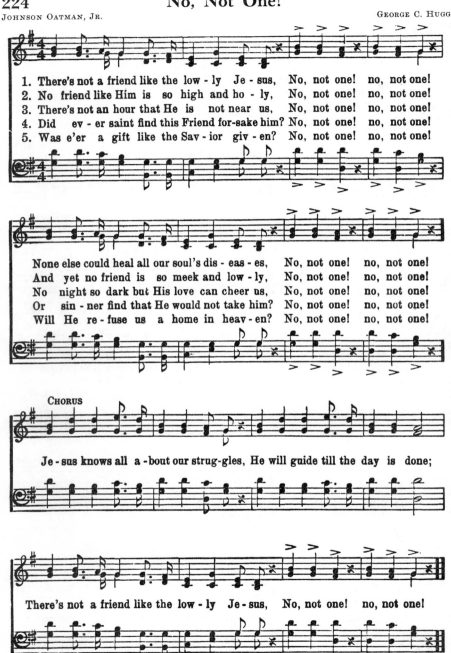

1. There's not a friend like the low-ly Je-sus, No, not one! no, not one!
2. No friend like Him is so high and ho-ly, No, not one! no, not one!
3. There's not an hour that He is not near us, No, not one! no, not one!
4. Did ev-er saint find this Friend for-sake him? No, not one! no, not one!
5. Was e'er a gift like the Sav-ior giv-en? No, not one! no, not one!

None else could heal all our soul's dis-eas-es, No, not one! no, not one!
And yet no friend is so meek and low-ly, No, not one! no, not one!
No night so dark but His love can cheer us, No, not one! no, not one!
Or sin-ner find that He would not take him? No, not one! no, not one!
Will He re-fuse us a home in heav-en? No, not one! no, not one!

CHORUS

Je-sus knows all a-bout our strug-gles, He will guide till the day is done;

There's not a friend like the low-ly Je-sus, No, not one! no, not one!

Only a Sinner

225

JAMES M. GRAY

DANIEL B. TOWNER

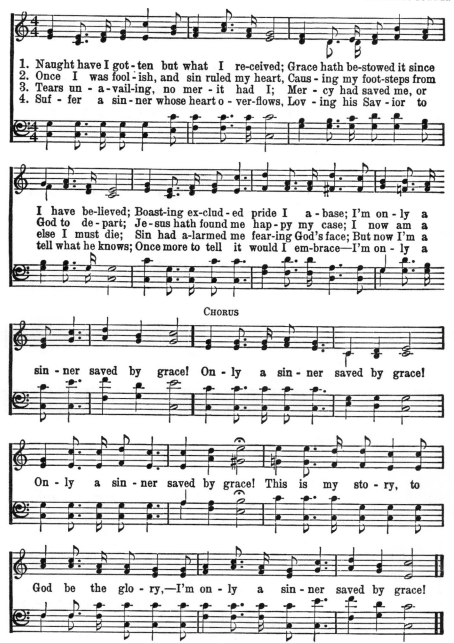

1. Naught have I got-ten but what I re-ceived; Grace hath be-stowed it since
2. Once I was fool-ish, and sin ruled my heart, Caus-ing my foot-steps from
3. Tears un-a-vail-ing, no mer-it had I; Mer-cy had saved me, or
4. Suf-fer a sin-ner whose heart o-ver-flows, Lov-ing his Sav-ior to

I have be-lieved; Boast-ing ex-clud-ed pride I a-base; I'm on-ly a
God to de-part; Je-sus hath found me hap-py my case; I now am a
else I must die; Sin had a-larmed me fear-ing God's face; But now I'm a
tell what he knows; Once more to tell it would I em-brace—I'm on-ly a

CHORUS

sin-ner saved by grace! On-ly a sin-ner saved by grace!

On-ly a sin-ner saved by grace! This is my sto-ry, to

God be the glo-ry,—I'm on-ly a sin-ner saved by grace!

226 Oh, How I Love Jesus

FREDERICK WHITFIELD

TRADITIONAL MELODY

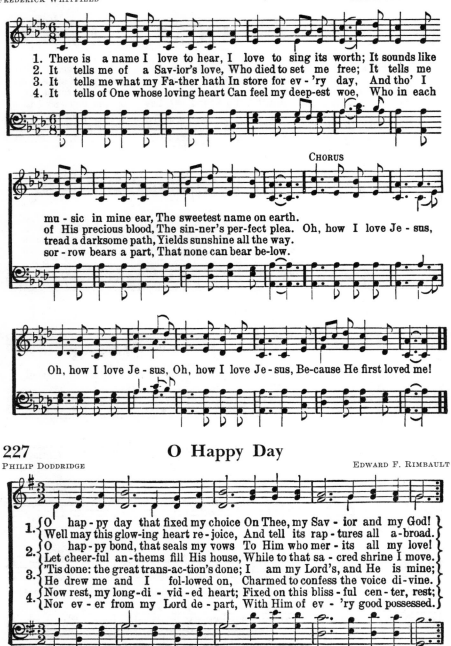

1. There is a name I love to hear, I love to sing its worth; It sounds like
2. It tells me of a Sav-ior's love, Who died to set me free; It tells me
3. It tells me what my Fa-ther hath In store for ev - 'ry day, And tho' I
4. It tells of One whose loving heart Can feel my deep-est woe, Who in each

CHORUS

mu - sic in mine ear, The sweetest name on earth.
of His precious blood, The sin-ner's per-fect plea. Oh, how I love Je - sus,
tread a darksome path, Yields sunshine all the way.
sor - row bears a part, That none can bear be-low.

Oh, how I love Je - sus, Oh, how I love Je - sus, Be-cause He first loved me!

227 O Happy Day

PHILIP DODDRIDGE

EDWARD F. RIMBAULT

1. { O hap - py day that fixed my choice On Thee, my Sav - ior and my God! }
   { Well may this glow-ing heart re - joice, And tell its rap - tures all a - broad. }
2. { O hap - py bond, that seals my vows To Him who mer - its all my love! }
   { Let cheer-ful an - thems fill His house, While to that sa - cred shrine I move. }
3. { 'Tis done: the great trans-ac-tion's done; I am my Lord's, and He is mine; }
   { He drew me and I fol-lowed on, Charmed to confess the voice di - vine. }
4. { Now rest, my long-di - vid - ed heart; Fixed on this bliss - ful cen - ter, rest; }
   { Nor ev - er from my Lord de - part, With Him of ev - 'ry good possessed. }

O Happy Day

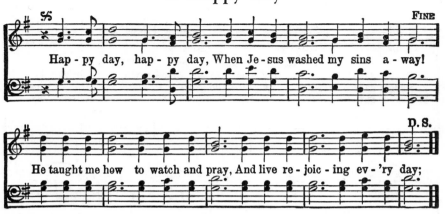

Hap - py day, hap - py day, When Je - sus washed my sins a - way!

He taught me how to watch and pray, And live re - joic - ing ev - 'ry day;

We'll Work till Jesus Comes

228

ELIZABETH MILLS

WILLIAM MILLER

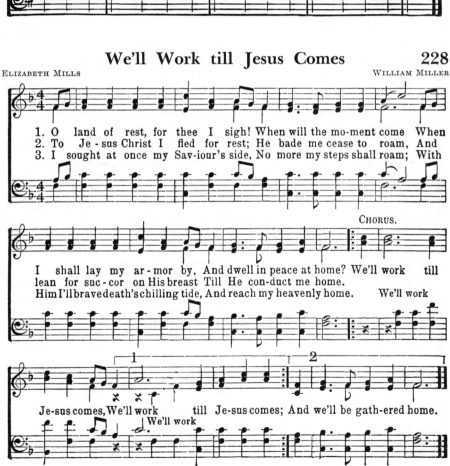

1. O land of rest, for thee I sigh! When will the mo-ment come When
2. To Je-sus Christ I fled for rest; He bade me cease to roam, And
3. I sought at once my Sav-iour's side, No more my steps shall roam; With

CHORUS.

I shall lay my ar - mor by, And dwell in peace at home? We'll work till
lean for suc - cor on His breast Till He con-duct me home.
Him I'll brave death's chilling tide, And reach my heavenly home. We'll work

1.
2.

Je-sus comes, We'll work till Je-sus comes; And we'll be gath-ered home.
We'll work

229

Saved!

OSWALD J. SMITH

ROGER M. HICKMAN

1. Saved! saved! saved!   my sins are all for-giv'n;   Christ is
2. Saved! saved! saved!   by grace and grace a - lone;   Oh, what
3. Saved! saved! saved!   oh, joy be-yond com-pare!   Christ my

mine!   I'm on my way to heav'n;   Once a guilt - y
won - drous love to me was shown,   In my stead Christ
life,   and I His con-stant care;   Yield - ing all and

sin-ner, lost, un-done,   Now a child   of God, saved thro' His Son.
Je - sus bled and died,   Bore my sins,   for me was cru - ci-fied.
trust-ing Him a-lone,   Liv - ing now   each moment as His own.

CHORUS

Saved! I'm saved thro' Christ, my all in all; .... Saved! I'm saved, what-
my all in all;

ev - er may be - fall;   He died up - on the cross for me, He bore the aw - ful

Saved!

rit.

pen - al - ty; And now I'm saved e - ter - nal - ly—I'm saved! saved! saved!

Now I Belong to Jesus

230

NORMAN J. CLAYTON

NORMAN J. CLAYTON

1. Je - sus my Lord will love me for - ev - er, From Him no pow'r of e - vil can
2. Once I was lost in sin's deg-ra-da-tion, Je - sus came down to bring me sal -
3. Joy floods my soul for Je-sus has saved me, Freed me from sin that long had en-

sev - er, He gave His life to ran-som my soul, Now I be-long to Him;
va - tion, Lift-ed me up from sor-row and shame, Now I be-long to Him;
slaved me, His pre-cious blood He gave to redeem, Now I be-long to Him;

CHORUS

Now I be-long to Je - sus, Je - sus be-longs to me,

Not for the years of time a - lone, But for e - ter - ni - ty.

231 Saved, Saved!

JACK P. SCHOLFIELD

JACK P. SCHOLFIELD

1. I've found a friend who is all to me,.... His
2. He saves me from ev-'ry sin and harm,. Se-
3. When poor and need-y and all a-lone,... In

love is ev-er true;..... I love to tell how He
cures my soul each day;..... I'm lean-ing strong on His
love He said to me,....... "Come un-to me and I'll

lift-ed me.... And what His grace can do for you...
might-y arm;.. I know He'll guide me all the way...
lead you home, To live with me e-ter-nal-ly."...

CHORUS.

Saved .... by His pow'r di-vine, Saved .... to new life sub-lime!
Saved by His pow'r, Saved to new life,

rit.

Life now is sweet and my joy is com-plete, For I'm Saved, saved, saved!

Since I Have Been Redeemed

EDWIN O. EXCELL

EDWIN O. EXCELL

1. I have a song I love to sing, Since I have been re-deemed,
2. I have a Christ that sat-is-fies, Since I have been re-deemed,
3. I have a wit-ness bright and clear, Since I have been re-deemed,
4. I have a home pre-pared for me, Since I have been re-deemed,

Of my Re-deem-er, Sav-ior, King, Since I have been re-deemed.
To do His will my high-est prize, Since I have been re-deemed.
Dis-pel-ling ev-'ry doubt and fear, Since I have been re-deemed.
Where I shall dwell e-ter-nal-ly, Since I have been re-deemed.

CHORUS.

Since I . . . . have been re-deemed,
Since I have been redeemed, Since I have been redeemed,
Since I have been re-

deemed, I will glo-ry in His name; Since I . . . . . . have been re-
Since I have been redeemed, Since

deemed, I will glo-ry in my Sav-ior's name.
I have been re-deemed,

233 Since the Fullness of His Love Came In

ELIZA E. HEWITT

BENTLEY D. ACKLEY

1. Once my way was dark and drear - y, For my heart was full of sin,
2. There is grace for all the low - ly, Grace to keep the trust-ing soul:
3. Let me spread a - broad the sto - ry, Oth - er souls to Je - sus win;

But the sky is bright and cheer-y, Since the full-ness of His love came in.
Pow'r to cleanse and make me ho - ly, Je - sus shall my yield-ed life con - trol.
For the cross is now my glo - ry, Since the full-ness of His love came in.

CHORUS

I can nev-er tell how much I love Him, I can nev-er tell His love for me;

For it pass-eth hu-man measure, Like a deep, unfathomed sea;

deep, unfathomed sea;

'Tis re-deeming love in Christ my Sav-ior, In my soul the heav'nly joys be-gin;

Since the Fullness of His Love Came In

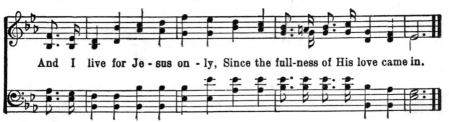

And I live for Je-sus on-ly, Since the full-ness of His love came in.

Jesus Loves Even Me

234

PHILIP P. BLISS

PHILIP P. BLISS

1. I am so glad that our Fa-ther in heav'n Tells of His love in the
2. Tho' I for-get Him and wan-der a-way, Still He doth love me wher-
3. Oh, if there's on-ly one song I can sing, When in His beau-ty I

Book He has giv'n, Won-der-ful things in the Bi-ble I see;
ev-er I stray; Back to His dear lov-ing arms would I flee,
see the Great King, This shall my song in e-ter-ni-ty be:

CHORUS.

This is the dear-est—that Je-sus loves me.
When I re-mem-ber that Je-sus loves me. I am so glad that
"Oh, what a won-der that Je-sus loves me!"

Je-sus loves me, Je-sus loves me, Je-sus loves me; e-ven me.

235 Sweeter as the Years Go By

LEILA N. MORRIS

LEILA N. MORRIS

1. Of Je - sus' love that sought me, When I was lost in sin; Of wondrous
2. He trod in old Ju - de - a Life's pathway long a - go; The peo - ple
3. 'Twas wondrous love which led Him For us to suf - fer loss—To bear with-

grace that brought me Back to His fold a - gain; Of heights and depths of
thronged a - bout Him, His sav - ing grace to know; He healed the bro - ken
out a mur-mur The an - guish of the cross; With saints redeemed in

mer - cy, Far deep - er than the sea, And high - er than the heav-ens. My
heart-ed, And caused the blind to see; And still His great heart yearneth In
glo - ry, Let us our voi - ces raise, Till heav'n and earth re - ech - o With

CHORUS

theme shall ev - er be. Sweet-er as the years go by,......
love for e - ven me. Sweet - er as the years go by, 'Tis
our Re-deem-er's praise. Sweet - er as the years go by,

Sweet-er as the years go by; Rich-er, full - er, deep - er,
sweet - er as the years go by;

Sweeter as the Years Go By

Je - sus' love is sweet - er, Sweet - er as the years go by.

Must I Go, and Empty-Handed? 236

CHARLES C. LUTHER

GEORGE C. STEBBINS

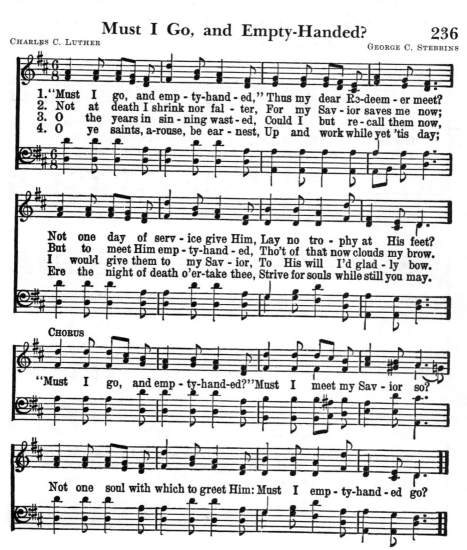

1. "Must I go, and emp - ty-hand - ed," Thus my dear Re-deem - er meet?
2. Not at death I shrink nor fal - ter, For my Sav - ior saves me now;
3. O the years in sin - ning wast - ed, Could I but re - call them now,
4. O ye saints, a-rouse, be ear - nest, Up and work while yet 'tis day;

Not one day of serv - ice give Him, Lay no tro - phy at His feet?
But to meet Him emp - ty-hand - ed, Tho't of that now clouds my brow.
I would give them to my Sav - ior, To His will I'd glad - ly bow.
Ere the night of death o'er-take thee, Strive for souls while still you may.

CHORUS

"Must I go, and emp - ty-hand - ed?" Must I meet my Sav - ior so?

Not one soul with which to greet Him: Must I emp - ty-hand - ed go?

237 Tell Me the Story of Jesus

FANNY J. CROSBY   JOHN R. SWENEY

1. Tell me the sto - ry of Je - sus, Write on my heart ev - 'ry word;
2. Fast-ing a - lone in the des - ert, Tell of the days that are past,
3. Tell of the cross where they nailed Him, Writh-ing in an-guish and pain;

CHO.—*Tell me the sto - ry of Je - sus, Write on my heart ev - 'ry word;*

Tell me the sto - ry most pre - cious, Sweet-est that ev - er was heard.
How for our sins He was tempt - ed, Yet was tri - um-phant at last.
Tell of the grave where they laid Him, Tell how He liv - eth a - gain.

Tell me the sto - ry most pre - cious, Sweet-est that ev - er was heard.

Tell how the an - gels, in cho - rus, Sang as they welcomed His birth,
Tell of the years of His la - bor, Tell of the sor - row He bore,
Love in that sto - ry so ten - der, Clear - er than ev - er I see:

D. C. for Chorus

"Glo - ry to God in the high - est! Peace and good ti - dings to earth."
He was de-spised and af - flict - ed, Home-less, re - ject - ed and poor.
Stay, let me weep while you whis - per, Love paid the ran - som for me.

"Whosoever" Meaneth Me 238

J. Edwin McConnell

J. Edwin McConnell

1. I am hap - py to - day and the sun shines bright, The clouds have been
2. All my hopes have been raised, O His name be praised, His glo - ry has
3. O what won - der - ful love, O what grace di - vine, That Je - sus should

rolled a - way; For the Sav - ior said Who - so - ev - er will, May
filled my soul; I've been lift - ed up and from sin set free, His
die for me! I was lost in sin, for the world I pined, But

Chorus

come with Him to stay (to stay).
blood hath made me whole (me whole). "Who-so - ev - er," sure-ly mean-eth me,
now I am set free (set free).

Sure - ly mean-eth me, O sure - ly mean-eth me; "Who - so - ev - er,"

sure - ly mean - eth me, "Who - so - ev - er," mean-eth me.
mean - eth me.

239 I've Discovered the Way of Gladness

FLOYD W. HAWKINS

FLOYD W. HAWKINS

1. Man-kind is search-ing ev-ery day In quest of some-thing new, But
2. I've found the Pearl of great-est price, "E - ter-nal life" so fair; 'Twas

I have found the "liv-ing way," The path of pleas-ures true.
through the Sav-iour's sac-ri-fice, I found this jew-el rare.

REFRAIN

LOWER VOICES

HIGH VOICES

I've dis-cov-ered the way of glad-ness, I've dis - cov-ered the way of

LOWER VOICES

DUET

joy, I've dis-cov-ered re-lief from sad-ness, 'Tis a hap-pi-ness with-out al-

PARTS

loy; I've dis-cov-ered the fount of bless-ing, I've dis-cov-ered the "Liv-ing

I've Discovered the Way of Gladness

Word", 'Twas the great-est of all dis-cov-er-ies When I found Je-sus my Lord.

Jesus, Revealed in Me

240

GIPSY SMITH

E. EDWIN YOUNG

1. Christ, the Trans-form-ing Light, Touch-es this heart of mine;
2. Here, Lord, I bring my heart, My love, my strength, my will;
3. Life is no long-er mine, I yield it all to Thee;
4. Tri - um-phant peace is mine, Now Je-sus reigns with-in;

Pierc-ing the dark-est night, Mak-ing His glo-ry shine.
Cleanse me in ev-er-y part, With all Thy Spir-it fill.
Fill me, that I may shine, Un-til Thy face I see.
He giv-eth joy di - vine, And vic-t'ry o-ver sin.

REFRAIN

Oh, to re-flect His grace, Caus-ing the world to see
His grace, to see

Love that will glow, till oth-ers shall know Je-sus, re-vealed in me.

241   'Tis So Sweet to Trust in Jesus

LOUISA M. R. STEAD

WILLIAM J. KIRKPATRICK

1. 'Tis so sweet to trust in Je - sus, Just to take Him at His Word;
2. O how sweet to trust in Je - sus, Just to trust His cleans-ing blood;
3. Yes,'tis sweet to trust in Je - sus, Just from sin and self to cease;
4. I'm so glad I learned to trust Thee, Pre - cious Je - sus, Sav - ior, Friend;

Just to rest up - on His prom-ise; Just to know,"Thus saith the Lord."
Just in sim - ple faith to plunge me 'Neath the heal-ing, cleans-ing flood!
Just from Je - sus sim - ply tak-ing Life and rest, and joy and peace.
And I know that Thou art with me, Wilt be with me to the end.

CHORUS

Je - sus, Je - sus, how I trust Him! How I've proved Him o'er and o'er!

Je - sus, Je - sus, pre - cious Je - sus! O for grace to trust Him more!

242   I Am Trusting Thee, Lord Jesus

FRANCES R. HAVERGAL

ETHELBERT W. BULLINGER

1. I am trust - ing Thee, Lord Je - sus! Trust - ing on - ly Thee!
2. I am trust - ing Thee, Lord Je - sus! At Thy feet I bow,
3. I am trust - ing Thee to guide me: Thou a - lone shalt lead,
4. I am trust - ing Thee, Lord Je - sus! Nev - er let me fall!

I Am Trusting Thee, Lord Jesus

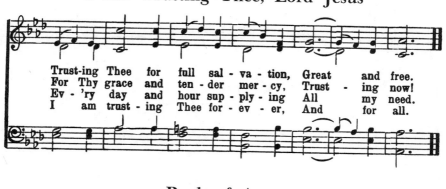

Trust-ing Thee for full sal - va - tion, Great and free.
For Thy grace and ten - der mer - cy, Trust - ing now!
Ev - 'ry day and hour sup - ply - ing All my need.
I am trust - ing Thee for - ev - er, And for all.

Rock of Ages

243

AUGUSTUS M. TOPLADY

THOMAS HASTINGS

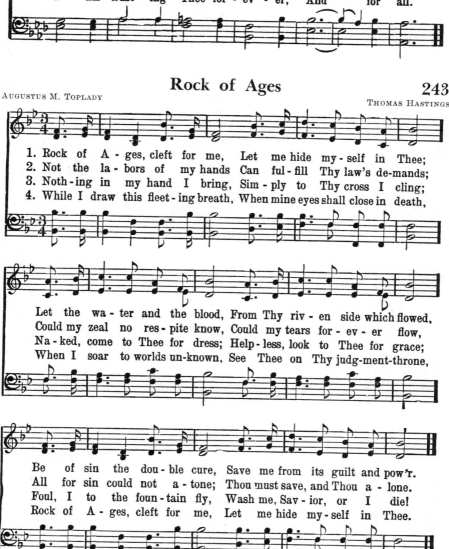

1. Rock of A - ges, cleft for me, Let me hide my - self in Thee;
2. Not the la - bors of my hands Can ful - fill Thy law's de-mands;
3. Noth - ing in my hand I bring, Sim - ply to Thy cross I cling;
4. While I draw this fleet - ing breath, When mine eyes shall close in death,

Let the wa - ter and the blood, From Thy riv - en side which flowed,
Could my zeal no res - pite know, Could my tears for - ev - er flow,
Na - ked, come to Thee for dress; Help - less, look to Thee for grace;
When I soar to worlds un-known, See Thee on Thy judg-ment-throne,

Be of sin the dou - ble cure, Save me from its guilt and pow'r.
All for sin could not a - tone; Thou must save, and Thou a - lone.
Foul, I to the foun - tain fly, Wash me, Sav - ior, or I die!
Rock of A - ges, cleft for me, Let me hide my - self in Thee.

244

The Haven of Rest

Henry L. Gilmour   George D. Moore

1. My soul in sad ex - ile was out on life's sea, So
2. I yield - ed my - self to His ten - der em - brace, And
3. The song of my soul, since the Lord made me whole, Has
4. How pre - cious the thought that we all may re - cline, Like
5. Oh, come to the Sav - ior, He pa - tient - ly waits To

bur-dened with sin and dis - trest, Till I heard a sweet voice say-ing,
faith tak - ing hold of the Word, My fet - ters fell off, and I
been the old sto - ry so blest, Of Je - sus, who'll save who-so-
John the be - lov - ed and blest, On Je - sus' strong arm, where no
save by His pow - er di - vine; Come, an - chor your soul in the

D. S. — *The   tem - pest may sweep o'er the*

FINE.

"Make me your choice;" And I en-tered the "Ha - ven of Rest!"
an - chored my soul; The "Ha - ven of Rest" is my Lord.
ev - er will have A home in the "Ha - ven of Rest!"
tem - pest can harm,— Se - cure in the "Ha - ven of Rest!"
"Ha - ven of Rest," And say, "My Be - lov - ed is mine."

wild,   storm-y   deep,   In   Je - sus   I'm   safe   ev - er - more.

CHORUS   **D. S.**

I've anchored my soul in the "Ha-ven of Rest," I'll sail the wide seas no more;

Trusting Jesus

EDGAR P. STITES

IRA D. SANKEY

1. Sim - ply trust - ing ev - 'ry day, Trust - ing through a storm - y way;
2. Bright-ly doth His Spir - it shine In - to this poor heart of mine;
3. Sing - ing if my way is clear; Pray - ing if the path be drear;
4. Trust-ing Him while life shall last, Trust - ing Him till earth be past;

E - ven when my faith is small, Trust-ing Je - sus, that is all.
While He leads I can - not fall; Trust-ing Je - sus, that is all.
If in dan - ger, for Him call; Trust-ing Je - sus, that is all.
Till with - in the jas - per wall: Trust-ing Je - sus, that is all.

CHORUS

Trust - ing as the mo - ments fly, Trust - ing as the days go by;

Trust - ing Him what - e'er be - fall, Trust - ing Je - sus, that is all.

246 Trust in the Lord

Thomas O. Chisholm

Wendell P. Loveless

1. "Trust in the Lord with all thine heart," This is God's gra-cious com-mand;
2. "Trust in the Lord" who rul-eth all, See-eth all things as they are,
3. "Trust in the Lord" and peace-ful be, Fret not thy spir-it in vain,
4. "Trust in the Lord"—His eye will guide All thro' the path-way a-head,

"In all thy ways ac-know-ledge Him, So shalt thou dwell in the land."
Be it a bird-ling in its nest, Or yon-der ut-ter-most star.
What tho' the an-swer tar-ries long, Still shalt thou praise Him a-gain.
He hath re-deemed and He will keep, Trust Him and be not a-fraid.

REFRAIN

"Trust in the Lord," O trou-bled soul, Rest in the arms of His care; . What-care, of His care;

ev-er thy lot, It mat-ter-eth not, For noth-ing can trou-ble thee there;

"Trust in the Lord," O trou-bled soul, Noth-ing can trou-ble thee there.

He Hideth My Soul

FANNY J. CROSBY　　　　　　　　　　　　　　　　　WILLIAM J. KIRKPATRICK

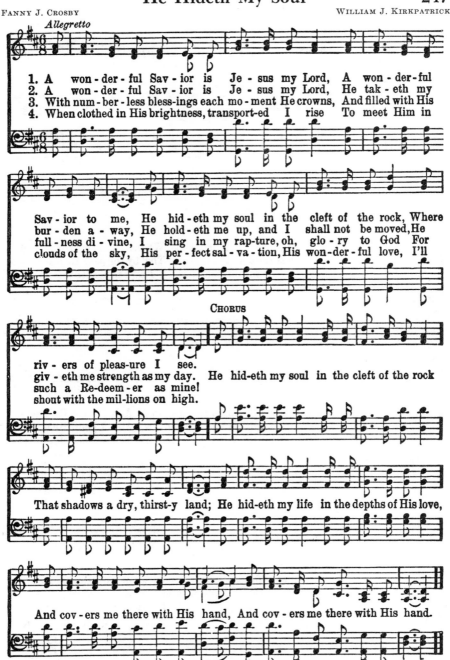

Allegretto

1. A won-der-ful Sav-ior is Je-sus my Lord, A won-der-ful
2. A won-der-ful Sav-ior is Je-sus my Lord, He tak-eth my
3. With num-ber-less bless-ings each mo-ment He crowns, And filled with His
4. When clothed in His brightness, transport-ed I rise To meet Him in

Sav-ior to me, He hid-eth my soul in the cleft of the rock, Where
bur-den a-way, He hold-eth me up, and I shall not be moved, He
full-ness di-vine, I sing in my rap-ture, oh, glo-ry to God For
clouds of the sky, His per-fect sal-va-tion, His won-der-ful love, I'll

riv-ers of pleas-ure I see.
giv-eth me strength as my day.
such a Re-deem-er as mine!
shout with the mil-lions on high.

CHORUS

He hid-eth my soul in the cleft of the rock

That shadows a dry, thirst-y land; He hid-eth my life in the depths of His love,

And cov-ers me there with His hand, And cov-ers me there with His hand.

His Eye Is on the Sparrow

CIVILLA D. MARTIN

CHARLES H. GABRIEL

1. Why should I feel discouraged, Why should the shadows come, Why should my
2. "Let not your heart be troubled," His ten-der word I hear, And rest-ing
3. When-ev-er I am temp-ted, When-ev-er clouds a - rise, When songs give

heart be lonely And long for Heav'n and home, When Jesus is my portion? My
on His goodness, I lose my doubts and fears; Tho' by the path He leadeth But
place to sighing, When hope within me dies, I draw the clo-ser to Him, From

constant Friend is He: His eye is on the spar-row, And I know He watches
one step I may see: His eye is on the spar-row, And I know He watches
care He sets me free; His eye is on the spar-row, And I know He cares for

me; His eye is on the sparrow, And I know He watches me.
me; His eye is on the sparrow, And I know He watches me.
me; His eye is on the sparrow, And I know He cares for me.

His Eye Is on the Sparrow

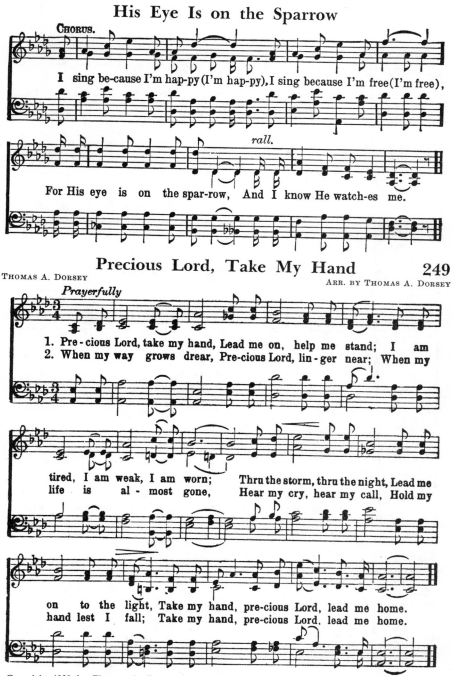

CHORUS.

I sing be-cause I'm hap-py (I'm hap-py), I sing because I'm free (I'm free),

rall.

For His eye is on the spar-row, And I know He watch-es me.

Precious Lord, Take My Hand

249

THOMAS A. DORSEY

ARR. BY THOMAS A. DORSEY

Prayerfully

1. Pre-cious Lord, take my hand, Lead me on, help me stand; I am
2. When my way grows drear, Pre-cious Lord, lin-ger near; When my

tired, I am weak, I am worn; Thru the storm, thru the night, Lead me
life is al-most gone, Hear my cry, hear my call, Hold my

on to the light, Take my hand, pre-cious Lord, lead me home.
hand lest I fall; Take my hand, pre-cious Lord, lead me home.

250 I Know Who Holds Tomorrow

IRA STANPHILL   IRA STANPHILL

1. I don't know a-bout to-mor-row, I just live from day to - day.
2. Ev-'ry step is get-ting bright-er, As the gold-en stairs I climb;
3. I don't know a-bout to-mor-row, It may bring me pov-er-ty;

I don't bor-row from its sun-shine, For its skies may turn to gray.
Ev-'ry bur-den's get-ting light-er; Ev-'ry cloud is sil-ver lined.
But the one who feeds the spar-row, Is the one who stands by me.

I don't wor-ry o'er the fu-ture, For I know what Je-sus said,
There the sun is al-ways shin-ing, There no tear will dim the eye,
And the path that be my por-tion, May be through the flame or flood,

And to-day I'll walk be-side Him, For He knows what is a-head.
At the end-ing of the rain-bow, Where the mountains touch the sky.
But His pres-ence goes be-fore me, And I'm cov-ered with His blood.

CHORUS

Man-y things a-bout to-mor-row, I don't seem to un-der-stand;

I Know Who Holds Tomorrow

But I know who holds to-mor - row, And I know who holds my hand.

In the Hollow of His Hand

251

WILLIAM M. RUNYAN

GEORGE S. SCHULER

ALTO SOLO or TRIO

1. Our God hath giv - en prom - ise—And His grace for this hath planned:
2. O soul, be thou not troub - led, Tho' thou dost not un - der - stand;
3. E'en tho' stern du - ty call thee, And each day make full de - mand,
4. The joy that pass-eth knowl-edge, Peace that none can un - der - stand,

His child shall rest se - cure - ly In the hol - low of His hand.
No tur - moil shall mo - lest thee In the hol - low of His hand.
The soul may find its shel - ter In the hol - low of His hand.
For thee, for thee are wait - ing In the hol - low of His hand.

CHORUS

Let come what may— or wave, or tem-pest—"Peace, be still!" 'tis His command;

My soul is held in peace e - ter - nal In the hol - low of His hand.

Cleanse Me

J. EDWIN ORR

MAORI MELODY

1. Search me, O God, and know my heart to-day; Try me, O
2. I praise Thee, Lord, for cleans-ing me from sin: Ful-fill Thy
3. Lord, take my life, and make it whol-ly Thine: Fill my poor
4. O Ho-ly Ghost, re-viv-al comes from Thee: Send a re-

Sav-ior, know my thoughts, I pray: See if there be some wick-ed
Word, and make me pure with-in; Fill me with fire, where once I
heart with Thy great love di-vine; Take all my will, my pas-sion,
viv-al—start the work in me: Thy Word de-clares Thou wilt sup-

way in me: Cleanse me from ev-'ry sin, and set me free.
burned with shame: Grant my de-sire to mag-ni-fy Thy name.
self and pride; I now sur-ren-der: Lord, in me a-bide.
ply our need: For bless-ing now, O Lord, I hum-bly plead.

253

Holy Bible, Book Divine

JOHN BURTON

WILLIAM B. BRADBURY

1. Ho-ly Bi-ble, Book di-vine, Pre-cious treas-ure, thou art mine:
2. Mine to chide me when I rove, Mine to show a Sav-ior's love,
3. Mine to com-fort in dis-tress—Suf-fer-ing in this wil-der-ness,
4. Mine to tell of joys to come, And the reb-el sin-ner's doom:

Holy Bible, Book Divine

Mine to tell me whence I came, Mine to teach me what I am,
Mine thou art to guide and guard, Mine to pun-ish or re-ward,
Mine to show—by liv - ing faith— Man can tri-umph o - ver death,
O thou ho - ly Book di - vine, Pre-cious treas-ure, thou art mine.

Lord, Dismiss Us with Thy Blessing   254

JOHN FAWCETT, ASC.
ALT. BY GODFREY THRING

ARR. FROM A SICILIAN MELODY

1. Lord, dis-miss us with Thy bless-ing; Fill our hearts with joy and peace;
2. Thanks we give and ad - o - ra - tion For Thy gos-pel's joy-ful sound;
3. So that when Thy love shall call us, Sav-ior, from the world a - way,

Let us each, Thy love pos-sess-ing, Tri-umph in re - deem-ing grace:
May the fruits of Thy sal-va - tion In our hearts and lives a - bound:
Let no fear of death ap-pall us, Glad Thy sum - mons to o - bey:

O re - fresh us, O re - fresh us, Trav-el-ing through this wil-der-ness.
Ev - er faith-ful, Ev - er faith-ful To the truth may we be found.
May we ev - er, May we ev - er Reign with Thee in end-less day. A-MEN.

255   The Sands of Time

ANNE ROSS COUSIN

CHRETIEN URHAN
ARR. BY EDWARD F. RIMBAULT

1. The sands of time are sink-ing, The dawn of heav-en breaks;
2. O Christ! He is the foun-tain, The deep, sweet well of love!
3. Oh, I am my Be-lov-ed's, And my Be-lov-ed's mine!
4. The Bride eyes not her gar-ment, But her dear Bridegroom's face;

The sum-mer morn I've sighed for, The fair, sweet morn a-wakes:
The streams on earth I've tast-ed, More deep I'll drink a-bove:
He brings a poor vile sin-ner In-to His "house of wine."
I will not gaze at glo-ry, But on my King of grace.

Dark, dark hath been the mid-night, But day-spring is at hand,
There, to an o-cean ful-ness, His mer-cy doth ex-pand,
I stand up-on His mer-it, I know no oth-er stand,
Not at the crown He giv-eth, But on His pierc-ed hand,

And glo-ry, glo-ry dwell-eth In Im-man-uel's land.
And glo-ry, glo-ry dwell-eth In Im-man-uel's land.
Not e'en where glo-ry dwell-eth In Im-man-uel's land.
The Lamb is all the glo-ry Of Im-man-uel's land. A-MEN.

My Savior First of All

FANNY J. CROSBY

JOHN R. SWENEY

1. When my life-work is end-ed, and I cross the swell-ing tide, When the
2. Oh, the soul-thrill-ing rap-ture when I view His bless-ed face, And the
3. Oh, the dear ones in glo-ry, how they beck-on me to come, And our
4. Thro' the gates to the cit-y in a robe of spot-less white, He will

bright and glorious morning I shall see; I shall know my Re-deem-er when I
lus-ter of His kind-ly beaming eye; How my full heart will praise Him for the
part-ing at the riv-er I re-call; To the sweet vales of E-den they will
lead me where no tears will ev-er fall; In the glad song of a-ges I shall

reach the oth-er side, And His smile will be the first to wel-come me.
mer-cy, love, and grace, That pre-pare for me a man-sion in the sky.
sing my wel-come home; But I long to meet my Sav-ior first of all.
min-gle with de-light; But I long to meet my Sav-ior first of all.

CHORUS

I shall know .. Him, I shall know Him, And redeemed by His side I shall stand,
I shall know Him,

I shall know .. Him, I shall know Him By the print of the nails in His hand.
I shall know Him,

257 Gone, Yes, Gone Forevermore!

Joseph C. Macaulay

John F. Wilson

1. Now let songs of tri-umph swell loud and clear, loud and clear, Christ has
2. Sins as black as death's dark shroud blot-ted out, blot-ted out! As the
3. Far as east is from the west they are gone, they are gone. O, how

con-quered sin and hell, sing it loud and clear. Once for us in mor-tal fray,
thick-est thun-der cloud, all are blot-ted out. From God's mem-o-ry e-rased—
rich-ly we are blest, for our sins are gone. In the deep, un-fath-omed sea

Climbed He Cal-v'ry's rug-ged way. Praise Him now in glad-some lay;
At such mer-cy stand a-mazed! Be His name for-ev-er praised;
They are cast, and we are free. Join our glo-rious ju-bi-lee—

REFRAIN

Sing it loud and clear!
All are blot-ted out! Gone, yes, gone for-ev-er-more!   Ful-ly set-tled is the
All our sins are gone!   Ev-er-more!

score! Since He purged my guilt-y stains, Not a spot re-mains;

Not a spot re-mains;

Gone, Yes, Gone Forevermore!

Gone, yes, gone! Gone, yes, gone! Gone, yes, gone for-ev-er-more!

Who at My Door Is Standing? 258

MARY B. C. SLADE

ASA B. EVERETT

1. Who at my door is stand-ing, Pa-tient-ly draw-ing near,
2. Lone-ly with-out He's stay-ing: Lone-ly with-in am I;
3. All through the dark hours drea-ry, Knock-ing a-gain is He;
4. Door of my heart, I has-ten! Thee will I o-pen wide.

En-trance with-in de-mand-ing? Whose is the voice I hear?
While I am still de-lay-ing, Will He not pass me by?
Je-sus, art Thou not wea-ry, Wait-ing so long for me?
Tho' He re-buke and chas-ten, He shall with me a-bide.

REFRAIN

Sweet-ly the tones are fall-ing: "O-pen the door for me!

If thou wilt heed My call-ing, I will a-bide with thee."

Living for Jesus

259

THOMAS O. CHISHOLM

C. HAROLD LOWDEN

Not fast

1. Liv-ing for Je-sus a life that is true, Striv-ing to please Him in
2. Liv-ing for Je-sus who died in my place, Bear-ing on Cal-v'ry my
3. Liv-ing for Je-sus wher-ev-er I am, Do-ing each du-ty in
4. Liv-ing for Je-sus through earth's lit-tle while, My dear-est treas-ure, the

all that I do; Yield-ing al-le-giance, glad-heart-ed and free,
sin and dis-grace; Such love con-strains me to an-swer His call,
His ho-ly name; Will-ing to suf-fer af-flic-tion and loss,
light of His smile; Seek-ing the lost ones He died to re-deem,

CHORUS Unison. Slower

This is the path-way of bless-ing for me.
Fol-low His lead-ing and give Him my all. O Je-sus, Lord and
Deem-ing each tri-al a part of my cross.
Bring-ing the wea-ry to find rest in Him.

Sav-ior, I give my-self to Thee, For Thou, in Thy a-tone-ment, Didst

give Thy-self for me; I own no oth-er Mas-ter, My heart shall be Thy

Living for Jesus

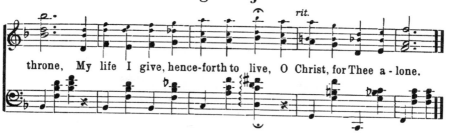

throne, My life I give, hence-forth to live, O Christ, for Thee a-lone.

I Would Be True

260

HOWARD A. WALTER

JOSEPH YATES PEEK

1. I would be true, for there are those who trust me; I would be
2. I would be friend of all—the foe, the friend-less; I would be
3. I would be prayer-ful thru each bus-y mo-ment; I would be

pure, for there are those who care; I would be strong, for
giv-ing, and for-get the gift; I would be hum-ble,
con-stant-ly in touch with God; I would be tuned to

there is much to suf-fer; I would be brave, for there is
for I know my weak-ness; I would look up, and laugh, and
hear His slight-est whis-per; I would have faith to keep the

much to dare; I would be brave, for there is much to dare.
love, and lift; I would look up, and laugh, and love, and lift.
path Christ trod; I would have faith to keep the path Christ trod.

261 "Are Ye Able," Said the Master

Earl Marlatt

Harry S. Mason

1. "Are ye a-ble," said the Mas-ter, "To be cru-ci-fied with me?"
2. "Are ye a-ble" to re-mem-ber, When a thief lifts up his eyes,
3. "Are ye a-ble" when the shad-ows Close a-round you with the sod,
4. "Are ye a-ble?" Still the Mas-ter Whis-pers down e-ter-ni-ty,

"Yea," the stur-dy dream-ers an-swered, "To the death we fol-low Thee."
That his par-doned soul is wor-thy Of a place in par-a-dise?
To be-lieve that spir-it tri-umphs, To com-mend your soul to God?
And he-ro-ic spir-its an-swer Now, as then, in Gal-i-lee.

REFRAIN

"Lord, we are a-ble." Our spir-its are Thine. Re-mold them,

make us, Like Thee, di-vine. Thy guid-ing ra-diance A-bove us shall

be A bea-con to God, To love and loy-al-ty.

Higher Ground

Johnson Oatman, Jr.

Charles H. Gabriel

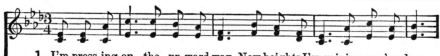

1. I'm press-ing on the up-ward way, New heights I'm gaining ev-'ry day;
2. My heart has no de-sire to stay Where doubts a-rise and fears dis-may;
3. I want to live a-bove the world, Tho' Sa-tan's darts at me are hurled;
4. I want to scale the utmost height, And catch a gleam of glo-ry bright;

Still pray-ing as I'm on-ward bound, "Lord, plant my feet on high-er ground."
Tho' some may dwell where these abound, My prayer, my aim, is high-er ground.
For faith has caught the joy-ful sound, The song of saints on high-er ground.
But still I'll pray till Heav'n I've found, "Lord, lead me on to high-er ground."

Chorus

Lord, lift me up and let me stand, By faith, on Heav-en's ta-ble-land,

A high-er plane than I have found; Lord, plant my feet on high-er ground.

263 Bring Your Vessels, Not a Few

Leila N. Morris

Leila N. Morris

1. Are you look-ing for the full-ness of the bless-ing of the Lord
2. Bring your emp-ty earth-en ves-sels, clean thro' Je-sus' pre-cious blood,
3. Like the cruse of oil un-fail-ing is His grace for-ev-er-more,

In your heart and life to-day? Claim the prom-ise of your Fa-ther,
Come, ye need-y, one and all; And in hu-man con-se-cra-tion
And His love un-chang-ing still; And ac-cord-ing to His prom-ise

come ac-cord-ing to His word, In the bless-ed old-time way.
wait be-fore the throne of God, Till the Ho-ly Ghost shall fall.
with the Ho-ly Ghost and pow'r, He will ev-'ry ves-sel fill.

Chorus

He will fill your heart to-day to o-ver-flow - - - ing, As the
He will fill   your   heart to o-ver-flow-ing,

Lord commandeth you, "Bring your vessels, not a few;" He will fill your heart to-
He will fill

Bring Your Vessels, Not a Few

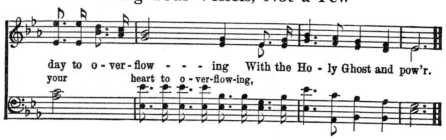

day to o-ver-flow - - - ing With the Ho-ly Ghost and pow'r.
your heart to o-ver-flow-ing,

Something for Thee 264

SYLVANUS D. PHELPS

ROBERT LOWRY

1. Sav - ior, Thy dy - ing love Thou gav - est me, Nor should I
2. At the blest mer - cy - seat, Plead - ing for me, My fee - ble
3. Give me a faith - ful heart,—Like - ness to Thee,— That each de-
4. All that I am and have,—Thy gifts so free,— In joy, in

aught with-hold, Dear Lord, from Thee: In love my soul would bow, My heart ful-
faith looks up, Je - sus, to Thee: Help me the cross to bear, Thy wondrous
part - ing day Hence-forth may see Some work of love be - gun, Some deed of
grief, thro' life, Dear Lord, for Thee! And when Thy face I see, My ran-somed

fill its vow, Some of-f'ring bring Thee now, Something for Thee.
love de - clare, Some song to raise, or prayer, Something for Thee.
kindness done, Some wand'rer sought and won, Something for Thee.
soul shall be, Thro' all e - ter - ni - ty, Something for Thee. A - MEN.

265 Draw Me Nearer

FANNY J. CROSBY

WILLIAM H. DOANE

1. I am Thine, O Lord, I have heard Thy voice, And it told Thy
2. Con-se-crate me now to Thy serv-ice, Lord, By the pow'r of
3. Oh, the pure de-light of a sin-gle hour That be-fore Thy
4. There are depths of love that I can-not know Till I cross the

love to me; But I long to rise in the arms of faith, And be
grace di-vine; Let my soul look up with a stead-fast hope, And my
throne I spend, When I kneel in prayer, and with Thee, my God, I com-
nar-row sea; There are heights of joy that I may not reach Till I

REFRAIN

clos-er drawn to Thee.
will be lost in Thine. Draw me near - er, near- er, bless-ed
mune as friend with friend!
rest in peace with Thee. near - er, near - er,

Lord, To the cross where Thou hast died; Draw me near - er, near - er,

near - er, bless - ed Lord, To Thy pre - cious, bleed - ing side.

I Need Jesus

George O. Webster

Charles H. Gabriel

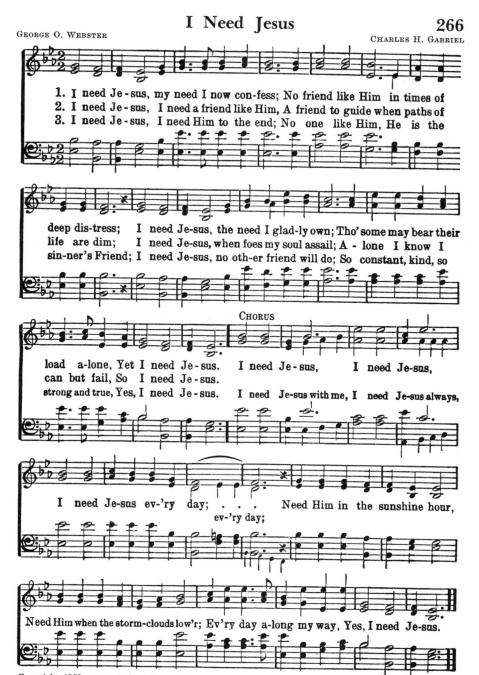

1. I need Je-sus, my need I now con-fess; No friend like Him in times of
2. I need Je-sus, I need a friend like Him, A friend to guide when paths of
3. I need Je-sus, I need Him to the end; No one like Him, He is the

deep dis-tress; I need Je-sus, the need I glad-ly own; Tho' some may bear their
life are dim; I need Je-sus, when foes my soul assail; A-lone I know I
sin-ner's Friend; I need Je-sus, no oth-er friend will do; So constant, kind, so

CHORUS

load a-lone, Yet I need Je-sus. I need Je-sus, I need Je-sus,
can but fail, So I need Je-sus.
strong and true, Yes, I need Je-sus. I need Je-sus with me, I need Je-sus always,

I need Je-sus ev-'ry day; . . . Need Him in the sunshine hour,
ev-'ry day;

Need Him when the storm-clouds low'r; Ev'ry day a-long my way, Yes, I need Je-sus.

267

Nearer, Still Nearer

LEILA N. MORRIS

LEILA N. MORRIS

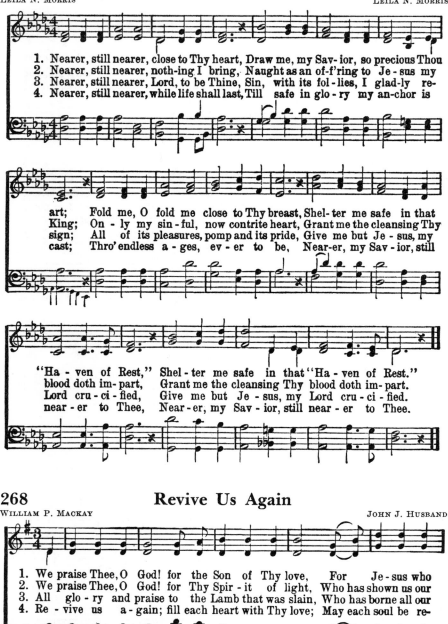

1. Nearer, still nearer, close to Thy heart, Draw me, my Sav-ior, so precious Thou
2. Nearer, still nearer, noth-ing I bring, Naught as an of-f'ring to Je-sus my
3. Nearer, still nearer, Lord, to be Thine, Sin, with its fol-lies, I glad-ly re-
4. Nearer, still nearer, while life shall last, Till safe in glo-ry my an-chor is

art; Fold me, O fold me close to Thy breast, Shel-ter me safe in that
King; On-ly my sin-ful, now contrite heart, Grant me the cleansing Thy
sign; All of its pleasures, pomp and its pride, Give me but Je-sus, my
cast; Thro' endless a-ges, ev-er to be, Near-er, my Sav-ior, still

"Ha-ven of Rest," Shel-ter me safe in that "Ha-ven of Rest."
blood doth im-part, Grant me the cleansing Thy blood doth im-part.
Lord cru-ci-fied, Give me but Je-sus, my Lord cru-ci-fied.
near-er to Thee, Near-er, my Sav-ior, still near-er to Thee.

268

Revive Us Again

WILLIAM P. MACKAY

JOHN J. HUSBAND

1. We praise Thee, O God! for the Son of Thy love, For Je-sus who
2. We praise Thee, O God! for Thy Spir-it of light, Who has shown us our
3. All glo-ry and praise to the Lamb that was slain, Who has borne all our
4. Re-vive us a-gain; fill each heart with Thy love; May each soul be re-

Revive Us Again

CHORUS

died, and is now gone a-bove.
Sav-ior, and scat-tered our night.
sins, and has cleansed ev-'ry stain.
kin-dled with fire from a-bove.

Hal-le-lu-jah! Thine the glo-ry; Hal-le-

lu-jah! A-men! Hal-le-lu-jah! Thine the glo-ry; Re-vive us a-gain.

More Holiness Give Me 269

PHILIP P. BLISS   PHILIP P. BLISS

1. More ho-li-ness give me, More striv-ing with-in;   More pa-tience in
2. More grat-i-tude give me, More trust in the Lord;   More pride in His
3. More pu-ri-ty give me, More strength to o'er-come;   More freedom from

suf-f'ring, More sor-row for sin; More faith in my Sav-ior,
glo-ry, More hope in His word; More tears for His sor-rows,
earth-stains, More long-ings for home; More fit for the king-dom,

rit.

More sense of His care; More joy in His serv-ice, More pur-pose in prayer.
More pain at His grief; More meekness in tri-al, More praise for re-lief.
More used would I be; More bless-ed and ho-ly, More, Sav-ior, like Thee.

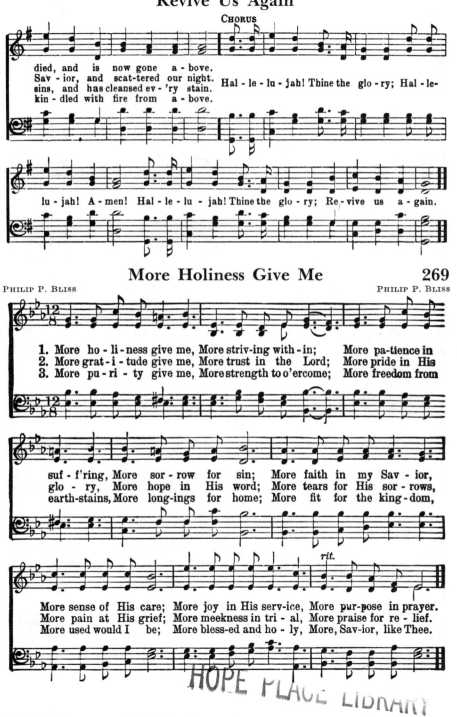

270 I Would Be Like Jesus

JAMES ROWE   BENTLEY D. ACKLEY

1. Earth-ly pleas-ures vain-ly call me; I would be like Je-sus;
2. He has bro-ken ev-'ry fet-ter, I would be like Je-sus;
3. All the way from earth to Glo-ry, I would be like Je-sus;
4. That in Heav-en He may meet me, I would be like Je-sus;
would be like Je-sus;

Noth-ing world-ly shall en-thrall me; I would be like Je-sus.
That my soul may serve Him bet-ter, I would be like Je-sus.
Tell-ing o'er and o'er the sto-ry, I would be like Je-sus.
That His words "Well done" may greet me, I would be like Je-sus.
would be like Je-sus.

CHORUS.

Be like Je-sus, this my song, In the home and in the throng;

Be like Je-sus, all day long! I would be like Je-sus. A-MEN.

Jesus, I My Cross Have Taken

Henry F. Lyte

Ascribed to Wolfgang A. Mozart
Arr. by Hubert P. Main

1. Je - sus, I my cross have ta - ken, All to leave, and fol - low Thee;
2. Let the world de-spise and leave me, They have left my Sav - ior, too;
3. Man may troub-le and dis - tress me, 'Twill but drive me to Thy breast;
4. Haste thee on from grace to glo - ry, Armed by faith, and winged by prayer;

Des - ti - tute, de-spised, for - sa - ken, Thou, from hence, my all shalt be:
Hu - man hearts and looks de - ceive me; Thou art not, like man, un-true;
Life with tri - als hard may press me, Heav'n will bring me sweet-er rest.
Heav'n's e - ter - nal day's be - fore thee, God's own hand shall guide thee there.

Per - ish ev - 'ry fond am - bi - tion, All I've sought, and hoped, and known;
And, while Thou shalt smile up-on me, God of wis - dom, love, and might,
O 'tis not in grief to harm me, While Thy love is left to me;
Soon shall close thy earth-ly mis - sion, Swift shall pass thy pil - grim days,

Yet how rich is my con - di - tion, God and heav'n are still my own!
Foes may hate, and friends may shun me; Show Thy face, and all is bright.
O 'twere not in joy to charm me, Were that joy un - mixed with Thee.
Hope shall change to glad fru - i - tion, Faith to sight, and prayer to praise.

272 Nearer, My God, to Thee

SARAH F. ADAMS   LOWELL MASON

1. Near - er, my God, to Thee, Near - er to Thee! E'en though it
2. Though like the wan - der - er, The sun gone down, Dark - ness be
3. There let the way ap - pear, Steps un - to Heav'n: All that Thou
4. Then, with my wak - ing tho'ts Bright with Thy praise, Out of my
5. Or if on joy - ful wing, Cleav - ing the sky, Sun, moon, and

be a cross That rais - eth me; Still all my song shall be,
o - ver me, My rest a stone; Yet in my dreams I'd be
send - est me, In mer - cy giv'n: An - gels to beck - on me,
ston - y griefs Beth - el I'll raise; So by my woes to be
stars for - got, Up - ward I fly, Still all my song shall be,

Near - er, my God, to Thee, Near - er, my God, to Thee, Near - er to Thee!

273 Lord, Speak to Me

FRANCES R. HAVERGAL   ROBERT SCHUMANN

1. Lord, speak to me, that I may speak In liv - ing ech - oes of Thy tone;
2. O teach me, Lord, that I may teach The pre - cious things Thou dost im - part;
3. O fill me with Thy full-ness, Lord, Un - til my ver - y heart o'er-flow
4. O use me, Lord, use e - ven me, Just as Thou wilt, and when, and where;

Lord, Speak to Me

As Thou hast sought, so let me seek Thy err-ing chil-dren lost and lone.
And wing my words, that they may reach The hid-den depths of many a heart.
In kindling thought and glowing word, Thy love to tell, Thy praise to show.
Un-til Thy bless-ed face I see, Thy rest, Thy joy, Thy glo-ry share.

O Jesus, I Have Promised

274

JOHN E. BODE

ARTHUR H. MANN

1. O Je-sus, I have prom-ised To serve Thee to the end; Be Thou for-ev-er
2. O let me feel Thee near me, The world is ev-er near; I see the sights that
3. O Je-sus, Thou hast promised To all who fol-low Thee, That where Thou art in

near me, My Mas-ter and my Friend: I shall not fear the bat-tle If Thou art
daz-zle, The tempting sounds I hear: My foes are ev-er near me, A-round me
glo-ry, There shall Thy servant be; And, Je-sus, I have promised To serve Thee

by my side, Nor wan-der from the path-way If Thou wilt be my guide.
and with-in; But, Je-sus, draw Thou near-er, And shield my soul from sin.
to the end; O give me grace to fol-low My Mas-ter and my Friend.

More About Jesus

ELIZA E. HEWITT

JOHN R. SWENEY

1. More a-bout Je-sus would I know, More of His grace to oth-ers show;
2. More a-bout Je-sus let me learn, More of His ho-ly will dis-cern;
3. More a-bout Je-sus; in His word, Holding com-mun-ion with my Lord;
4. More a-bout Je-sus on His throne, Rich-es in glo-ry all His own;

More of His sav-ing full-ness see, More of His love who died for me.
Spir-it of God, my teach-er be, Show-ing the things of Christ to me.
Hear-ing His voice in ev-'ry line, Mak-ing each faith-ful say-ing mine.
More of His kingdom's sure in-crease; More of His com-ing, Prince of Peace.

FINE

D.S.—*More of His sav-ing full-ness see, More of His love who died for me.*

REFRAIN

D.S.

More, more a-bout Je-sus, More, more a-bout Je-sus;

O for a Closer Walk with God

WILLIAM COWPER

ARR. FROM WILLIAM GARDINER

1. O for a clos-er walk with God, A calm and heav'n-ly frame,
2. Where is the bless-ed-ness I knew When first I saw the Lord?
3. The dear-est i-dol I have known, What-e'er that i-dol be,
4. So shall my walk be close with God, Calm and se-rene my frame;

O for a Closer Walk with God

A light to shine up-on the road That leads me to the Lamb!
Where is the soul-re-fresh-ing view Of Je-sus and His word?
Help me to tear it from Thy throne, And wor-ship on-ly Thee.
So pur-er light shall mark the road That leads me to the Lamb.

Lead, Kindly Light

JOHN H. NEWMAN

JOHN B. DYKES

1. Lead, kindly Light, amid th'encircling gloom, Lead Thou me on! The night is
2. I was not ev-er thus, nor prayed that Thou Shouldst lead me on; I loved to
3. So long Thy pow'r hath blest me, sure it still Will lead me on O'er moor and

dark, and I am far from home; Lead Thou me on! Keep Thou my feet; I
choose and see my path; but now Lead Thou me on! I loved the gar-ish
fen, o'er crag and torrent, till The night is gone, And with the morn those

do not ask to see . . . The dis-tant scene; one step e-nough for me.
day, and, spite of fears, . . Pride ruled my will. Remember not past years!
an-gel fa-ces smile, . Which I have loved long since, and lost a-while!

278 Open My Eyes, That I May See

CLARA H. SCOTT   CLARA H. SCOTT

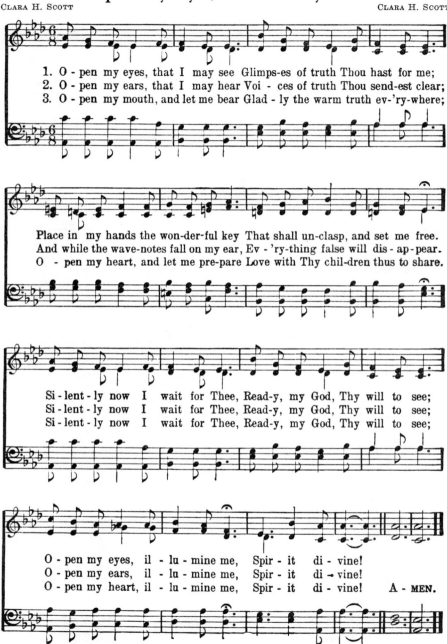

1. O - pen my eyes, that I may see Glimps-es of truth Thou hast for me;
2. O - pen my ears, that I may hear Voi - ces of truth Thou send-est clear;
3. O - pen my mouth, and let me bear Glad - ly the warm truth ev-'ry-where;

Place in my hands the won-der-ful key That shall un-clasp, and set me free.
And while the wave-notes fall on my ear, Ev - 'ry-thing false will dis - ap-pear.
O - pen my heart, and let me pre-pare Love with Thy chil-dren thus to share.

Si - lent - ly now I wait for Thee, Read-y, my God, Thy will to see;
Si - lent - ly now I wait for Thee, Read-y, my God, Thy will to see;
Si - lent - ly now I wait for Thee, Read-y, my God, Thy will to see;

O - pen my eyes, il - lu - mine me, Spir - it di - vine!
O - pen my ears, il - lu - mine me, Spir - it di - vine!
O - pen my heart, il - lu - mine me, Spir - it di - vine!   A - MEN.

There Shall Be Showers of Blessing

Daniel W. Whittle

James McGranahan

1. "There shall be show-ers of bless-ing:" This is the prom-ise of love;
2. "There shall be show-ers of bless-ing"—Pre-cious re - viv-ing a - gain;
3. "There shall be show-ers of bless-ing:" Send them up-on us, O Lord;
4. "There shall be show-ers of bless-ing:" Oh, that to - day they might fall,

There shall be sea-sons re-fresh-ing, Sent from the Sav-ior a - bove.
O - ver the hills and the val - leys, Sound of a - bun-dance of rain.
Grant to us now a re-fresh-ing, Come, and now hon - or Thy Word.
Now as to God we're con-fess-ing, Now as on Je - sus we call!

CHORUS

Show - - ers of bless-ing, Show-ers of bless-ing we need:
Show - ers, show-ers of bless - ing,

Mer-cy-drops round us are fall - ing, But for the show-ers we plead.

280 More Like the Master

Charles H. Gabriel

Charles H. Gabriel

1. More like the Mas-ter I would ev-er be, More of His meek-ness,
2. More like the Mas-ter is my dai-ly prayer; More strength to car-ry
3. More like the Mas-ter I would live and grow; More of His love to

more hu-mil-i-ty; More zeal to la-bor, more cour-age to be true,
cross-es I must bear; More ear-nest ef-fort to bring His kingdom in;
oth-ers I would show; More self-de-ni-al, like His in Gal-i-lee,

rit.   CHORUS.

More con-se-cra-tion for work He bids me do. . . . . . Take Thou my
More of His Spir-it, the wan-der-er to win. . . . .
More like the Mas-ter I long to ev-er be. . . . Take my heart, O

heart, . . I would be Thine a-lone; . . Take Thou my heart . . and
take my heart, I would be Thine a-lone; Take my heart, O take my heart and

make it all Thine own; . . Purge me from sin, . . . O Lord, I now im-
make it all Thine own; Purge Thou me from ev'ry sin, O Lord, I

More Like the Master

plore, . . . Wash me and keep . . . me Thine for-ev - er - more.
now im-plore, Wash and keep, O wash and keep me Thine for-ev - er - more.

In the Hour of Trial   281

JAMES MONTGOMERY   SPENCER LANE

1. In   the hour of   tri - al, Je - sus, plead for   me; Lest, by base de-
2. With for - bid- den pleas-ures Would this vain world charm; Or   its   sor - did
3. Should Thy mer-cy send   me Sor - row, toil, and   woe; Or should pain at-
4. When my last hour com - eth, Fraught with strife and pain, When my dust re-

ni - al,   I   de - part from Thee; When Thou see'st me wa - ver, With a
treas-ures   Spread to work me harm; Bring to my   re-mem-brance Sad Geth-
tend   me   On my path be - low; Grant that I   may nev - er   Fail Thy
turn - eth   To the dust a - gain; On Thy truth re - ly - ing Thro' that

look re - call; Nor for fear or   fa - vor Suf - fer me   to fall.
sem - a - ne,   Or, in dark-er sem-blance, Cross-crowned Calvary.
hand to   see; Grant that I may ev - er Cast my care on Thee.
mor - tal strife; Lord, re-ceive me, dy - ing, To   e - ter - nal life. A-MEN.

282   More Love to Thee

Elizabeth P. Prentiss   William H. Doane

1. More love to Thee, O Christ, More love to Thee! Hear Thou the
2. Once earth-ly joy I craved, Sought peace and rest; Now Thee a-
3. Let sor-row do its work, Send grief and pain; Sweet are Thy
4. Then shall my lat-est breath Whis-per Thy praise; This be the

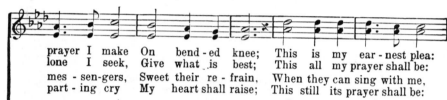

prayer I make On bend-ed knee; This is my ear-nest plea:
lone I seek, Give what is best; This all my prayer shall be:
mes-sen-gers, Sweet their re-frain, When they can sing with me,
part-ing cry My heart shall raise; This still its prayer shall be:

More love, O Christ, to Thee, More love to Thee, More love to Thee!

283   I'll Live for Him

Ralph E. Hudson   C. R. Dunbar

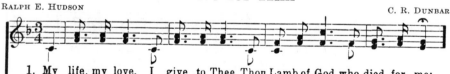

1. My life, my love, I give to Thee, Thou Lamb of God who died for me;
2. I now be-lieve Thou dost re-ceive, For Thou hast died that I might live;
3. O Thou who died on Cal-va-ry, To save my soul and make me free,

CHO. *I'll live for Him who died for me, How hap-py then my life shall be!*

I'll Live for Him

D. C. Chorus

Oh, may I ev - er faith - ful be, My Sav - ior and my God!
And now hence-forth I'll trust in Thee, My Sav - ior and my God!
I'll con - se - crate my life to Thee, My Sav - ior and my God!

I'll live for Him who died for me, My Sav - ior and my God!

Lord, I Hear of Showers of Blessing 284

ELIZABETH CODNER

WILLIAM B. BRADBURY

1. Lord, I hear of show'rs of bless - ing Thou art scat-t'ring full and free,
2. Pass me not, O ten - der Sav - ior! Let me love and cling to Thee;
3. Pass me not, O might - y Spir - it! Thou canst make the blind to see;
4. Love of God, so pure and changeless; Blood of Christ, so rich and free;
5. Pass me not! Thy lost one bring - ing, Bind my heart, O Lord, to Thee;

Show'rs the thirst-y land re - fresh - ing; Let some droppings fall on me—
I am long-ing for Thy fa - vor; Whilst Thou'rt calling, O call me.
Wit - ness - er of Je - sus' mer - it, Speak the word of pow'r to me.
Grace of God, so strong and bound-less; Mag - ni - fy them all in me.
While the streams of life are spring-ing, Bless-ing oth - ers, O bless me.

CHORUS

E - ven me, e - ven me, Let Thy bless - ing fall on me.

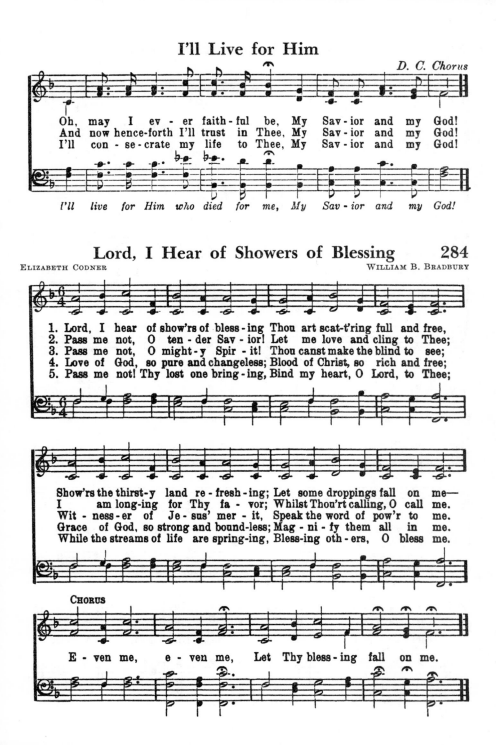

285 Just When I Need Him Most

WILLIAM C. POOLE   CHARLES H. GABRIEL

1. Just when I need Him, Je-sus is near, Just when I fal - ter,
2. Just when I need Him, Je-sus is true, Nev - er for - sak - ing
3. Just when I need Him, Je-sus is strong, Bear-ing my bur - dens
4. Just when I need Him, He is my all, An - swer-ing when up-

just when I fear; Read - y to help me, read - y to cheer,
all the way thro'; Giv - ing for bur - dens pleas-ures a - new,
all the day long; For all my sor - row giv - ing a song,
on Him I call; Ten - der - ly watch-ing lest I should fall,

CHORUS.

Just when I need Him most. Just when I need Him most,

Just when I need Him most; Je - sus is near to

com - fort and cheer, Just when I need Him most. A - MEN.

Anywhere with Jesus

JESSIE B. POUNDS

DANIEL B. TOWNER

1. An - y-where with Je - sus I can safe - ly go; An - y-where He
2. An - y-where with Je - sus I am not a - lone; Oth - er friends may
3. An - y-where with Je - sus o - ver land and sea, Tell - ing souls in
4. An - y-where with Je - sus I can go to sleep, When the dark-'ning

leads me in this world be - low; An - y-where with-out Him dear-est
fail me, He is still my own; Tho' His hand may lead me o - ver
dark-ness of sal - va - tion free; Read - y as He sum-mons me to
shad-ows round a - bout me creep; Know-ing I shall wak - en nev - er

joys would fade; An - y-where with Je - sus I am not a - fraid.
drear - y ways, An - y-where with Je - sus is a house of praise.
go or stay, An - y-where with Je - sus when He points the way.
more to roam, An - y-where with Je - sus will be home, sweet home.

CHORUS

An - y-where! an - y-where! Fear I can - not know;

An - y-where with Je - sus I can safe - ly go.

287

We Have an Anchor

PRISCILLA J. OWENS

WILLIAM J. KIRKPATRICK

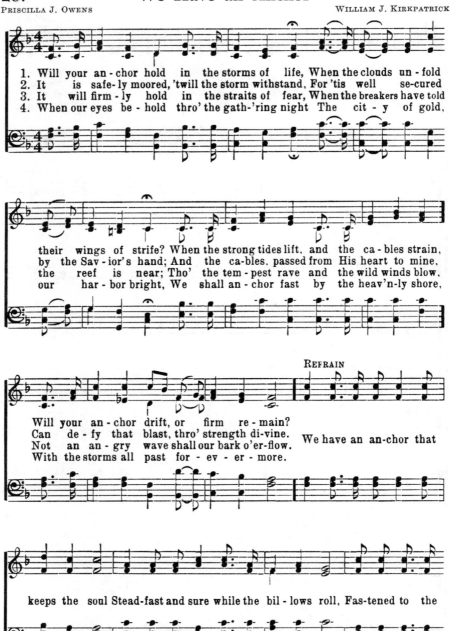

1. Will your an-chor hold in the storms of life, When the clouds un-fold
2. It is safe-ly moored, 'twill the storm withstand, For 'tis well se-cured
3. It will firm-ly hold in the straits of fear, When the breakers have told
4. When our eyes be-hold thro' the gath-'ring night The cit-y of gold,

their wings of strife? When the strong tides lift, and the ca-bles strain,
by the Sav-ior's hand; And the ca-bles, passed from His heart to mine,
the reef is near; Tho' the tem-pest rave and the wild winds blow,
our har-bor bright, We shall an-chor fast by the heav'n-ly shore,

REFRAIN

Will your an-chor drift, or firm re-main?
Can de-fy that blast, thro' strength di-vine.
Not an an-gry wave shall our bark o'er-flow.
With the storms all past for-ev-er-more.

We have an an-chor that

keeps the soul Stead-fast and sure while the bil-lows roll, Fas-tened to the

We Have an Anchor

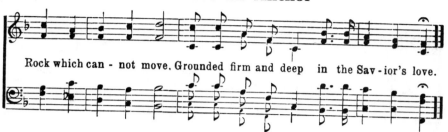

Rock which can - not move. Grounded firm and deep in the Sav - ior's love.

When I See My Savior

288

MAUD FRAZER

ROBERT HARKNESS

1. When I see my Sav - iour, hang-ing on Cal - va - ry,
2. I can see the blood - drops, red 'neath His thorn - y crown,
3. "Why hast thou for - sak - en?" list to that sad, sad moan!

Bear - ing there for sin - ners bit - ter - est ag - o - ny,
From the cru - el nail - wounds now they are fall - ing down;
Oh, His heart was bro - ken, suf - fer - ing there a - lone:

Grat - i - tude o'er-whelms me, makes mine eyes grow dim,
Lord, when I would wan - der from Thy love a - way,
Bro - ken then that mor - tals ne'er need cry in vain

All my ran - somed be - ing cap - tive is to Him.
Let me see those blood - drops shed for me that day.
For God's love and com - fort, in the hour of pain.

289 Blessed Assurance

FANNY J. CROSBY

PHOEBE P. KNAPP

1. Bless-ed as-sur-ance, Je-sus is mine! Oh, what a fore-taste of
2. Per-fect sub-mis-sion, per-fect de-light, Vi-sions of rap-ture now
3. Per-fect sub-mis-sion, all is at rest, I in my Sav-ior am

glo-ry di-vine! Heir of sal-va-tion, pur-chase of God,
burst on my sight; An-gels de-scend-ing, bring from a-bove
hap-py and blest; Watching and wait-ing, look-ing a-bove,

CHORUS

Born of His Spir-it, washed in His blood.
Ech-oes of mer-cy, whis-pers of love. This is my sto-ry, this is my
Filled with His goodness, lost in His love.

song, Prais-ing my Sav-ior all the day long; This is my sto-ry,

this is my song, Prais-ing my Sav-ior all the day long.

Each Step I Take

290

W. Elmo Mercer

W. Elmo Mercer

1. Each step I take my Sa-viour goes be-fore me, And with His loving hand
2. At times I feel my faith be-gin to wa-ver, When up a-head I see
3. I trust in God, no mat-ter come what may, For life e-ter-nal

He leads the way. And with each breath I whis-per "I a-dore Thee;" Oh, what
a chas-m wide. It's then I turn and look up to my Sav-iour, I am
is in His hand. He holds the key that o-pens up the way, That will

rit. CHORUS

joy to walk with Him each day......
strong when He is by my side...... Each step I take I know that He will
lead me to the promised land......

guide me; To higher ground He ev-er leads me on. Un-til some day the last

rit.

step will be tak-en, Each step I take just leads me clos-er home.

291
My Anchor Holds

W. C. MARTIN, ALT.

DANIEL B. TOWNER

1. Tho' the an - gry sur - ges roll On my tem - pest-driv - en soul,
2. Might-y tides a - bout me sweep, Per - ils lurk with - in the deep,
3. I can feel the an - chor fast As I meet each sud - den blast,
4. Troub-les al-most 'whelm the soul; Griefs like bil - lows o'er me roll;

I am peace - ful, for I know, Wild - ly though the winds may blow,
An - gry clouds o'er-shade the sky, And the tem - pest ris - es high;
And the ca - ble, though un - seen, Bears the heav - y strain be - tween;
Tempters seek to lure a - stray; Storms ob - scure the light of day:

I've an an - chor safe and sure, That can ev - er-more en - dure.
Still I stand the tem-pest's shock, For my an - chor grips the Rock.
Thro' the storm I safe - ly ride, Till the turn - ing of the tide.
But in Christ I can be bold, I've an an - chor that shall hold.

CHORUS

And it holds, my an - chor holds; Blow your wild - est, then, O
And it holds,........ my an - chor holds; Blow your wild - - - est,

gale, On my bark so small and frail: By His grace I shall not
then, O gale,

My Anchor Holds

fail, For my an - chor holds, my an - chor holds.
For my an - chor holds, it firm - ly holds,

Leaning on the Everlasting Arms

292

ELISHA A. HOFFMAN

ANTHONY J. SHOWALTER

1. What a fel-low-ship, what a joy di-vine, Leaning on the ev-er-last-ing arms;
2. Oh, how sweet to walk in this pilgrim way, Leaning on the ev-er-last-ing arms;
3. What have I to dread, what have I to fear, Leaning on the ev-er-last-ing arms?

What a bless-ed-ness, what a peace is mine, Leaning on the ev-er-last-ing arms.
Oh, how bright the path grows from day to day, Leaning on the ev-er-last-ing arms.
I have bless-ed peace with my Lord so near, Leaning on the ev-er-last-ing arms.

REFRAIN

Lean - ing, lean - ing, Safe and se-cure from all a-larms;
Lean-ing on Je - sus, lean-ing on Je - sus,

Lean - ing, lean - ing, Lean-ing on the ev- er-last-ing arms.
Lean-ing on Je - sus, lean-ing on Je - sus,

293 God Will Take Care of You

Civilla D. Martin

W. Stillman Martin

1. Be not dis-mayed what-e'er be-tide, God will take care of you;
2. Thro' days of toil when heart doth fail, God will take care of you;
3. All you may need He will pro-vide, God will take care of you;
4. No mat-ter what may be the test, God will take care of you;

Be-neath His wings of love a-bide, God will take care of you.
When dan-gers fierce your path as-sail, God will take care of you.
Noth-ing you ask will be de-nied, God will take care of you.
Lean, wear-y one, up-on His breast, God will take care of you.

Chorus

God will take care of you, Thro' ev-'ry day, O'er all the way;

He will take care of you, God will take care of you.
take care of you,

The Rock That Is Higher Than I

ERASTUS JOHNSON

WILLIAM G. FISCHER

1. O some-times the shadows are deep, And rough seems the path to the goal,
2. O sometimes how long seems the day, And sometimes how wea-ry my feet;
3. O near to the Rock let me keep, If bless-ings or sor-rows pre-vail;

And sorrows, sometimes how they sweep Like tempests down o-ver the soul!
But toil-ing in life's dust-y way, The Rock's blessed shadow, how sweet!
Or climb-ing the mountain way steep, Or walk-ing the shad-ow-y vale.

REFRAIN

O then to the Rock let me fly, let me fly, To the

Rock that is high-er than I; is high-er than I; O then to the

Rock let me fly, let me fly, To the Rock that is high-er than I!

Jesus, I Come

WILLIAM T. SLEEPER

GEORGE C. STEBBINS

1. Out of my bond-age, sor-row and night, Je-sus, I come, Je-sus, I come;
2. Out of my shame-ful fail-ure and loss, Je-sus, I come, Je-sus, I come;
3. Out of un-rest and ar - ro-gant pride, Je-sus, I come, Je-sus, I come;
4. Out of the fear and dread of the tomb, Je-sus, I come, Je-sus, I come;

In - to Thy free-dom, glad-ness and light, Je - sus, I come to Thee;
In - to the glo - rious gain of Thy cross, Je - sus, I come to Thee;
In - to Thy bless - ed will to a - bide, Je - sus, I come to Thee;
In - to the joy and light of Thy home, Je - sus, I come to Thee;

Out of my sick-ness in - to Thy health, Out of my want and in - to Thy wealth,
Out of earth's sorrows in-to Thy balm, Out of life's storms and in - to Thy calm,
Out of my - self to dwell in Thy love, Out of de-spair in-to rap-tures a-bove,
Out of the depths of ru - in un - told, In - to the peace of Thy sheltering fold,

Out of my sin and in - to Thy-self, Je - sus, I come to Thee.
Out of dis-tress to ju - bi - lant psalm, Je - sus, I come to Thee.
Up-ward for aye on wings like a dove, Je - sus, I come to Thee.
Ev - er Thy glo - rious face to be-hold, Je - sus, I come to Thee.

He Keeps Me Singing

LUTHER B. BRIDGERS

296

LUTHER B. BRIDGERS

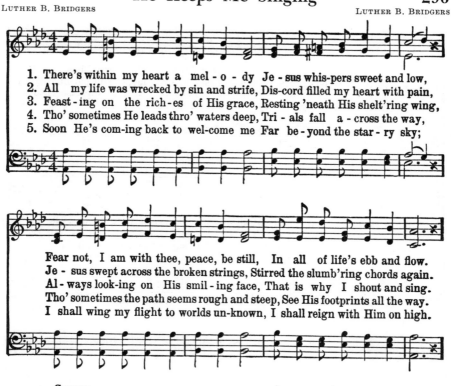

1. There's within my heart a mel - o - dy Je - sus whis-pers sweet and low,
2. All my life was wrecked by sin and strife, Dis-cord filled my heart with pain,
3. Feast - ing on the rich - es of His grace, Resting 'neath His shelt'ring wing,
4. Tho' sometimes He leads thro' waters deep, Tri - als fall a - cross the way,
5. Soon He's com-ing back to wel-come me Far be - yond the star - ry sky;

Fear not, I am with thee, peace, be still, In all of life's ebb and flow.
Je - sus swept across the broken strings, Stirred the slumb'ring chords again.
Al - ways look-ing on His smil - ing face, That is why I shout and sing.
Tho' sometimes the path seems rough and steep, See His footprints all the way.
I shall wing my flight to worlds un-known, I shall reign with Him on high.

CHORUS.

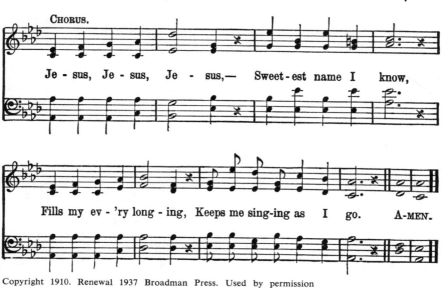

Je - sus, Je - sus, Je - sus,— Sweet-est name I know,

Fills my ev - 'ry long - ing, Keeps me sing-ing as I go. A-MEN.

297 My Jesus, I Love Thee

WILLIAM R. FEATHERSTONE

ADONIRAM J. GORDON

1. My Je - sus, I love Thee, I know Thou art mine, For Thee all the
2. I love Thee, be - cause Thou hast first lov - ed me, And pur-chased my
3. I'll love Thee in life, I will love Thee in death, And praise Thee as
4. In man - sions of glo - ry and end - less de - light, I'll ev - er a-

fol - lies of sin I re - sign; My gra - cious Re - deem - er, my
par - don on Cal - va - ry's tree; I love Thee for wear - ing the
long as Thou lend - est me breath; And say when the death - dew lies
dore Thee in heav - en so bright; I'll sing with the glit - ter-ing

Sav - ior art Thou; If ev - er I loved Thee, my Je - sus, 'tis now.
thorns on Thy brow; If ev - er I loved Thee, my Je - sus, 'tis now.
cold on my brow, If ev - er I loved Thee, my Je - sus, 'tis now.
crown on my brow, If ev - er I loved Thee, my Je - sus, 'tis now.

298 Close to Thee

FANNY J. CROSBY

SILAS J. VAIL

1. Thou, my ev - er - last - ing por - tion, More than friend or life to me;
2. Not for ease or world - ly pleas-ure, Nor for fame my prayer shall be;
3. Lead me thro' the vale of shad-ows, Bear me o'er life's fit - ful sea;

Close to Thee

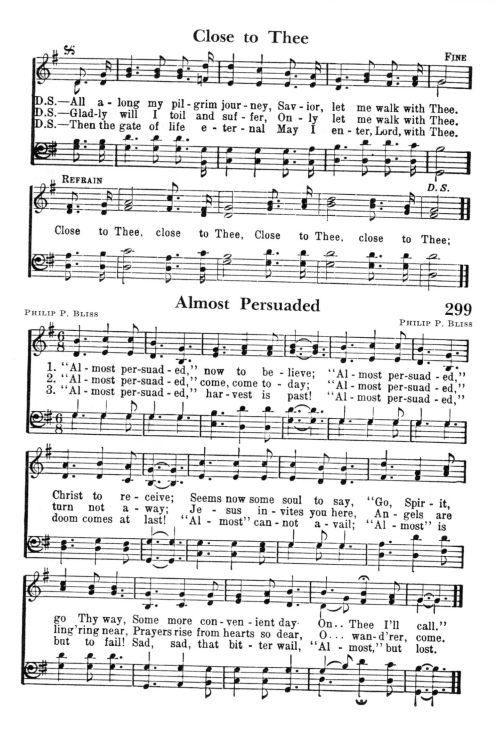

D.S.—All a-long my pil-grim jour-ney, Sav-ior, let me walk with Thee.
D.S.—Glad-ly will I toil and suf-fer, On-ly let me walk with Thee.
D.S.—Then the gate of life e-ter-nal May I en-ter, Lord, with Thee.

REFRAIN

Close to Thee, close to Thee, Close to Thee, close to Thee;

Almost Persuaded

299

PHILIP P. BLISS

PHILIP P. BLISS

1. "Al-most per-suad-ed," now to be-lieve; "Al-most per-suad-ed,"
2. "Al-most per-suad-ed," come, come to-day; "Al-most per-suad-ed,"
3. "Al-most per-suad-ed," har-vest is past! "Al-most per-suad-ed,"

Christ to re-ceive; Seems now some soul to say, "Go, Spir-it,
turn not a-way; Je-sus in-vites you here, An-gels are
doom comes at last! "Al-most" can-not a-vail; "Al-most" is

go Thy way, Some more con-ven-ient day. On.. Thee I'll call."
ling'ring near, Prayers rise from hearts so dear, O... wan-d'rer, come.
but to fail! Sad, sad, that bit-ter wail, "Al-most," but lost.

300 Give Me Thy Heart

Eliza E. Hewitt

William J. Kirkpatrick

1. "Give me thy heart," says the Fa-ther a-bove, No gift so pre-cious to
2. "Give me thy heart," says the Sav-ior of men, Call-ing in mer-cy a-
3. "Give me thy heart," says the Spir-it di-vine, "All that thou hast, to my

Him as our love, Soft-ly He whis-pers wher-ev-er thou art,
gain and a-gain; "Turn now from sin, and from e-vil de-part,
keep-ing re-sign; Grace more a-bound-ing is mine to im-part,

CHORUS

"Grate-ful-ly trust me, and give me thy heart."
Have I not died for thee? give me thy heart." "Give me thy heart,
Make full sur-ren-der and give me thy heart."

p

Give me thy heart," Hear the soft whisper, wher-ev-er thou art; From this dark

rit.

world He would draw thee a-part, Speak-ing so ten-der-ly, "Give me thy heart."

Why Not Now?

Daniel W. Whittle

301

Charles C. Case

1. While we pray and while we plead, While you see your soul's deep need,
2. You have wan-dered far a - way; Do not risk an - oth - er day;
3. In the world you've failed to find Aught of peace for troub-led mind;
4. Come to Christ, con - fes - sion make; Come to Christ, and par - don take;

While our Fa - ther calls you home, Will you not, my broth-er, come?
Do not turn from God thy face, But to - day ac - cept His grace.
Come to Christ, on Him be - lieve, Peace and joy you shall re - ceive.
Trust in Him from day to day, He will keep you all the way.

CHORUS

Why not now?... Why not now?... Why not come to Je - sus now?
Why not now?   Why not now?

Why not now?... Why not now?... Why not come to Je - sus now?
Why not now?   Why not now?

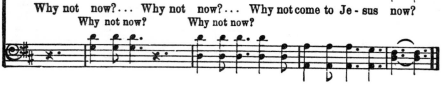

302 "Whosoever Will"

PHILIP P. BLISS   PHILIP P. BLISS

1. "Who-so-ev-er hear-eth," shout, shout the sound! Spread the bless-ed ti-dings
2. Who-so-ev-er com-eth, need not de-lay, Now the door is o-pen,
3. "Who-so-ev-er will," the prom-ise is se-cure; "Who-so-ev-er will," for-

all the world a-round; Tell the joy-ful news wher-ev-er man is found,
en-ter while you may; Je-sus is the true, the on-ly Liv-ing Way:
ev-er must en-dure; "Who-so-ev-er will," 'tis life for-ev-er-more;

CHORUS

"Who-so-ev-er will may come." "Who-so-ev-er will, who-so-ev-er will!"

Send the proc-la-ma-tion o-ver vale and hill; 'Tis a lov-ing

Fa-ther calls the wan-d'rer home: "Who-so-ev-er will may come."

Softly and Tenderly Jesus Is Calling

WILL L. THOMPSON

303

WILL L. THOMPSON

1. Soft-ly and ten-der-ly Je-sus is call-ing, Call-ing for you and for me;
2. Why should we tarry when Jesus is plead-ing, Pleading for you and for me?
3. Time is now fleeting, the moments are passing, Passing from you and from me;
4. Oh! for the won-der-ful love He has promised, Promised for you and for me;

See, on the portals He's waiting and watching, Watching for you and for me.
Why should we linger and heed not His mercies, Mer-cies for you and for me?
Shadows are gathering, death-beds are coming, Com-ing for you and for me.
Tho' we have sinned, He has mercy and pardon, Par-don for you and for me.

Chorus *m*   *cresc.*

Come home,.. come home,...... Ye who are wear-y, come home;...
Come home,   come home,

pp   *ppp*   *rit.*   *pp*

Ear-nest-ly, ten-der-ly, Je-sus is call-ing, Call-ing, O sin-ner, come home!

304 What Will You Do with Jesus?

Author Unknown

M. L. Stocks

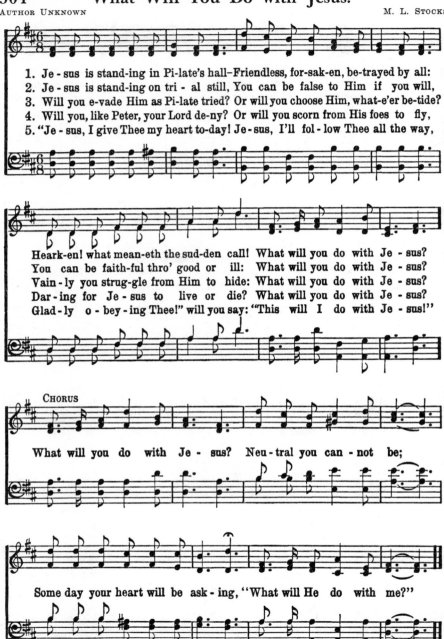

1. Je - sus is stand-ing in Pi-late's hall–Friendless, for-sak-en, be-trayed by all:
2. Je - sus is stand-ing on tri - al still, You can be false to Him if you will,
3. Will you e-vade Him as Pi-late tried? Or will you choose Him, what-e'er be-tide?
4. Will you, like Peter, your Lord de-ny? Or will you scorn from His foes to fly,
5. "Je - sus, I give Thee my heart to-day! Je-sus, I'll fol-low Thee all the way,

Heark-en! what mean-eth the sud-den call! What will you do with Je - sus?
You can be faith-ful thro' good or ill: What will you do with Je - sus?
Vain - ly you strug-gle from Him to hide: What will you do with Je - sus?
Dar - ing for Je - sus to live or die? What will you do with Je - sus?
Glad - ly o - bey-ing Thee!" will you say: "This will I do with Je - sus!"

CHORUS

What will you do with Je - sus? Neu - tral you can - not be;

Some day your heart will be ask - ing, "What will He do with me?"

Come to the Feast

305

Charles H. Gabriel

William A. Ogden

1. "All things are read-y," come to the feast! Come, for the ta-ble now is
2. "All things are read-y," come to the feast! Come, for the door is o-pen
3. "All things are read-y," come to the feast! Come, while He waits to wel-come
4. "All things are read-y," come to the feast! Leave ev-'ry care and world-ly

spread; Ye fam-ish-ing, ye wea-ry, come, And thou shalt be rich-ly fed.
wide; A place of hon-or is re-served For you at the Mas-ter's side.
thee; De-lay not while this day is thine, To-mor-row may nev-er be.
strife; Come, feast up-on the love of God, And drink ev-er-last-ing life.

Chorus

Hear . . . . . the in-vi-ta - - - tion, Come,
Hear the in-vi-ta - - tion, "Who-so-ev-er will,"

"who - - so - ev-er will;" . . . . Praise God . . .
Hear the in-vi-ta - tion, "Who-so-ev-er will;" Praise God for full sal-

. . for full sal-va - - tion For "who-so-ev-er will."
va - tion, For "who-so-ev-er will,"

306 Seeking the Lost

Come to the Savior

George F. Root

George F. Root

1. Come to the Sav - ior, make no de - lay— Here in His word He's
2. "Suf - fer the chil - dren!" O hear His voice, Let ev - 'ry heart leap
3. Think once a - gain, He's with us to - day— Heed now His blest com-

shown us the way; Here in our midst He's stand - ing to - day,
forth and re - joice, And let us free - ly make Him our choice:
mands, and o - bey; Hear now His ac - cents ten - der - ly say,

Chorus

Ten - der - ly say - ing, "Come!"
Do not de - lay, but come. Joy - ful, joy - ful
"Will you, My chil - dren, come?"

will the meet-ing be, When from sin our hearts are pure and free,

And we shall gath - er, Sav - ior, with Thee, In our e - ter - nal home.

308 The Savior Is Waiting

RALPH CARMICHAEL · RALPH CARMICHAEL

1. The Sav-iour is wait-ing to en-ter your heart,
2. If you'll take one step t'ward the Sav-iour, my friend,

Why don't you let Him come in? There's noth-ing in this world to
You'll find His arms o - pen wide; Re - ceive Him, and all of your

keep you a - part, What is your an-swer to Him?
dark-ness will end, With-in your heart He'll a - bide.

CHORUS

Time af-ter time He has wait-ed be-fore, And now He is wait-ing a - gain

___ To see if you're will-ing to o-pen the door, Oh, how He wants to come in.

Don't Turn the Savior Away

HARRY D. CLARKE

HARRY D. CLARKE
ARR. BY JOHN F. WILSON

309

1. The Sav-iour is call-ing, is call-ing for you, In ac-cents so ten-der, so
2. The Sav-iour is call-ing, why turn Him a-way? Sin's bur-den is heav-y, why
3. The Sav-iour is call-ing, O, can it be true That life ev-er-last-ing is
4. The Sav-iour is call-ing from Cal-va-ry's cross, Where He died to save you at

lov-ing and true, How can you re-fuse Him? O heed His sweet call! O,
long-er de-lay? O heart full of sor-row, there's com-fort to-day; O,
wait-ing for you? Come now and re-ceive Him, to Sa-tan say nay; O,
in-fi-nite cost; His heart there was bro-ken for you and for me; O,

REFRAIN

don't turn the Sav-iour a - way. Don't turn the Sav-iour a -

way from your heart, Don't turn the Sav-iour a - way from your heart;

O hear Him plead-ing, O list' to His call, O, don't turn the Sav-iour a - way.

310 The Solid Rock

Edward Mote

WILLIAM B. BRADBURY

1. My hope is built on noth-ing less Than Je-sus' blood and right-eous-ness;
2. When darkness veils His love-ly face, I rest on His un-chang-ing grace;
3. His oath, His cov-e-nant, His blood, Sup-port me in the whelm-ing flood;
4. When He shall come with trumpet sound, Oh, may I then in Him be found;

I dare not trust the sweet-est frame, But whol-ly lean on Je-sus' name.
In ev-'ry high and storm-y gale, My an-chor holds with-in the veil.
When all a-round my soul gives way, He then is all my hope and stay.
Dressed in His right-eous-ness a-lone, Fault-less to stand be-fore the throne.

REFRAIN

On Christ, the sol-id Rock, I stand; All oth-er ground

is sink-ing sand, All oth-er ground is sink-ing sand.

Under His Wings

William O. Cushing

Ira D. Sankey

1. Un - der His wings I am safe - ly a - bid - ing; Tho' the night
2. Un - der His wings, what a ref - uge in sor - row! How the heart
3. Un - der His wings, O what pre - cious en - joy - ment! There will I

deep - ens and tem - pests are wild, Still I can trust Him; I
yearn - ing - ly turns to His rest! Oft - en when earth has no
hide till life's tri - als are o'er; Shel - tered, pro - tect - ed, no

know He will keep me; He has re - deemed me, and I am His child.
balm for my heal - ing, There I find com - fort, and there I am blest.
e - vil can harm me; Rest - ing in Je - sus I'm safe ev - er - more.

CHORUS

Un - der His wings, un - der His wings, Who from His love can sev - er?

Un - der His wings my soul shall a - bide, Safe - ly a - bide for - ev - er.

312   Never Alone!

AUTHOR UNKNOWN

AUTHOR UNKNOWN
ARR. BY FRED JACKY

1. I've seen the light-ning flash-ing, I've heard the thun-der roll,
2. The world's fierce winds are blow-ing; Temp-ta-tion sharp and keen;
3. When in af-flic-tion's val-ley I tread the road of care,
4. He died on Cal-v'ry's moun-tain, For me they pierced His side,

I've felt sin's break-ers dash-ing, Which al-most con-quered my soul;
I have a peace in know-ing My Sav-ior stands be-tween—
My Sav-ior helps me to car-ry The cross so heav-y to bear;
For me He opened that foun-tain, The crim-son, cleans-ing tide;

I've heard the voice of my Sav-ior Bid-ding me still to fight on;
He stands to shield me from dan-ger When my friends are all gone;
Tho' all a-round me is dark-ness, Earth-ly joys all flown;
For me He wait-eth in glo-ry, Seat-ed up-on His throne;

He prom-ised nev-er to leave me, Nev-er to leave me a-lone!
He prom-ised nev-er to leave me, Nev-er to leave me a-lone!
My Sav-ior whis-pers His prom-ise, Nev-er to leave me a-lone!
He prom-ised nev-er to leave me, Nev-er to leave me a-lone!

Never Alone!

Chorus

No, nev-er a-lone,............ No, nev-er a-lone,...... He prom-ised nev-er to
No, nev-er a-lone, No, no, nev-er a-lone,

leave me, He'll claim me for His own. No, nev-er a-lone,...... No, nev-er a-
No, nev-er a-lone, No, no,

lone,...... He prom-ised nev-er to leave me, Nev-er to leave me a-lone.
nev-er a-lone.

I Love Thy Kingdom, Lord   313

Timothy Dwight

Aaron Williams

1. I love Thy king-dom, Lord, The house of Thine a-bode,
2. I love Thy Church, O God! Her walls be-fore Thee stand,
3. For her my tears shall fall; For her my prayers as-cend;
4. Be-yond my high-est joy I prize her heav'n-ly ways,
5. Sure as Thy truth shall last, To Zi-on shall be giv'n

The Church our blest Re-deem-er saved With His own pre-cious blood.
Dear as the ap-ple of Thine eye, And grav-en on Thy hand.
To her my cares and toils be giv'n, Till toils and cares shall end.
Her sweet com-mun-ion, sol-emn vows, Her hymns of love and praise.
The bright-est glo-ries earth can yield, And bright-er bliss of heav'n. A-MEN.

314 His Mighty Hand

GEORGE W. WHITCOMB

ALBERT S. REITZ

1. I am saved from sin, I have peace with-in, And I walk with Je-sus
2. Man-y passed me by, heed-ing not my cry, But the Sav-iour heard and
3. There's a prom-ise sure and it shall en-dure, "Lo, I will be with thee
4. There is sweet-er peace, there is per-fect peace, And my Fa-ther's word is

day by day; O His hand so strong holds me all day long, And with
res-cued me; I was lost and blind, Je-sus was so kind, Lo, He
all the way;" And tho' foes as-sail, I shall still pre-vail, For I
won-drous dear; There is might-y pow'r for each try-ing hour, There is

REFRAIN

Him I will not go a-stray.
touched my eyes and now I see. He will hold me with His might-y hand!
know He helps me watch and pray.
love that "cast-eth out all fear!"

He will hold me with His might-y hand! In temp-ta-tion He will

help me stand! For He will hold me with His might-y hand.

I Never Walk Alone

ALFRED H. ACKLEY

315

ALFRED H. ACKLEY

1. I nev-er walk a-lone, I have the Sav-iour, Who walks be-side me ev-ery-where I go; My heart re-joic-es in His lov-ing fa - vor, And all who will His sav-ing grace may know.

2. I nev-er walk a-lone, in storm-y wea-ther, When winds of trou-ble sweep a-bout my head; I know I'm safe, be-cause we are to - geth - er, And 'round me His pro-tect-ing love is spread.

REFRAIN

I nev-er walk a-lone, Christ walks be-side me, He is the dear-est Friend I've ev-er known, With such a Friend to com-fort and to guide me, I nev-er, no, I nev-er walk a - lone.

316   The Nail-Scarred Hand

BAYLUS B. McKINNEY   BAYLUS B. McKINNEY

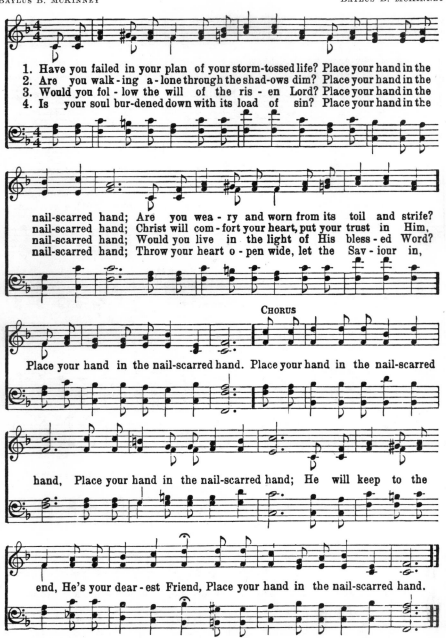

1. Have you failed in your plan of your storm-tossed life? Place your hand in the
2. Are you walk-ing a-lone through the shad-ows dim? Place your hand in the
3. Would you fol-low the will of the ris-en Lord? Place your hand in the
4. Is your soul bur-dened down with its load of sin? Place your hand in the

nail-scarred hand; Are you wea-ry and worn from its toil and strife?
nail-scarred hand; Christ will com-fort your heart, put your trust in Him,
nail-scarred hand; Would you live in the light of His bless-ed Word?
nail-scarred hand; Throw your heart o-pen wide, let the Sav-iour in,

CHORUS

Place your hand in the nail-scarred hand. Place your hand in the nail-scarred
hand, Place your hand in the nail-scarred hand; He will keep to the
end, He's your dear-est Friend, Place your hand in the nail-scarred hand.

The Old Rugged Cross

GEORGE BENNARD

317

GEORGE BENNARD

1. On a hill far a-way stood an old rug-ged cross, The em-blem of
2. Oh, that old rug-ged cross so de-spised by the world, Has a wondrous at-
3. In the old rug-ged cross, stained with blood so di-vine, A won-drous
4. To the old rug-ged cross I will ev-er be true, Its shame and re-

suf-f'ring and shame; And I love that old cross where the dear-est and best
trac-tion for me; For the dear Lamb of God left His glo-ry a-bove,
beau-ty I see; For 'twas on that old cross Je-sus suf-fered and died,
proach gladly bear; Then He'll call me some day to my home far a-way,

CHORUS

For a world of lost sin-ners was slain.
To bear it to dark Cal-va-ry. So I'll cher-ish the old rug-ged
To par-don and sanc-ti-fy me.
Where His glo-ry for-ev-er I'll share. cross, the

cross,.... Till my tro-phies at last I lay down; I will cling to the
old rugged cross,

old rug-ged cross,...... And ex-change it some day for a crown.
cross, the old rug-ged cross,

318
Buried with Christ

T. RYDER

WILLIAM J. KIRKPATRICK

1. Bur-ied with Christ and raised with Him too, What is there left for
2. Ris-en with Christ my glo-ri-ous Head, Ho-li-ness now the
3. Liv-ing with Christ, who di-eth no more, Fol-low-ing Christ, who

me . . . to do? Sim-ply to cease from strug-gling and strife,
path-way I tread; Beau-ti-ful thought while walk-ing there-in,
go-eth be-fore; Not un-der law, I'm now un-der grace,

CHORUS

Sim-ply to walk in new-ness of life.
He that is dead is freed from all sin. Bur-ied with Christ and
Sin is de-throned and Christ takes its place.

dead un-to sin; Dy-ing but liv-ing, Je-sus with-in; Rul-ing and

reign-ing day aft-er day, Guid-ing and keep-ing all of the way.

O Word of God Incarnate 319

William W. How

"Neuvermehrtes Meiningisches Gesangbuch"
Har. by Felix Mendelssohn-Bartholdy

1. O Word of God in-car-nate, O Wis-dom from on high,
2. The Church from her dear Mas-ter Re-ceived the gift di-vine,
3. It float-eth like a ban-ner Be-fore God's host un-furled;
4. O make Thy Church, dear Sav-ior, A lamp of pur-est gold,

O Truth un-changed, un-chang-ing, O Light of our dark sky;
And still that light she lift-eth O'er all the earth to shine.
It shin-eth like a bea-con A-bove the dark-'ning world.
To bear be-fore the na-tions Thy true light, as of old.

We praise Thee for the ra-diance That from the hal-lowed page,
It is the gold-en cask-et, Where gems of truth are stored;
It is the chart and com-pass That o'er life's surg-ing sea,
O teach Thy wan-d'ring pil-grims By this their path to trace,

A lan-tern to our foot-steps, Shines on from age to age.
It is the heav'n-drawn pic-ture Of Christ, the liv-ing Word.
'Mid mists and rocks and quick-sands, Still guides, O Christ, to Thee.
Till, clouds and dark-ness end-ed, They see Thee face to face. A-men.

320 Break Thou the Bread of Life

MARY ANN LATHBURY

WILLIAM F. SHERWIN

1. Break Thou the bread of life, Dear Lord, to me, As Thou didst break the loaves Be-side the sea; Be-yond the sa-cred page I seek Thee, Lord; My spir-it pants for Thee, O liv-ing Word.
2. Bless Thou the truth, dear Lord To me— to me— As Thou didst bless the bread By Gal-i-lee; Then shall all bond-age cease, All fet-ters fall; And I shall find my peace, My All in All.
3. Thou art the bread of life, O Lord, to me, Thy ho-ly Word the truth That sav-eth me; Give me to eat and live With Thee a-bove; Teach me to love Thy truth, For Thou art love.
4. O send Thy Spir-it, Lord, Now un-to me, That He may touch my eyes, And make me see: Show me the truth con-cealed With-in Thy Word, And in Thy book re-vealed I see the Lord.

321 'Tis Midnight; and on Olive's Brow

WILLIAM B. TAPPAN

WILLIAM B. BRADBURY

1. 'Tis midnight; and on Ol-ive's brow The star is dimmed that late-ly shone:
2. 'Tis midnight; and from all re-moved, The Sav-ior wres-tles lone with fears;
3. 'Tis midnight; and for oth-ers' guilt The Man of Sor-rows weeps in blood;
4. 'Tis midnight; and from e-ther-plains Is borne the song that an-gels know;

'Tis Midnight; and on Olive's Brow

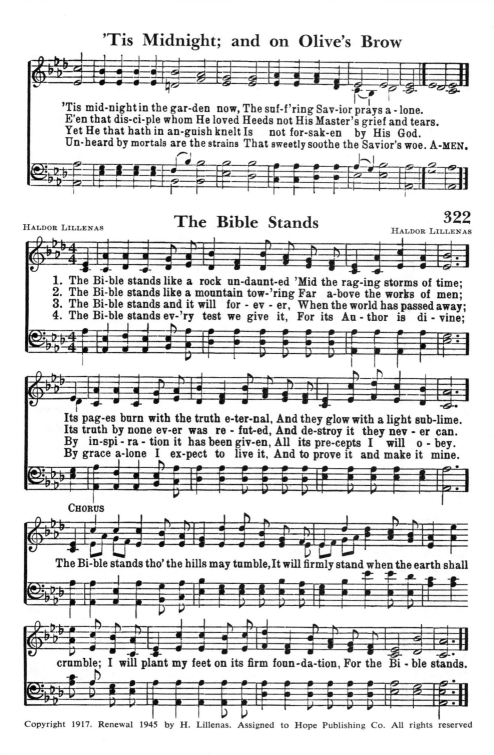

'Tis mid-night in the gar-den now, The suf-f'ring Sav-ior prays a - lone.
E'en that dis-ci-ple whom He loved Heeds not His Master's grief and tears.
Yet He that hath in an-guish knelt Is not for-sak-en by His God.
Un-heard by mortals are the strains That sweetly soothe the Savior's woe. A-MEN.

The Bible Stands

322

HALDOR LILLENAS

HALDOR LILLENAS

1. The Bi-ble stands like a rock un-daunt-ed 'Mid the rag-ing storms of time;
2. The Bi-ble stands like a mountain tow-'ring Far a-bove the works of men;
3. The Bi-ble stands and it will for - ev - er, When the world has passed away;
4. The Bi-ble stands ev-'ry test we give it, For its Au - thor is di - vine;

Its pag-es burn with the truth e-ter-nal, And they glow with a light sub-lime.
Its truth by none ev-er was re - fut-ed, And de-stroy it they nev - er can.
By in-spi - ra - tion it has been giv-en, All its pre-cepts I will o - bey.
By grace a-lone I ex-pect to live it, And to prove it and make it mine.

CHORUS

The Bi-ble stands tho' the hills may tumble, It will firmly stand when the earth shall

crumble; I will plant my feet on its firm foun-da-tion, For the Bi - ble stands.

323 Standing on the Promises

R. KELSO CARTER

R. KELSO CARTER

1. Stand-ing on the prom-is-es of Christ my King, Thro' e-ter-nal a-ges
2. Stand-ing on the prom-is-es that can-not fail, When the howling storms of
3. Stand-ing on the prom-is-es of Christ the Lord, Bound to Him e-ter-nal-
4. Stand-ing on the prom-is-es I can-not fall, Lis-t'ning ev-'ry mo-ment

let His prais-es ring; Glo-ry in the high-est, I will shout and sing,
doubt and fear as-sail, By the liv-ing word of God I shall pre-vail.
ly by love's strong cord, O-ver-com-ing dai-ly with the Spir-it's sword,
to the Spir-it's call, Rest-ing in my Sav-ior, as my all in all,

CHORUS

Stand-ing on the prom-is-es of God. Stand - - ing, stand - - ing,
Standing on the promises, standing on the promises,

Stand-ing on the prom-is-es of God my Sav-ior; Stand - - ing,
Stand-ing on the prom-is-es,

stand - - ing, I'm stand-ing on the prom-is-es of God.
stand-ing on the prom-is-es,

Thy Word Have I Hid in My Heart

324

FROM PSALM 119
ADAPTED BY ERNEST O. SELLERS

ERNEST O. SELLERS

1. Thy Word is a lamp to my feet, A light to my path al - way,
2. For - ev - er, O Lord, is Thy Word Es-tab-lished and fixed on high;
3. At morn-ing, at noon, and at night I ev - er will give Thee praise;
4. Thro' Him whom Thy Word hath foretold, The Sav-ior and Morn-ing Star,

To guide and to save me from sin, And show me the heav'n-ly way.
Thy faith-ful-ness un - to all men A - bid - eth for - ev - er nigh.
For Thou art my por-tion, O Lord, And shall be thro' all my days!
Sal - va-tion and peace have been bro't To those who have strayed a - far.

CHORUS—Ps. 119: 11.

Thy Word have I hid in my heart (in my heart), That I might not

sin a - gainst Thee (a - gainst Thee); That I might not sin, That

ad lib.

I might not sin, Thy Word have I hid in my heart.

325 Beautiful Words of Jesus

ELIZA E. HEWITT

ISAAC H. MEREDITH

1. Beau-ti-ful words of Je-sus, Spo-ken so long a-go, Yet, as we sing them
2. Beau-ti-ful words of Je-sus, Cheering us, day by day; Throwing a gleam of
3. Beau-ti-ful words of Je-sus, To-kens of end-less rest, When, by and by, we

DUET. LADIES' VOICES

o-ver, Dearer to us they grow, Calling the heav-y-la-den, Call-ing to hearts op-
sunshine Over a cloud-y way; Casting on Him the burden We are too weak to
en-ter In-to His presence blest; There shall we see His beauty, Meet with Him face to

ALL VOICES   **CHORUS**

pressed, "Come un-to me, ye wea-ry, Come, I will give you rest."
bear,   He will give grace sufficient, He will re-gard our prayer. Hear the
face,   There shall we sing His glory, Praising His matchless grace.

call .... of His voice, so   sweet; .   Bring your   load .... to the

Sav-ior's feet;   Lean your   heart ... on His lov - ing

Beautiful Words of Jesus

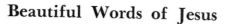

breast,.. Come, O come and He will give you rest.....

Wonderful Words of Life

326

PHILIP P. BLISS

PHILIP P. BLISS

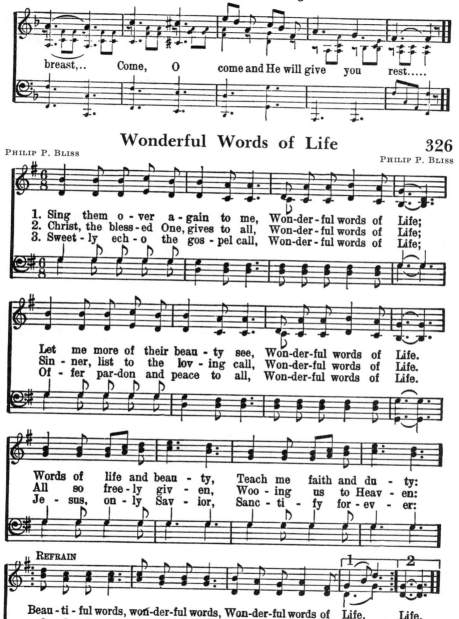

1. Sing them o-ver a-gain to me, Won-der-ful words of Life;
2. Christ, the bless-ed One, gives to all, Won-der-ful words of Life;
3. Sweet-ly ech-o the gos-pel call, Won-der-ful words of Life;

Let me more of their beau-ty see, Won-der-ful words of Life.
Sin-ner, list to the lov-ing call, Won-der-ful words of Life.
Of-fer par-don and peace to all, Won-der-ful words of Life.

Words of life and beau-ty, Teach me faith and du-ty:
All so free-ly giv-en, Woo-ing us to Heav-en:
Je-sus, on-ly Sav-ior, Sanc-ti-fy for-ev-er:

REFRAIN

Beau-ti-ful words, won-der-ful words, Won-der-ful words of Life. Life.

327   Thy Word Is Like a Garden, Lord

EDWIN HODDER   GOTTFRIED W. FINK

1. Thy Word is like a gar-den, Lord, With flow-ers bright and fair;
2. Thy Word is like a star-ry host: A thou-sand rays of light
3. Oh, may I love Thy pre-cious Word, May I ex-plore the mine,

And ev-'ry one who seeks may pluck A love-ly clus-ter there.
Are seen to guard the trav-el-er, And make his path-way bright.
May I its fra-grant flow-ers glean, May light up-on me shine!

Thy Word is like a deep, deep mine, And jew-els rich and rare
Thy Word is like an ar-mor-y, Where sol-diers may re-pair,
Oh, may I find my ar-mor there! Thy Word my trust-y sword,

Are hid-den in its might-y depths For ev-'ry search-er there.
And find, for life's long bat-tle-day, All need-ful weap-ons there.
I'll learn to fight with ev-'ry foe The bat-tle of the Lord.

Are You Washed in the Blood?

ELISHA A. HOFFMAN

ELISHA A. HOFFMAN

1. Have you been to Je-sus for the cleansing pow'r? Are you washed in the
2. Are you walk-ing dai-ly by the Sav-ior's side? Are you washed in the
3. When the Bridegroom cometh will your robes be white? Are you washed in the
4. Lay a-side the garments that are stained with sin, And be washed in the

blood of the Lamb? Are you ful-ly trust-ing in His grace this hour? Are you
blood of the Lamb? Do you rest each mo-ment in the Cru-ci-fied? Are you
blood of the Lamb? Will your soul be read-y for the mansions bright, And be
blood of the Lamb; There's a fountain flow-ing for the soul un-clean, O be

CHORUS

washed in the blood of the Lamb? Are you washed in the blood,

Are you washed in the blood,

In the soul-cleans-ing blood of the Lamb? Are your gar-ments

of the Lamb?

spot-less? Are they white as snow? Are you washed in the blood of the Lamb?

329 Saved by the Blood

S. J. HENDERSON

DANIEL B. TOWNER

1. Saved by the blood of the Cru - ci - fied One! Now ran - somed from
2. Saved by the blood of the Cru - ci - fied One! The an - gels re -
3. Saved by the blood of the Cru - ci - fied One! The Fa - ther He
4. Saved by the blood of the Cru - ci - fied One! All hail to the

sin and a new work be - gun, Sing praise to the Fa - ther and
joic - ing be - cause it is done; A child of the Fa - ther, joint -
spake, and His will it was done; Great price of my par - don, His
Fa - ther, all hail to the Son, All hail to the Spir - it, the

praise to the Son, Saved by the blood of the Cru - ci - fied One!
heir with the Son, Saved by the blood of the Cru - ci - fied One!
own pre - cious Son; Saved by the blood of the Cru - ci - fied One!
great Three in One! Saved by the blood of the Cru - ci - fied One!

CHORUS

Saved! . . saved! . . My sins are all pardoned, my guilt is all gone!
Glo - ry, I'm saved! glo - ry, I'm saved!

Saved! . . saved! . . I am saved by the blood of the Cru - ci - fied One!
Glo - ry, I'm saved! glo - ry, I'm saved!

There Is Power in the Blood

Lewis E. Jones

Lewis E. Jones

1. Would you be free from the bur-den of sin? There's pow'r in the blood,
2. Would you be free from your pas-sion and pride? There's pow'r in the blood,
3. Would you be whit-er, much whiter than snow? There's pow'r in the blood,
4. Would you do serv-ice for Je-sus your King? There's pow'r in the blood,

pow'r in the blood; Would you o'er e-vil a vic-to-ry win? There's
pow'r in the blood; Come for a cleans-ing to Cal-va-ry's tide; There's
pow'r in the blood; Sin-stains are lost in its life-giv-ing flow; There's
pow'r in the blood; Would you live dai-ly His prais-es to sing? There's

Chorus.

won-der-ful pow'r in the blood. There is pow'r, pow'r, Wonder-working pow'r
there is

In the blood of the Lamb; There is pow'r, pow'r,
In the blood of the Lamb; there is

Won-der-work-ing pow'r In the pre-cious blood of the Lamb.

When I See the Blood

331

JOHN FOOTE

J. G. FOOTE

1. Christ our Re-deem-er died on the cross, Died for the sin-ner,
2. Chief-est of sin-ners, Je-sus will save; All He has prom-ised,
3. Judg-ment is com-ing, all will be there, Each one re-ceiv-ing
4. O great com-pas-sion! O bound-less love! O lov-ing kind-ness,

paid all his due; Sprin-kle your soul with the blood of the Lamb,
that He will do; Wash in the foun-tain o-pened for sin,
just-ly his due; Hide in the sav-ing sin-cleans-ing blood,
faith-ful and true! Find peace and shel-ter un-der the blood,

CHORUS

And I will pass, will pass o-ver you. When I see the
When I

blood, When I see the blood, When I see the
see the blood, When I see the blood, When I

rit.

blood, I will pass, I will pass o-ver you.
see the blood, o-ver you.

'Twas Jesus' Blood

Harry D. Loes   Harry D. Loes

1. A sin-ner, lost, condemned was I, Doomed an e-ter-nal death to die;
2. I ne'er could be at peace with God, But for the cleansing, crimson flood,
3. No doubter's scorn or creed of man Can shake my faith in Cal-v'ry's plan;

But Je-sus died for me, He bore sin's pen-al-ty. On Cal-v'ry's hill was
No one but Christ could win A-tone-ment for all sin—He signed my par-don
His blood re-deemed my soul, It made me pure and whole; By faith my life in

CHORUS

lift-ed high. 'Twas Je-sus' blood...... that ransomed me......
with His blood.
Him be-gan. 'Twas Jesus' blood that ransomed me,

From chains of sin He set me free........ While a-ges roll........
He set me free. While a-ges roll

my song shall be: ....'Twas Je-sus' blood that ransomed me......
My song shall be: ransomed me.

333 Yield Not to Temptation

HORATIO R. PALMER

HORATIO R. PALMER

1. Yield not to temp-ta - tion, For yield-ing is sin, Each vic-t'ry will
2. Shun e - vil com-pan-ions, Bad lan-guage dis-dain, God's name hold in
3. To him that o'er-com-eth God giv-eth a crown, Thro' faith we shall

help you Some oth - er to win; Fight man-ful - ly on-ward,
rev-'rence, Nor take it in vain; Be thought-ful and ear - nest.
con - quer, Though of - ten cast down; He who is our Sav - ior,

Dark pas-sions sub-due, Look ev - er to Je - sus, He will car-ry you through.
Kind-heart-ed and true, Look ev - er to Je - sus, He will car-ry you through.
Our strength will re - new, Look ev - er to Je - sus, He will car-ry you through.

CHORUS

Ask the Sav - ior to help you, Com - fort, strengthen, and keep you,

He is will-ing to aid you, He will car - ry you through.

He Died for Me

JOHN NEWTON

EDWIN O. EXCELL

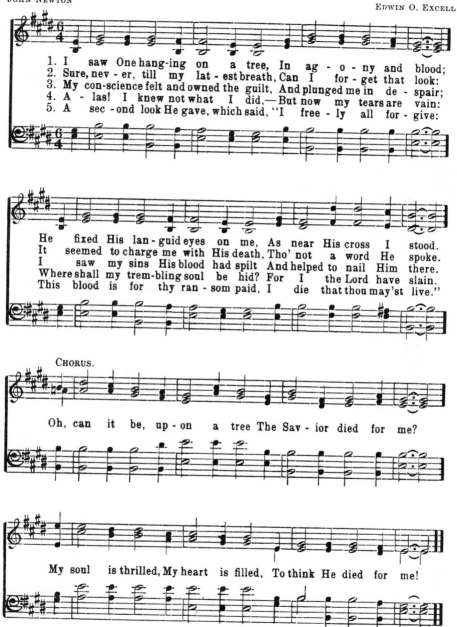

1. I saw One hang-ing on a tree, In ag - o - ny and blood;
2. Sure, nev - er, till my lat - est breath, Can I for - get that look;
3. My con-science felt and owned the guilt, And plunged me in de - spair;
4. A - las! I knew not what I did,—But now my tears are vain:
5. A sec - ond look He gave, which said, "I free - ly all for - give:

He fixed His lan - guid eyes on me, As near His cross I stood.
It seemed to charge me with His death, Tho' not a word He spoke.
I saw my sins His blood had spilt And helped to nail Him there.
Where shall my trem-bling soul be hid? For I the Lord have slain.
This blood is for thy ran - som paid, I die that thou may'st live."

CHORUS.

Oh, can it be, up - on a tree The Sav - ior died for me?

My soul is thrilled, My heart is filled, To think He died for me!

335 Glorious Things of Thee Are Spoken

JOHN NEWTON

FRANZ JOSEPH HAYDN

1. Glo-rious things of thee are spo-ken, Zi - on, cit - y of our God;
2. See, the streams of liv - ing wa-ters, Springing from e - ter - nal love,
3. Round each hab - i - ta - tion hov-'ring, See the cloud and fire ap - pear

He, whose word can-not be bro-ken, Formed thee for His own a - bode;
Well sup-ply thy sons and daughters, And all fear of want re-move:
For a glo - ry and a cov-'ring, Show-ing that the Lord is near!

On the Rock of A - ges found-ed, What can shake thy sure re - pose?
Who can faint, while such a riv - er Ev - er flows their thirst t' as-suage?
Glo-rious things of thee are spo-ken, Zi - on, cit - y of our God;

With sal-va-tion's walls sur-round-ed, Thou may'st smile at all thy foes.
Grace which, like the Lord, the Giv-er, Nev - er fails from age to age.
He, whose word can-not be bro-ken, Formed thee for His own a - bode. A-MEN.

The Church's One Foundation

SAMUEL J. STONE

SAMUEL S. WESLEY

1. The Church-'s one foun - da - tion Is Je - sus Christ her Lord;
2. E - lect from ev - 'ry na - tion, Yet one o'er all the earth,
3. 'Mid toil and trib - u - la - tion, And tu - mult of her war,
4. Yet she on earth hath un - ion With God the Three in One,

She is His new cre - a - tion By wa - ter and the word:
Her char - ter of sal - va - tion, One Lord, one faith, one birth;
She waits the con - sum - ma - tion Of peace for - ev - er - more;
And mys - tic sweet com - mun - ion With those whose rest is won:

From Heav'n He came and sought her To be His ho - ly bride; With
One ho - ly name she bless - es, Par - takes one ho - ly food, And
Till, with the vi - sion glo - rious, Her long - ing eyes are blest, And
O hap - py ones and ho - ly! Lord, give us grace that we, Like

His own blood He bought her, And for her life He died.
to one hope she press - es, With ev - 'ry grace en - dued.
the great church vic - to - rious Shall be the church at rest.
them, the meek and low - ly, On high may dwell with Thee. A-MEN.

Lead Me to Calvary

JENNIE E. HUSSEY

WILLIAM J. KIRKPATRICK

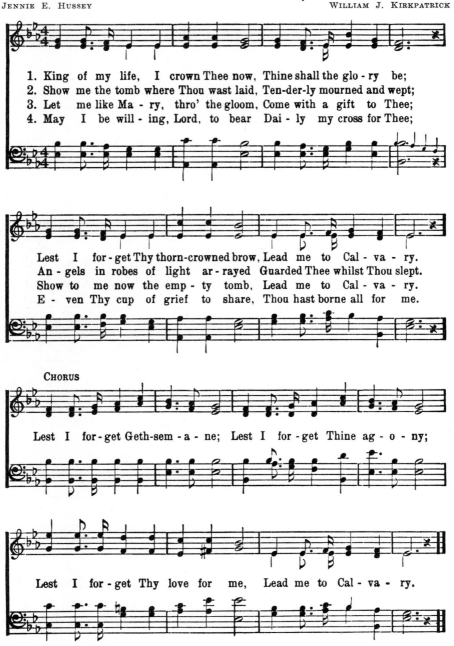

1. King of my life, I crown Thee now, Thine shall the glo-ry be;
2. Show me the tomb where Thou wast laid, Ten-der-ly mourned and wept;
3. Let me like Ma-ry, thro' the gloom, Come with a gift to Thee;
4. May I be will-ing, Lord, to bear Dai-ly my cross for Thee;

Lest I for-get Thy thorn-crowned brow, Lead me to Cal-va-ry.
An-gels in robes of light ar-rayed Guarded Thee whilst Thou slept.
Show to me now the emp-ty tomb, Lead me to Cal-va-ry.
E-ven Thy cup of grief to share, Thou hast borne all for me.

CHORUS

Lest I for-get Geth-sem-a-ne; Lest I for-get Thine ag-o-ny;

Lest I for-get Thy love for me, Lead me to Cal-va-ry.

O Sacred Head, Now Wounded

ASCRIBED TO BERNARD OF CLAIRVAUX
TR. (GERMAN) BY PAUL GERHARDT
TR. (ENGLISH) BY JAMES W. ALEXANDER

HANS L. HASSLER
HAR. BY J. S. BACH

To be sung slowly

1. O sa-cred Head, now wound-ed, With grief and shame weighed down.
2. O no-blest Brow and dear-est, In oth-er days the world
3. What Thou, my Lord, hast suf-fered Was all for sin-ners' gain.
4. What lan-guage shall I bor-row To thank Thee, dear-est Friend,

Now scorn-ful-ly sur-round-ed With thorns, Thine on-ly crown;
All feared when Thou ap-pear-edst; What shame on Thee is hurled!
Mine, mine was the trans-gres-sion, But Thine the dead-ly pain.
For this Thy dy-ing sor-row, Thy pit-y with-out end?

O sa-cred Head, what glo-ry, What bliss till now was Thine!
How art Thou pale with an-guish, With sore a-buse and scorn;
Lo, here I fall, my Sav-ior! 'Tis I de-serve Thy place;
O make me Thine for-ev-er; And should I faint-ing be,

Yet, though de-spised and go-ry, I joy to call Thee mine.
How does that vis-age lan-guish Which once was bright as morn!
Look on me with Thy fa-vor, Vouch-safe to me Thy grace.
Lord, let me nev-er, nev-er Out-live my love to Thee.

339 Surely Goodness and Mercy

JOHN W. PETERSON
ALFRED B. SMITH

JOHN W. PETERSON
ALFRED B. SMITH

1. A pil-grim was I and a-wan-d'ring, In the cold night of
2. He re-stor-eth my soul when I'm wea-ry, He giv-eth me
3. When I walk thro' the dark lone-some val-ley, My Sav-ior will

sin I did roam, When Je-sus the kind Shep-herd found me,
strength day by day; He leads me be-side the still wa-ters,
walk with me there; And safe-ly His great hand will lead me

CHORUS

And now I am on my way home.
He guards me each step of the way. Sure-ly good-ness and
To the man-sions He's gone to pre-pare.

mer-cy shall fol-low me All the days, all the days of my

life; Sure-ly good-ness and mer-cy shall fol-low

Surely Goodness and Mercy

me All the days, all the days of my life. And I shall

dwell in the house of the Lord for - ev - er, And I shall

feast at the ta-ble spread for me; Sure - ly good-ness

and mer-cy shall fol - low me All the days, all the

CODA (after last chorus only)

days of my life. All the days, all the days of my life.

★ Opt. D.C. The following section may be reserved for use with final chorus only.

340 There Is a Green Hill Far Away

CECIL F. ALEXANDER

GEORGE C. STEBBINS

1. There is a green hill far a - way, With-out a cit - y wall,
2. We may not know we can - not tell What pains He had to bear;
3. He died that we might be for-giv'n, He died to make us good,
4. There was no oth - er good e-nough, To pay the price of sin;

Where the dear Lord was cru - ci - fied, Who died to save us all.
But we be-lieve it was for us He hung and suf-fered there.
That we might go at last to Heav'n, Saved by His pre-cious blood.
He on - ly could un - lock the gate Of Heav'n and let us in.

CHORUS

Oh, dear - ly, dear - ly has He loved, And we must love Him, too;

rit . . .

And trust in His re - deem-ing blood, And try His works to do.

As a Volunteer

W. S. Brown

Charles H. Gabriel

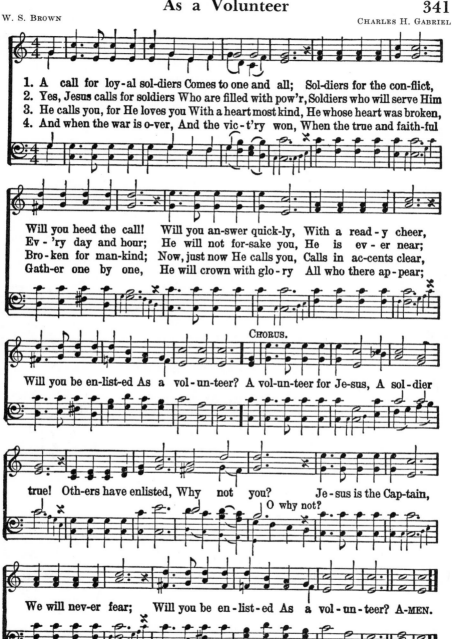

1. A call for loy-al sol-diers Comes to one and all; Sol-diers for the con-flict,
2. Yes, Jesus calls for soldiers Who are filled with pow'r, Soldiers who will serve Him
3. He calls you, for He loves you With a heart most kind, He whose heart was broken,
4. And when the war is o-ver, And the vic-t'ry won, When the true and faith-ful

Will you heed the call! Will you an-swer quick-ly, With a read-y cheer,
Ev-'ry day and hour; He will not for-sake you, He is ev-er near;
Bro-ken for man-kind; Now, just now He calls you, Calls in ac-cents clear,
Gath-er one by one, He will crown with glo-ry All who there ap-pear;

CHORUS.

Will you be en-list-ed As a vol-un-teer? A vol-un-teer for Je-sus, A sol-dier

true! Oth-ers have enlisted, Why not you? O why not? Je-sus is the Cap-tain,

We will nev-er fear; Will you be en-list-ed As a vol-un-teer? A-MEN.

342 Take Time to Be Holy

WILLIAM D. LONGSTAFF

GEORGE C. STEBBINS

1. Take time to be ho-ly, Speak oft with thy Lord; A - bide in Him al - ways, And feed on His Word. Make friends of God's chil-dren; Help those who are weak; For - get-ting in noth-ing His bless-ing to seek.

2. Take time to be ho-ly, The world rush-es on;.. Spend much time in se - cret With Je - sus a - lone; By look - ing to Je - sus, Like Him thou shalt be;.. Thy friends in thy con-duct His likeness shall see..

3. Take time to be ho-ly, Let Him be thy Guide, And run not be-fore Him, What - ev - er be - tide;.. In joy or in sor - row, Still fol - low thy Lord, And, look-ing to Je - sus, Still trust in His Word.

4. Take time to be ho-ly, Be calm in thy soul;. Each tho't and each mo - tive Be - neath His con - trol;.. Thus led by His Spir - it To foun-tains of love, Thou soon shalt be fit - ted For serv-ice a - bove.

343 Jesus Calls Us

CECIL F. ALEXANDER

WILLIAM H. JUDE

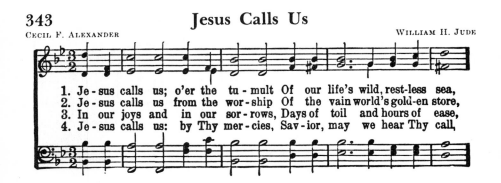

1. Je - sus calls us; o'er the tu - mult Of our life's wild, rest-less sea,

2. Je - sus calls us from the wor - ship Of the vain world's gold-en store,

3. In our joys and in our sor - rows, Days of toil and hours of ease,

4. Je - sus calls us: by Thy mer - cies, Sav - ior, may we hear Thy call,

Jesus Calls Us

Day by day His sweet voice sound-eth, Say-ing, "Chris-tian, fol - low Me."
From each i - dol that would keep us, Say-ing, "Chris-tian, love Me more."
Still He calls, in cares and pleasures, "Chris-tian, love Me more than these."
Give our hearts to Thy o - be-dience, Serve and love Thee best of all.

My Faith Looks Up to Thee   344

RAY PALMER   LOWELL MASON

1. My faith looks up to Thee, Thou Lamb of Cal - va - ry,
2. May Thy rich grace im - part Strength to my faint - ing heart,
3. While life's dark maze I tread, And griefs a - round me spread,
4. When ends life's tran-sient dream, When death's cold, sul - len stream

Sav - ior di - vine! Now hear me while I pray, Take all my
My zeal in - spire; As Thou hast died for me, O may my
Be Thou my Guide; Bid dark - ness turn to day, Wipe sor - row's
Shall o'er me roll; Blest Sav - ior, then, in love, Fear and dis-

guilt a - way, O let me from this day Be whol - ly Thine!
love to Thee Pure, warm, and changeless be, A liv - ing fire!
tears a - way, Nor let me ev - er stray From Thee a - side.
trust re - move; O bear me safe a - bove, A ran - somed soul!

345

Hold the Fort

PHILIP P. BLISS

PHILIP P. BLISS

1. Ho, my com-rades! see the sig-nal Wav-ing in the sky!
2. See the might-y host ad-vanc-ing, Sa-tan lead-ing on;
3. See the glo-rious ban-ner wav-ing! Hear the trump-et blow!
4. Fierce and long the bat-tle rag-es, But our help is near;

Re-in-force-ments now ap-pear-ing, Vic-to-ry is nigh.
Might-y men a-round us fall-ing, Cour-age al-most gone!
In our Lead-er's name we tri-umph O-ver ev-'ry foe.
On-ward comes our great Com-mand-er, Cheer, my com-rades, cheer!

CHORUS

"Hold the fort, for I am com-ing," Je-sus sig-nals still;

Wave the an-swer back to heav-en, "By Thy grace we will."

346

Fight the Good Fight

JOHN S. B. MONSELL

WILLIAM BOYD

1. Fight the good fight with all thy might! Christ is thy strength, and Christ thy right;
2. Run the straight race thro' God's good grace, Lift up thine eyes, and seek His face;
3. Cast care a-side, lean on thy Guide, His bound-less mer-cy will pro-vide;
4. Faint not nor fear, His arms are near, He chang-eth not, and thou art dear;

Fight the Good Fight

Lay hold on life, and it shall be Thy joy and crown e - ter - nal - ly.
Life with its way be - fore us lies, Christ is the path, and Christ the prize.
Trust, and thy trust-ing soul shall prove Christ is its life, and Christ its love.
On - ly be - lieve, and thou shalt see That Christ is all in all to thee. A-MEN.

Jesus Bids Us Shine 347

SUSAN WARNER

EDWIN O. EXCELL

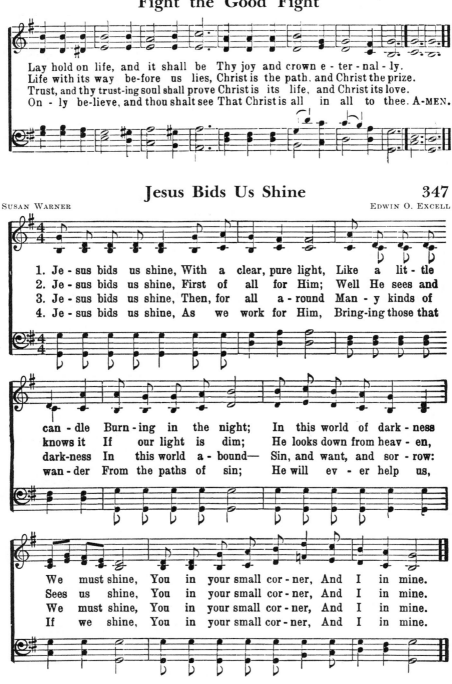

1. Je - sus bids us shine, With a clear, pure light, Like a lit - tle
2. Je - sus bids us shine, First of all for Him; Well He sees and
3. Je - sus bids us shine, Then, for all a - round Man - y kinds of
4. Je - sus bids us shine, As we work for Him, Bring-ing those that

can - dle Burn - ing in the night; In this world of dark - ness
knows it If our light is dim; He looks down from heav - en,
dark - ness In this world a - bound— Sin, and want, and sor - row:
wan - der From the paths of sin; He will ev - er help us,

We must shine, You in your small cor - ner, And I in mine.
Sees us shine, You in your small cor - ner, And I in mine.
We must shine, You in your small cor - ner, And I in mine.
If we shine, You in your small cor - ner, And I in mine.

348 Give of Your Best to the Master

Howard B. Grose

Charlotte A. Bernard

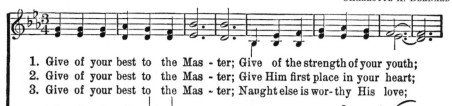

1. Give of your best to the Mas - ter; Give of the strength of your youth;
2. Give of your best to the Mas - ter; Give Him first place in your heart;
3. Give of your best to the Mas - ter; Naught else is wor-thy His love;

REF.—*Give of your best to the Mas - ter; Give of the strength of your youth;*

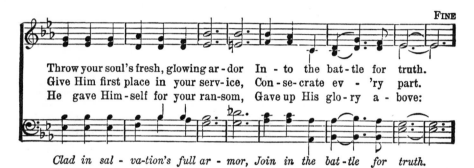

Throw your soul's fresh, glowing ar - dor In - to the bat - tle for truth.
Give Him first place in your serv - ice, Con - se - crate ev - 'ry part.
He gave Him-self for your ran-som, Gave up His glo - ry a - bove:

Clad in sal - va-tion's full ar - mor, Join in the bat - tle for truth.

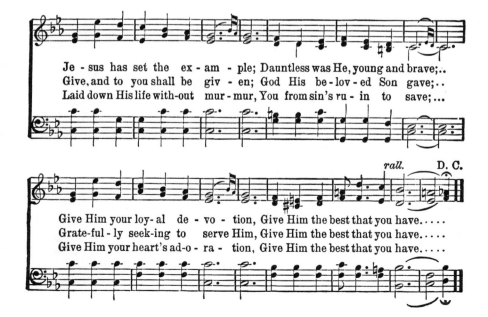

Je - sus has set the ex - am - ple; Dauntless was He, young and brave;..
Give, and to you shall be giv - en; God His be - lov - ed Son gave;..
Laid down His life with-out mur - mur, You from sin's ru - in to save;...

Give Him your loy- al de - vo - tion, Give Him the best that you have.....
Grate-ful-ly seek-ing to serve Him, Give Him the best that you have.....
Give Him your heart's ad-o - ra - tion, Give Him the best that you have.....

I Am Resolved

PALMER HARTSOUGH

JAMES H. FILLMORE

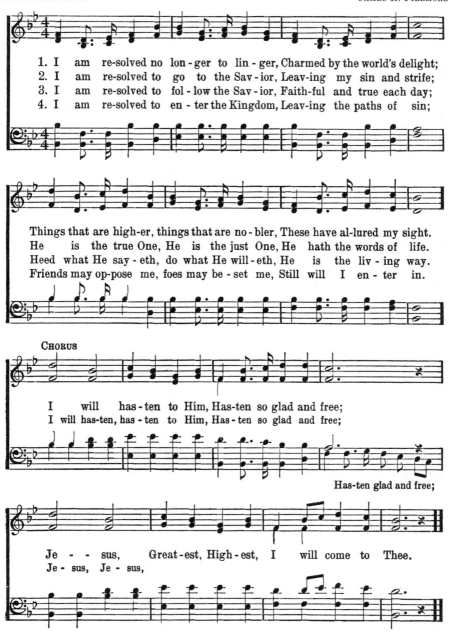

1. I am re-solved no lon-ger to lin-ger, Charmed by the world's delight;
2. I am re-solved to go to the Sav-ior, Leav-ing my sin and strife;
3. I am re-solved to fol-low the Sav-ior, Faith-ful and true each day;
4. I am re-solved to en-ter the Kingdom, Leav-ing the paths of sin;

Things that are high-er, things that are no-bler, These have al-lured my sight.
He is the true One, He is the just One, He hath the words of life.
Heed what He say-eth, do what He will-eth, He is the liv-ing way.
Friends may op-pose me, foes may be-set me, Still will I en-ter in.

CHORUS

I will has-ten to Him, Has-ten so glad and free;
I will has-ten, has-ten to Him, Has-ten so glad and free;

Has-ten glad and free;

Je - - sus, Great-est, High-est, I will come to Thee.
Je - sus, Je - sus,

350   My Soul, Be on Thy Guard

GEORGE HEATH   LOWELL MASON

1. My soul, be on thy guard; Ten thou-sand foes a - rise; The
2. O watch, and fight, and pray; The bat - tle ne'er give o'er; Re-
3. Ne'er think the vic - t'ry won, Nor lay thine ar - mor down; The
4. Fight on, my soul, till death Shall bring thee to thy God; He'll

hosts of sin are press - ing hard To draw thee from the skies.
new it bold - ly ev - 'ry day, And help di - vine im - plore.
work of faith will not be done, Till thou ob - tain the crown.
take thee, at thy part - ing breath, To His di - vine a - bode.

351   Rise Up, O Men of God

WILLIAM P. MERRILL   AARON WILLIAMS

1. Rise up, O men of God! Have done with less - er things;
2. Rise up, O men of God! His king - dom tar - ries long;
3. Rise up, O men of God! The Church for you doth wait,
4. Lift high the cross of Christ! Tread where His feet have trod;

Give heart and mind and soul and strength To serve the King of kings.
Bring in the day of broth - er - hood And end the night of wrong.
Her strength un - e - qual to her task; Rise up, and make her great!
As broth - ers of the Son of man, Rise up, O men of God!

In Times Like These

352

RUTH CAYE JONES

RUTH CAYE JONES

1. In times like these you need a Saviour, In times like
2. In times like these you need the Bi - ble, In times like
3. In times like these I have a Sav - iour, In times like

these you need an an - chor; [D.S.] Be ver - y sure (Be ver - y sure),
these, oh, be not i - dle; [D.S.] Be ver - y sure (Be ver - y sure),
these, I have an an - chor; [D.S.] I'm ver - y sure (I'm ver - y sure),

Be ver - y sure (Be ver - y sure), Your an - chor holds
Be ver - y sure (Be ver - y sure), Your an - chor holds
I'm ver - y sure (I'm ver - y sure), My an - chor holds

and grips the Sol - id Rock!
and grips the Sol - id Rock!
and grips the Sol - id Rock! This Rock is Je - sus,

FINE   REFRAIN

Yes, He's the One, This Rock is Je - sus,—The on - ly One;

D. S.

353 Onward, Christian Soldiers

SABINE BARING-GOULD

ARTHUR S. SULLIVAN

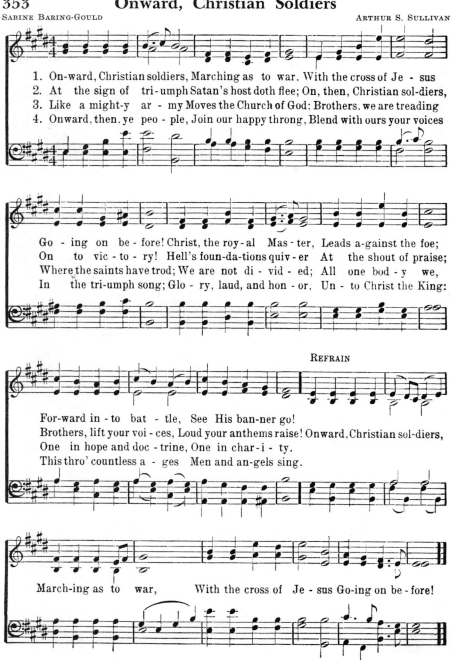

1. On-ward, Christian soldiers, Marching as to war, With the cross of Je - sus
2. At the sign of tri-umph Satan's host doth flee; On, then, Christian sol-diers,
3. Like a might-y ar - my Moves the Church of God; Brothers, we are treading
4. Onward, then, ye peo - ple, Join our happy throng, Blend with ours your voices

Go - ing on be - fore! Christ, the roy-al Mas - ter, Leads a-gainst the foe;
On to vic - to - ry! Hell's foun-da-tions quiv-er At the shout of praise;
Where the saints have trod; We are not di - vid - ed; All one bod-y we,
In the tri-umph song; Glo - ry, laud, and hon - or, Un - to Christ the King:

REFRAIN

For-ward in - to bat - tle, See His ban-ner go!
Brothers, lift your voi - ces, Loud your anthems raise! Onward, Christian sol-diers,
One in hope and doc - trine, One in char - i - ty.
This thro' countless a - ges Men and an-gels sing.

March-ing as to war, With the cross of Je - sus Go-ing on be - fore!

Into My Heart

354

HARRY D. CLARKE

HARRY D. CLARKE

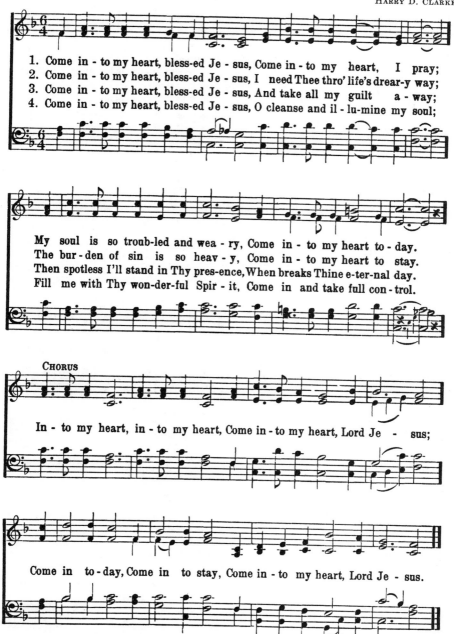

1. Come in - to my heart, bless-ed Je - sus, Come in - to my heart, I pray;
2. Come in - to my heart, bless-ed Je - sus, I need Thee thro' life's drear-y way;
3. Come in - to my heart, bless-ed Je - sus, And take all my guilt a - way;
4. Come in - to my heart, bless-ed Je - sus, O cleanse and il - lu-mine my soul;

My soul is so troub-led and wea - ry, Come in - to my heart to - day.
The bur - den of sin is so heav - y, Come in - to my heart to stay.
Then spotless I'll stand in Thy pres-ence, When breaks Thine e-ter-nal day.
Fill me with Thy won-der-ful Spir - it, Come in and take full con - trol.

CHORUS

In - to my heart, in - to my heart, Come in - to my heart, Lord Je - sus;

Come in to-day, Come in to stay, Come in - to my heart, Lord Je - sus.

355   Loyalty to Christ

E. TAYLOR CASSEL

FLORA H. CASSEL

1. From o-ver hill and plain There comes the signal strain, 'Tis loy-al-ty, loy-al-ty,
2. O hear, ye brave, the sound That moves the earth around, 'Tis loy-al-ty, loy-al-ty,
3. Come, join our loy-al throng, We'll rout the giant wrong, 'Tis loy-al-ty, loy-al-ty,
4. The strength of youth we lay At Je-sus' feet to-day, 'Tis loy-al-ty, loy-al-ty,

loy-al-ty to Christ; Its mu-sic rolls a-long, The hills take up the song,
loy-al-ty to Christ; A-rise to dare and do, Ring out the watch-word true,
loy-al-ty to Christ; Where Satan's banners float We'll send the bu-gle note,
loy-al-ty to Christ; His gos-pel we'll pro-claim Thro'-out the world's domain,

CHORUS.

Of loy-al-ty, loy-al-ty, Yes, loy-al-ty to Christ. "On to vic-to-ry! On to

vic-to-ry!" Cries our great Commander; "On!" . . . We'll move at His command,
great Commander; "On!"

We'll soon possess the land, Thro' loyalty, loyalty, Yes, loy-al-ty to Christ. A-MEN.

Soldiers of Christ, Arise!

Charles Wesley, Arr.

George J. Elvey

1. Sol - diers of Christ, a - rise, And put your ar - mor on,
2. Stand then in His great might, With all His strength en - dued,
3. Leave no un-guard - ed place, No weak - ness of the soul,

Strong in the strength which God sup-plies Through His e - ter - nal Son;
And take, to arm you for the fight, The pan - o - ply of God;
Take ev - 'ry vir - tue, ev - 'ry grace, And fort - i - fy the whole,

Strong in the Lord of hosts, And in His might - y pow'r,
That hav - ing all things done, And all your con - flicts past,
From strength to strength go on, Wres - tle and fight and pray,

Who in the strength of Je - sus trusts Is more than con -quer - or.
Ye may o'er-come through Christ a - lone, And stand en - tire at last.
Tread all the pow'rs of dark - ness down, And win the well-fought day.

357 Stand Up, Stand Up for Jesus

GEORGE DUFFIELD

ADAM GEIBEL

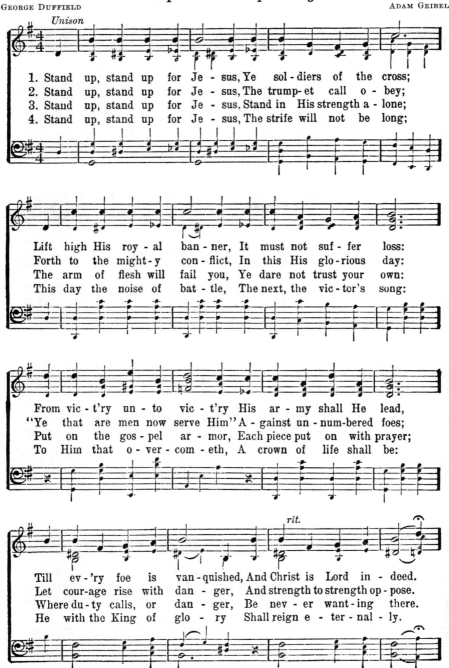

1. Stand up, stand up for Jesus, Ye soldiers of the cross;
2. Stand up, stand up for Jesus, The trumpet call obey;
3. Stand up, stand up for Jesus, Stand in His strength alone;
4. Stand up, stand up for Jesus, The strife will not be long;

Lift high His royal banner, It must not suffer loss:
Forth to the mighty conflict, In this His glorious day:
The arm of flesh will fail you, Ye dare not trust your own:
This day the noise of battle, The next, the victor's song:

From vic-t'ry unto vic-t'ry His army shall He lead,
"Ye that are men now serve Him" Against unnumbered foes;
Put on the gospel armor, Each piece put on with prayer;
To Him that overcometh, A crown of life shall be:

rit.

Till ev-'ry foe is vanquished, And Christ is Lord indeed.
Let courage rise with danger, And strength to strength oppose.
Where duty calls, or danger, Be never wanting there.
He with the King of glory Shall reign eternally.

Stand Up, Stand Up for Jesus

CHORUS

Stand up for Je - sus, Ye sol-diers of the cross;...
Stand up, stand up for Je - sus,

Lift high His roy - al ban - ner, It must not, It must not suf - fer loss.

Stand Up, Stand Up for Jesus

358

GEORGE DUFFIELD

GEORGE J. WEBB

1. Stand up, stand up for Je - sus, Ye sol-diers of the cross, Lift high His
2. Stand up, stand up for Je - sus, The trump-et call o - bey; Forth to the
3. Stand up, stand up for Je - sus, Stand in His strength a - lone; The arm of

roy - al ban - ner, It must not suf - fer loss; From vic-t'ry un - to vic-t'ry, His
might-y con - flict, In this His glo-rious day. "Ye that are men now serve Him," A-
flesh will fail you—Ye dare not trust your own; Put on the gos - pel ar-mor, And,

ar - my shall He lead, Till ev - 'ry foe is van-quished And Christ is Lord in - deed.
gainst un-num-bered foes; Let cour-age rise with dan-ger, And strength to strength oppose.
watching un - to prayer, Where du-ty calls, or dan-ger, Be nev - er want-ing there.

Sound the Battle Cry

WILLIAM F. SHERWIN   WILLIAM F. SHERWIN

1. Sound the bat-tle cry! See, the foe is nigh; Raise the standard high For the Lord; Gird your ar-mor on, Stand firm, ev-'ry one; Rest your cause up-on His ho-ly word.

2. Strong to meet the foe, Marching on we go, While our cause we know, Must pre-vail; Shield and banner bright, Gleam-ing in the light; Bat-tling for the right We ne'er can fail.

3. O! Thou God of all, Hear us when we call, Help us one and all By Thy grace; When the bat-tle's done, And the vic-t'ry's won, May we wear the crown Be-fore Thy face.

CHORUS ff

Rouse, then, sol-diers, ral-ly round the ban-ner, Read-y, stead-y, pass the word a-long; On-ward, for-ward, shout a-loud Ho-san-na! Christ is Cap-tain of the might-y throng.

The Banner of the Cross

Daniel W. Whittle

James McGranahan

1. There's a roy-al ban-ner giv-en for dis-play To the sol-diers
2. Though the foe may rage and gath-er as the flood, Let the stand-ard
3. O - ver land and sea, wher-ev - er man may dwell, Make the glo - rious
4. When the glo - ry dawns—'tis draw-ing ver - y near—It is has-t'ning

of the King; As an en - sign fair we lift it up to-day,
be dis-played; And be-neath its folds, as sol-diers of the Lord,
ti-dings known; Of the crim-son ban - ner now the sto - ry tell,
day by day— Then be - fore our King the foe shall dis - ap-pear,

CHORUS

While as ran-somed ones we sing.
For the truth be not dis-mayed! March-ing on, . . . march-ing
While the Lord shall claim His own! on, on,
And the cross the world shall sway!

on, . . For Christ count ev - 'ry-thing but loss! . . . . And to
on, on, ev - 'ry-thing, ev - 'ry-thing but loss!

crown Him King, toil and sing 'Neath the ban-ner of the cross!
we'll Be-neath

361 Am I a Soldier of the Cross?

ISAAC WATTS

THOMAS A. ARNE

1. Am I a sol-dier of the cross, A fol-low'r of the Lamb?
2. Must I be car-ried to the skies On flow-'ry beds of ease,
3. Are there no foes for me to face? Must I not stem the flood?
4. Sure I must fight, if I would reign; In-crease my cour-age, Lord;

And shall I fear to own His cause, Or blush to speak His name?
While oth-ers fought to win the prize, And sailed thro' blood-y seas?
Is this vile world a friend to grace, To help me on to God?
I'll bear the toil, en-dure the pain, Sup-port-ed by Thy word.

362 A Charge to Keep I Have

CHARLES WESLEY

LOWELL MASON

1. A charge to keep I have, A God to glo-ri-fy;
2. To serve the pres-ent age, My call-ing to ful-fill;
3. Arm me with jeal-ous care, As in Thy sight to live,
4. Help me to watch and pray, And on Thy-self re-ly,

A nev-er-dy-ing soul to save, And fit it for the sky.
O may it all my pow'rs en-gage, To do my Mas-ter's will!
And O, Thy serv-ant, Lord, pre-pare, A strict ac-count to give!
As-sured, if I my trust be-tray, I shall for-ev-er die.

To the Work!

Fanny J. Crosby

William H. Doane

1. To the work! to the work! we are serv-ants of God, Let us fol-low the
2. To the work! to the work! let the hun-gry be fed; To the foun-tain of
3. To the work! to the work! there is la-bor for all; For the king-dom of
4. To the work! to the work! in the strength of the Lord, And a robe and a

path that our Mas-ter has trod; With the balm of His coun-sel our
life let the wea-ry be led; In the cross and its ban-ner our
dark-ness and er-ror shall fall; And the name of Je-ho-vah ex-
crown shall our la-bor re-ward, When the home of the faith-ful our

strength to re-new, Let us do with our might what our hands find to do.
glo-ry shall be, While we her-ald the ti-dings, "Sal-va-tion is free!"
alt-ed shall be, In the loud swell-ing cho-rus, "Sal-va-tion is free!"
dwell-ing shall be, And we shout with the ransomed, "Sal-va-tion is free!"

Chorus

Toil-ing on, toil-ing on, Toil-ing on, toil-ing on;
Toil-ing on, toil-ing on, Toil-ing on, toil-ing on;

Let us hope, let us watch, And la-bor till the Mas-ter comes.
and trust, and pray,

364 True-Hearted, Whole-Hearted

FRANCES R. HAVERGAL

GEORGE C. STEBBINS

1. True-hearted, whole-hearted, faith-ful and loy-al, King of our lives, by Thy
2. True-hearted, whole-hearted, full-est al-le-giance Yielding henceforth to our
3. True-hearted, whole-hearted, Sav-ior all-glo-rious! Take Thy great pow-er and

grace we will be; Un-der the standard ex-alt-ed and roy-al, Strong in Thy
glo-ri-ous King; Val-iant en-deav-or and lov-ing o-be-dience, Free-ly and
reign there a-lone, O-ver our wills and af-fec-tions vic-to-rious, Free-ly sur-

CHORUS

strength we will bat-tle for Thee. Peal out the watch-word! si-lence it nev-er!
joy-ous-ly now would we bring.   Peal out the watch-word! si-lence it nev-er!
ren-dered and whol-ly Thine own.

Song of our spir-its, re-joic-ing and free; Peal out the watch-word!
Song of our spir-its,   re-joic-ing and free;   Peal out the watch-word!

loy-al for-ev-er, King of our lives, by Thy grace we will be.
loy-al for-ev-er,   King of our lives, by Thy grace we will be.

Trust and Obey

JOHN H. SAMMIS

DANIEL B. TOWNER

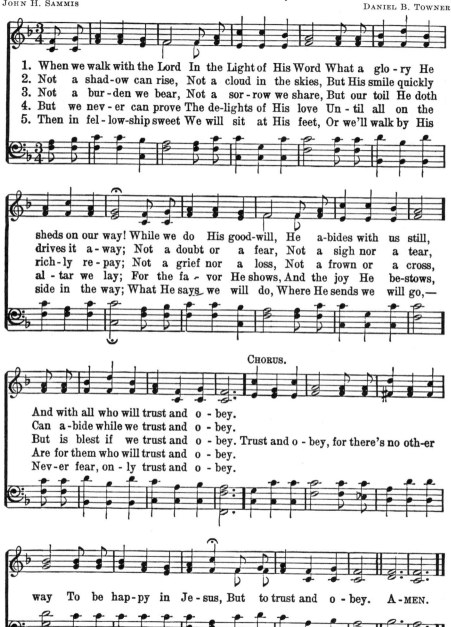

1. When we walk with the Lord In the Light of His Word What a glo-ry He
2. Not a shad-ow can rise, Not a cloud in the skies, But His smile quickly
3. Not a bur-den we bear, Not a sor-row we share, But our toil He doth
4. But we nev-er can prove The de-lights of His love Un-til all on the
5. Then in fel-low-ship sweet We will sit at His feet, Or we'll walk by His

sheds on our way! While we do His good-will, He a-bides with us still,
drives it a-way; Not a doubt or a fear, Not a sigh nor a tear,
rich-ly re-pay; Not a grief nor a loss, Not a frown or a cross,
al-tar we lay; For the fa-vor He shows, And the joy He be-stows,
side in the way; What He says we will do, Where He sends we will go,—

CHORUS.

And with all who will trust and o-bey.
Can a-bide while we trust and o-bey.
But is blest if we trust and o-bey. Trust and o-bey, for there's no oth-er
Are for them who will trust and o-bey.
Nev-er fear, on-ly trust and o-bey.

way To be hap-py in Je-sus, But to trust and o-bey. A-MEN.

Who Is on the Lord's Side?

366

FRANCES R. HAVERGAL

ARR. BY JOHN GOSS

1. Who is on the Lord's side? Who will serve the King? Who will be His help - ers
2. Not for weight of glo - ry, Not for crown and palm, En - ter we the ar - my,
3. Je - sus, Thou hast bought us, Not with gold or gem, But with Thine own life-blood,
4. Fierce may be the con - flict, Strong may be the foe, But the King's own ar - my

Oth - er lives to bring? Who will leave the world's side? Who will face the foe?
Raise the warrior psalm; But for love that claim-eth Lives for whom He died:
For Thy di - a - dem: With Thy blessing fill - ing Each who comes to Thee,
None can o - ver-throw: Round His standard rang-ing, Vic - t'ry to se - cure;

Who is on the Lord's side? Who for Him will go? By Thy call of mer - cy,
He whom Je - sus nam - eth Must be on His side. By Thy love constraining,
Thou hast made us will - ing. Thou hast made us free. By Thy grand redemption,
For His truth un-chang-ing Makes the tri - umph sure. Joy-ful-ly en - list - ing

By Thy grace di - vine, We are on the Lord's side, Sav - ior, we are Thine.

The Church in the Wildwood

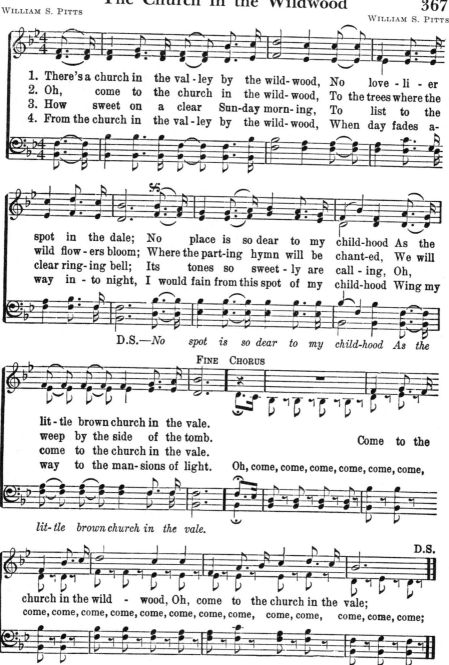

367

William S. Pitts

William S. Pitts

1. There's a church in the val-ley by the wild-wood, No love-li-er
2. Oh, come to the church in the wild-wood, To the trees where the
3. How sweet on a clear Sun-day morn-ing, To list to the
4. From the church in the val-ley by the wild-wood, When day fades a-

spot in the dale; No place is so dear to my child-hood As the
wild flow-ers bloom; Where the part-ing hymn will be chant-ed, We will
clear ring-ing bell; Its tones so sweet-ly are call-ing, Oh,
way in-to night, I would fain from this spot of my child-hood Wing my

D.S.—*No spot is so dear to my child-hood As the*

FINE CHORUS

lit-tle brown church in the vale.
weep by the side of the tomb.
come to the church in the vale.
way to the man-sions of light. Oh, come, come, come, come, come, come,

Come to the

lit-tle brown church in the vale.

D.S.

church in the wild - wood, Oh, come to the church in the vale;
come, come, come, come, come, come, come, come, come, come, come, come, come;

368

If Jesus Had Not Come!

Albert C. Norton

Donald P. Hustad

1. If Je-sus had not come, how dark had been the night! The wisemen, sad-ly dumb,
2. If Je-sus had not come, no free-dom had the slave; No wo-man's happy home;
3. If Je-sus had not come, no Great Phy-si-cian kind Had brought a healing balm,
4. If Je-sus had not come, how blank the Sa-cred page! The po-et had no song,
5. If Je-sus had not come, how sad had been our fate! Of judgment sore the sum

had seen no star-ry light! The shep-herds on the hill had heard no an-gel song! The
no hand a child to save; The peo-ple in the gloom had one e-ter-nal night: Death
a vi-sion for the blind! No soul with de-mon torn had found a sure re-lease! The
and si-lent were the sage! No ar-tist to a-dorn our wor-ship with de-light! No
for all our sin and hate! No lov-ing God of grace His precious Son had giv'n; No

Chorus

bells in si-lence chill, no joy-ous peal had rung!
met them at the tomb, no res-ur-rec-tion light!
hope-less and for-lorn had found no way of peace! But Je-sus came! He came to
cho-ral Psalm had borne His prais-es day or night!
hope to see His face; no joy to meet in heaven!

earth, And men be-held His man-ger birth! The shep-herds heard the an-gels sing, The

wise pro-claimed Him Lord and King! He died, He rose; and by His blood, We too be-come the

If Jesus Had Not Come!

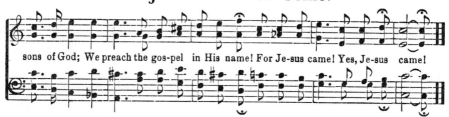

sons of God; We preach the gos-pel in His name! For Je-sus came! Yes, Je-sus came!

Wounded for Me

369

W. G. OVENS AND
GLADYS W. ROBERTS

W. G. OVENS

1. Wound-ed for me, wound-ed for me, There on the cross
2. Dy - ing for me, dy - ing for me. There on the cross
3. Ris - en for me, ris - en for me, Up from the grave
4. Liv - ing for me, liv - ing for me, Up in the skies
5. Com - ing for me, com - ing for me, One day to earth

He was wound - ed for me; Gone my trans - gres - sions, and
He was dy - ing for me; Now in His death my re-
He has ris - en for me; Now ev - er - more from death's
He is liv - ing for me; Dai - ly He's plead-ing and
He is com - ing for me; Then with what joy His dear

now I am free, All be-cause Je - sus was wound-ed for me.
demp-tion I see, All be-cause Je - sus was dy - ing for me.
sting I am free, All be-cause Je - sus has ris - en for me.
pray-ing for me, All be-cause Je - sus is liv - ing for me.
face I shall see, Oh, how I praise Him! He's com-ing for me.

370 I've Found a Friend

JAMES G. SMALL

GEORGE C. STEBBINS

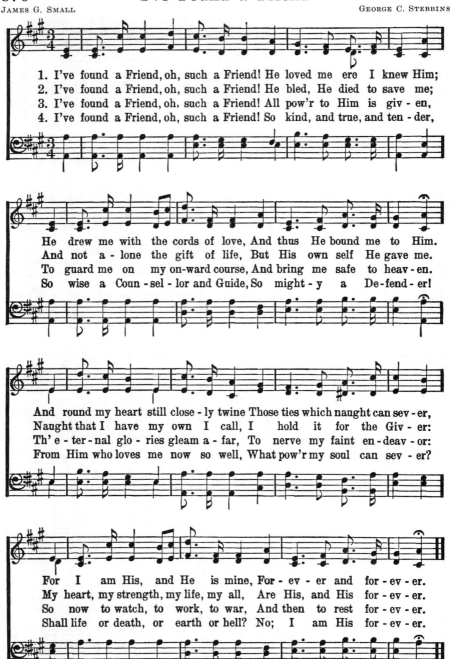

1. I've found a Friend, oh, such a Friend! He loved me ere I knew Him;
2. I've found a Friend, oh, such a Friend! He bled, He died to save me;
3. I've found a Friend, oh, such a Friend! All pow'r to Him is giv - en,
4. I've found a Friend, oh, such a Friend! So kind, and true, and ten - der,

He drew me with the cords of love, And thus He bound me to Him.
And not a - lone the gift of life, But His own self He gave me.
To guard me on my on-ward course, And bring me safe to heav - en.
So wise a Coun - sel - lor and Guide, So might - y a De-fend - er!

And round my heart still close - ly twine Those ties which naught can sev - er,
Naught that I have my own I call, I hold it for the Giv - er:
Th' e - ter - nal glo - ries gleam a - far, To nerve my faint en - deav - or:
From Him who loves me now so well, What pow'r my soul can sev - er?

For I am His, and He is mine, For - ev - er and for - ev - er.
My heart, my strength, my life, my all, Are His, and His for - ev - er.
So now to watch, to work, to war, And then to rest for - ev - er.
Shall life or death, or earth or hell? No; I am His for - ev - er.

In Tenderness He Sought Me

371

W. Spencer Walton

Adoniram J. Gordon

1. In ten-der-ness He sought me, Wea-ry and sick with sin,
2. He washed the bleed-ing sin-wounds, And poured in oil and wine;
3. He point-ed to the nail-prints, For me His blood was shed,
4. I'm sit-ting in His pres-ence, The sun-shine of His face,
5. So while the hours are pass-ing, All now is per-fect rest;

And on His shoul-ders brought me Back to His fold a-gain. While
He whis-pered to as-sure me, "I've found thee, thou art Mine;" I
A mock-ing crown so thorn-y Was placed up-on His head: I
While with a-dor-ing won-der His bless-ings I re-trace. It
I'm wait-ing for the morn-ing, The bright-est and the best. When

an-gels in His pres-ence sang Un-til the courts of heav-en rang.
nev-er heard a sweet-er voice; It made my ach-ing heart re-joice!
won-dered what He saw in me. To suf-fer such deep ag-o-ny.
seems as if e-ter-nal days Are far too short to sound His praise.
He will call us to His side, To be with Him, His spot-less bride.

CHORUS

Oh, the love that sought me! Oh, the blood that bought me! Oh, the grace that

brought me to the fold, Won-drous grace that brought me to the fold!

372   The King of Love My Shepherd Is

FROM PSALM 23
HENRY W. BAKER

JOHN B. DYKES

1. The King of love my Shep-herd is, Whose goodness fail-eth nev-er;
2. Where streams of liv-ing wa-ter flow My ran-somed soul He lead-eth,
3. In death's dark vale I fear no ill With Thee, dear Lord, be-side me;
4. And so through all the length of days, Thy good-ness fail-eth nev-er:

I noth-ing lack if I am His, And He is mine for-ev-er.
And, where the ver-dant pas-tures grow, With food ce-les-tial feed-eth.
Thy rod and staff my com-fort still, Thy cross be-fore to guide me.
Good Shep-herd, may I sing Thy praise With-in Thy house for-ev-er.

373   The Lord's My Shepherd

PSALM 23
"SCOTTISH PSALTER"

JESSIE S. IRVINE
HAR. BY DAVID GRANT

1. The Lord's my Shep-herd, I'll not want; He makes me down to lie
2. My soul He doth re-store a-gain. And me to walk, doth make,
3. Yea, tho' I walk in death's dark vale, Yet will I fear no ill;
4. My ta-ble Thou hast fur-nish-ed In pres-ence of my foes:
5. Good-ness and mer-cy all my life Shall sure-ly fol-low me,

In pas-tures green; He lead-eth me The qui-et wa-ters by.
With-in the paths of right-eous-ness, E'en for His own name's sake.
For Thou art with me, and Thy rod—And staff me com-fort still.
My head Thou dost with oil a-noint, And my cup o-ver flows.
And in God's house for ev-er-more My dwell-ing place shall be.

The Lord Is My Shepherd

PSALM 23
JAMES MONTGOMERY

THOMAS KOSCHAT
ARR. BY EDWIN O. EXCELL

1. The Lord is my Shep-herd, no want shall I know; I feed in green
2. Thro' the val-ley and shad-ow of death tho' I stray, Since Thou art my
3. In the midst of af - flic-tion my ta - ble is spread; With blessings un-
4. Let good-ness and mer-cy, my boun-ti - ful God, Still fol-low my

pas - tures, safe-fold - ed I rest; He lead - eth my soul where the
Guard-ian, no e - vil I fear; Thy rod shall de - fend me, Thy
meas-ured my cup run-neth o'er; With per-fume and oil Thou a-
steps till I meet Thee a - bove: I seek by the path which my

still wa - ters flow, Re - stores me when wan-d'ring, redeems when op-
staff be my stay; No harm can be - fall with my Com - fort - er
noint-est my head; O what shall I ask of Thy prov - i - dence
fore - fa - thers trod, Thro' the land of their so-journ, Thy king-dom of

pressed; Re - stores me when wan-d'ring, re - deems when op - pressed.
near; No harm can be - fall with my Com - fort - er near.
more? O what shall I ask of Thy prov - i - dence more?
love; Thro' the land of their so - journ, Thy king - dom of love.

375 Ivory Palaces

HENRY BARRACLOUGH

HENRY BARRACLOUGH

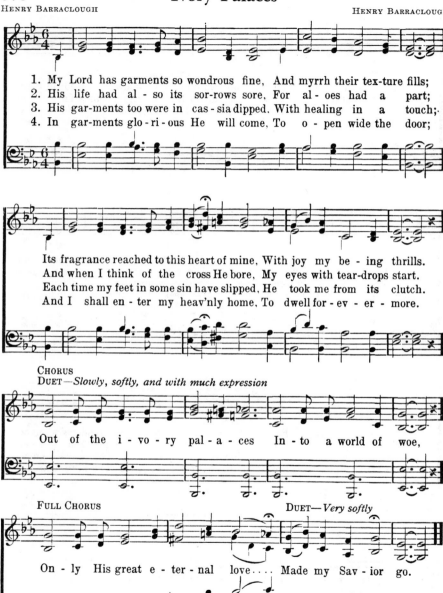

1. My Lord has garments so wondrous fine, And myrrh their tex-ture fills;
2. His life had al - so its sor-rows sore, For al - oes had a part;
3. His gar-ments too were in cas - sia dipped, With healing in a touch;·
4. In gar-ments glo - ri - ous He will come, To o - pen wide the door;

Its fragrance reached to this heart of mine, With joy my be - ing thrills.
And when I think of the cross He bore, My eyes with tear-drops start.
Each time my feet in some sin have slipped, He took me from its clutch.
And I shall en - ter my heav'nly home, To dwell for - ev - er - more.

CHORUS
DUET—*Slowly, softly, and with much expression*

Out of the i - vo - ry pal - a - ces In - to a world of woe,

FULL CHORUS

DUET—*Very softly*

On - ly His great e - ter - nal love.... Made my Sav - ior go.

What a Wonderful Savior!

376

ELISHA A. HOFFMAN

ELISHA A. HOFFMAN

1. Christ has for sin a-tone-ment made, What a won - der - ful Sav - ior!
2. I praise Him for the cleans-ing blood, What a won - der - ful Sav - ior!
3. He cleansed my heart from all its sin. What a won - der - ful Sav - ior!
4. He gives me o - ver - com - ing pow'r, What a won - der - ful Sav - ior!
5. To Him I've giv - en all my heart, What a won - der - ful Sav - ior!

We are re-deemed! the price is paid! What a won - der - ful Sav - ior!
That rec - on - ciled my soul to God; What a won - der - ful Sav - ior!
And now He reigns and rules there - in; What a won - der - ful Sav - ior!
And tri - umph in each try - ing hour; What a won - der - ful Sav - ior!
The world shall nev - er share a part; What a won - der - ful Sav - ior!

CHORUS

What a won - der - ful Sav - ior is Je - sus, my Je - sus!

What a won - der - ful Sav - ior is Je - sus, my Lord!

377 One Day!

J. WILBUR CHAPMAN   CHARLES H. MARSH

1. One day when heav-en was filled with His prais-es, One day when
2. One day they led Him up Cal-va-ry's moun-tain, One day they
3. One day they left Him a-lone in the gar-den, One day He
4. One day the grave could con-ceal Him no lon-ger, One day the
5. One day the trump-et will sound for His com-ing, One day the

sin was as black as could be,... Je-sus came forth to be
nailed Him to die on the tree;.. Suf-fer-ing an-guish, de-
rest-ed, from suf-fer-ing free;.. An-gels came down o'er His
stone rolled a-way from the door;. Then He a-rose, o-ver
skies with His glo-ries will shine; Won-der-ful day, my be-

born of a vir-gin—Dwelt amongst men, my ex-am-ple is He!...
spised and re-ject-ed: Bear-ing our sins, my Re-deem-er is He!...
tomb to keep vig-il; Hope of the hope-less, my Sav-ior is He!...
death He had con-quered; Now is as-cend-ed, my Lord ev-er-more!...
lov-ed ones bring-ing; Glo-ri-ous Sav-ior, this Je-sus is mine!

CHORUS

Liv-ing, He loved me; dy-ing, He saved me; Bur-ied, He

car-ried my sins far a-way;... Ris-ing, He jus-ti-fied

One Day!

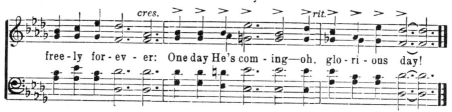

free-ly for-ev - er: One day He's com - ing—oh, glo-ri-ous day!

Take the Name of Jesus with You 378

LYDIA BAXTER

WILLIAM H. DOANE

1. Take the name of Je - sus with you, Child of sor-row and of woe;
2. Take the name of Je - sus ev - er, As a shield from ev-'ry snare;
3. O the precious name of Je - sus! How it thrills our souls with joy,
4. At the name of Je - sus bow-ing, Fall-ing pros-trate at His feet,

It will joy and com-fort give you, Take it, then, wher-e'er you go.
If temp-ta-tions round you gath-er, Breathe that ho - ly name in prayer.
When His lov-ing arms re-ceive us, And His songs our tongues em-ploy!
King of kings in Heav'n we'll crown Him, When our jour-ney is com-plete.

CHORUS

Pre-cious name, O how sweet! Hope of earth and joy of Heav'n;
Precious name, O how sweet!

Pre-cious name, O how sweet!... Hope of earth and joy of Heav'n.
Precious name, O how sweet, how sweet!

379 Jesus Christ Is Lord of All

DON WHITMAN — DON WHITMAN

1. Heav'n and earth pro-claim Je-sus Christ is Lord of all; King of
2. Glo - rious is His name Giv'n by God in heav'n a-bove. Name a-

Kings is He Whom an-gel hosts a - dore! Let men and na-tions bring
bove all names, And ev - er-more shall be. Come ev -'ry knee, and bow,

Prais-es to Christ the King, Who o - ver all shall reign For - ev - er-more.
Come ev'ry tongue, con-fess That Je-sus Christ is Lord E - ter-nal - ly.

CHORUS

WOMEN - UNISON or TWO PARTS — MEN - UNISON

Sing, my heart, oh praise His name; Je-sus Christ is Lord of all! Sing, ye

ALL PARTS

saints, His grace pro-claim; Je-sus Christ is Lord of all! At His

word the grave will o - pen, At His feet death's bonds will fall. King of

Jesus Christ Is Lord of All

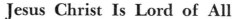

Kings, the might-y God, Je-sus Christ is Lord of all! Je-sus Christ is Lord of all!

Whom Have I but Thee? 380

AVIS B. CHRISTIANSEN

ROLF JORGENSON

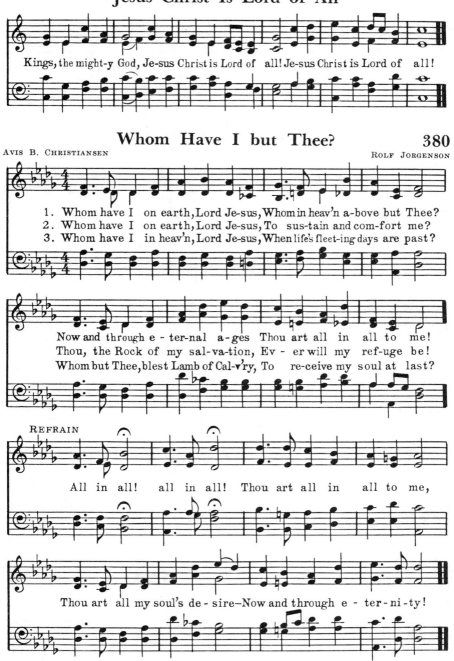

1. Whom have I on earth, Lord Je-sus, Whom in heav'n a-bove but Thee?
2. Whom have I on earth, Lord Je-sus, To sus-tain and com-fort me?
3. Whom have I in heav'n, Lord Je-sus, When life's fleet-ing days are past?

Now and through e-ter-nal a-ges Thou art all in all to me!
Thou, the Rock of my sal-va-tion, Ev-er will my ref-uge be!
Whom but Thee, blest Lamb of Cal-v'ry, To re-ceive my soul at last?

REFRAIN

All in all! all in all! Thou art all in all to me,

Thou art all my soul's de-sire—Now and through e-ter-ni-ty!

381 Jesus, Rose of Sharon

IDA A. GUIREY

CHARLES H. GABRIEL

1. Je-sus, Rose of Shar-on, bloom with-in my heart; Beau-ties of Thy
2. Je-sus, Rose of Shar-on, sweet-er far to me Than the fair-est
3. Je-sus, Rose of Shar-on, balm for ev-'ry ill, May Thy ten-der
4. Je-sus, Rose of Shar-on, bloom for-ev-er-more; Be Thy glo-ry

truth and ho-li-ness im-part, That where-e'er I go my life may
flow'rs of earth could ev-er be, Fill my life com-plete-ly, add-ing
mer-cy's heal-ing pow'r dis-til For af-flict-ed souls of wea-ry,
seen on earth from shore to shore, Till the na-tions own Thy Sov'-reign-

shed a-broad Fra-grance of the knowl-edge of the love of God.
more each day Of Thy grace di-vine and pur-i-ty, I pray.
bur-dened men, Giv-ing need-y mor-tals health and hope a-gain.
ty com-plete, Lay their hon-ors down and wor-ship at Thy feet.

REFRAIN

Je - sus, Rose of Shar-on,
Bless-ed Je - sus, Rose of Shar - on,

Bloom in ra - diance and in love with-in my heart.

We Gather Together

Author Unknown
Tr. by Theodore Baker

Netherlands Folk Song
Arr. by Edward Kremser

382

1. We gath - er to - geth - er to ask the Lord's bless - ing,
2. Be - side us to guide us, our God with us join - ing
3. We all do ex - tol Thee, Thou Lead - er in bat - tle,

He chas - tens and has - tens His will to make known;
Or - dain - ing, main - tain - ing His king - dom di - vine;
And pray that Thou still our De - fend - er wilt be.

The wick - ed op - press - ing cease them from dis - tress - ing,
So from the be - gin - ning the fight we were win - ning,
Let Thy con - gre - ga - tion es - cape trib - u - la - tion;

Sing prais - es to His name, He for - gets not His own.
Thou, Lord, wast at our side, — the glo - ry be Thine!
Thy name be ev - er praised. O Lord, make us free! A - men.

The first two stanzas should be sung in unison (alternately by the male and female voices if desired), and the last stanza in full harmony.

383 Leave It There

C. ALBERT TINDLEY

C. ALBERT TINDLEY

Moderato

1. If the world from you with-hold of its sil - ver and its gold, And you
2. If your bod - y suf - fers pain and your health you can't re-gain, And your
3. When your en - e - mies as - sail and your heart be - gins to fail, Don't for-
4. When your youthful days are gone and old age is steal-ing on, And your

have to get a-long with mea-ger fare. Just re-mem-ber, in His word, how He
soul is al-most sink-ing in de - spair. Je - sus knows the pain you feel, He can
get that God in heav-en answers prayer; He will make a way for you and will
bod - y bends beneath the weight of care; He will nev - er leave you then, He'll go

feeds the lit - tle bird; Take your bur - den to the Lord and leave it there.
save and He can heal; Take your bur - den to the Lord and leave it there.
lead you safe - ly thro'; Take your bur - den to the Lord and leave it there.
with you to the end; Take your bur - den to the Lord and leave it there.

CHORUS

Leave it there, . . . leave it there, ... Take your bur-den to the
Leave it there, leave it there,

Lord and leave it there; . . . . If you trust and nev - er doubt, He will
leave it there;

Leave It There

sure - ly bring you out; Take your burden to the Lord and leave it there. . . . .

leave it there.

Does Jesus Care?

384

FRANK E. GRAEFF

J. LINCOLN HALL

1. Does Je - sus care when my heart is pained Too deep-ly for mirth and song;
2. Does Je - sus care when my way is dark With a name-less dread and fear?
3. Does Je - sus care when I've tried and failed To re-sist some temp-ta - tion strong;
4. Does Je - sus care when I've said "good-by" To the dear-est on earth to me,

As the burdens press, and the cares distress, And the way grows wea-ry and long?
As the daylight fades into deep night shades, Does He care e-nough to be near?
When for my deep grief I find no re - lief, Tho' my tears flow all the night long?
And my sad heart aches till it nearly breaks–Is it aught to Him? Does He see?

CHORUS

O yes, He cares; I know He cares, His heart is touched with my grief;

ad lib.

rit.

When the days are wea-ry, the long nights dreary, I know my Sav-ior cares.

He cares.

385 His Way with Thee

Cyrus S. Nusbaum

Cyrus S. Nusbaum

1. Would you live for Je - sus, and be al-ways pure and good? Would you walk with
2. Would you have Him make you free, and fol-low at His call? Would you know the
3. Would you in His king-dom find a place of con-stant rest? Would you prove Him

Him with - in the nar-row road? Would you have Him bear your burden, car - ry
peace that comes by giv-ing all? Would you have Him save you, so that you need
true in prov - i - den-tial test? Would you in His serv - ice la - bor al-ways

Chorus.

all your load? Let Him have His way with thee.
nev - er fall? Let Him have His way with thee. His pow'r can make you what you
at your best? Let Him have His way with thee.

ought to be; His blood can cleanse your heart and make you free; His love can fill your

soul, and you will see 'Twas best for Him to have His way with thee. A - MEN.

rit.

Nothing Between

C. Albert Tindley   C. Albert Tindley

1. Noth - ing be - tween my soul and the Sav - ior, Naught of this world's de-
2. Noth - ing be - tween, like world - ly pleas - ure, Hab - its of life though
3. Noth - ing be - tween, like pride or sta - tion, Self or friends shall
4. Noth - ing be - tween, e'en man - y hard tri - als, Tho' the whole world a-

lu - sive dream; I have re-noun\ced all sin - ful pleas-ure,
harm-less they seem, Must not my heart from Him e'er sev - er,
not in - ter - vene, Tho' it may cost me much trib - u - la - tion,
gainst me con - vene; Watching with prayer and much self-de - ni - al, I'll

Chorus

Je - sus is mine; there's noth-ing be - tween.
He is my all; there's noth-ing be - tween.   Noth - ing be - tween my
I am re-solved; there's noth-ing be - tween.
tri - umph at last, with noth-ing be - tween.

soul and the Sav-ior, So that His bless - ed face may be seen; Noth-ing pre-

vent-ing the least of His fa - vor, Keep the way clear! Let nothing between.

387 Have Thine Own Way, Lord!

ADELAIDE A. POLLARD

GEORGE C. STEBBINS

Slowly

1. Have Thine own way, Lord! Have Thine own way! Thou art the
2. Have Thine own way, Lord! Have Thine own way! Search me and
3. Have Thine own way, Lord! Have Thine own way! Wound-ed and
4. Have Thine own way, Lord! Have Thine own way! Hold o'er my

Pot - ter; I am the clay Mould me and make me Aft - er Thy
try me, Mas-ter, to - day! Whit - er than snow, Lord, Wash me just
wea - ry, Help me, I pray! Pow - er—all pow - er—Sure - ly is
be - ing Ab - so - lute sway! Fill with Thy Spir - it Till all shall

will, While I am wait - ing, Yield - ed and still.
now, As in Thy pres - ence Hum - bly I bow.
Thine! Touch me and heal me, Sav - ior di - vine!
see Christ on - ly, al - ways, Liv - ing in me!

388 Take My Life, and Let It Be

FRANCES R. HAVERGAL

H. A. CÉSAR MALAN

1. Take my life, and let it be Con-se-crat-ed, Lord, to Thee; Take my hands, and
2. Take my feet, and let them be Swift and beau-ti-ful for Thee; Take my voice, and
3. Take my lips, and let them be Filled with messages for Thee; Take my sil - ver
4. Take my love, my God, I pour At Thy feet its treas-ure store; Take my-self and

Take My Life, and Let It Be

let them move At the im-pulse of Thy love, At the im-pulse of Thy love.
let me sing Al-ways, on - ly, for my King, Al-ways, on - ly, for my King.
and my gold, Not a mite would I with-hold, Not a mite would I with-hold.
I will be Ev - er, on - ly, all for Thee, Ev - er, on - ly, all for Thee.

Hiding in Thee

389

WILLIAM O. CUSHING

IRA D. SANKEY

1. O safe to the Rock that is high-er than I, My soul in its
2. In the calm of the noon-tide, in sor-row's lone hour, In times when temp-
3. How oft in the con-flict, when pressed by the foe, I have fled to my

con - flicts and sor - rows would fly; So sin - ful, so wea - ry, Thine,
ta - tion casts o'er me its pow'r; In the tem - pests of life, on its
Ref - uge and breathed out my woe; How oft - en, when tri - als like

Thine would I be; Thou blest "Rock of A - ges," I'm hid - ing in Thee.
wide, heaving sea, Thou blest "Rock of A - ges," I'm hid - ing in Thee.
sea - bil - lows roll, Have I hid - den in Thee, O Thou Rock of my soul.

CHORUS

Hid-ing in Thee, Hiding in Thee, Thou blest "Rock of Ages," I'm hid-ing in Thee.

390

Is Your All on the Altar?

ELISHA A. HOFFMAN

ELISHA A. HOFFMAN

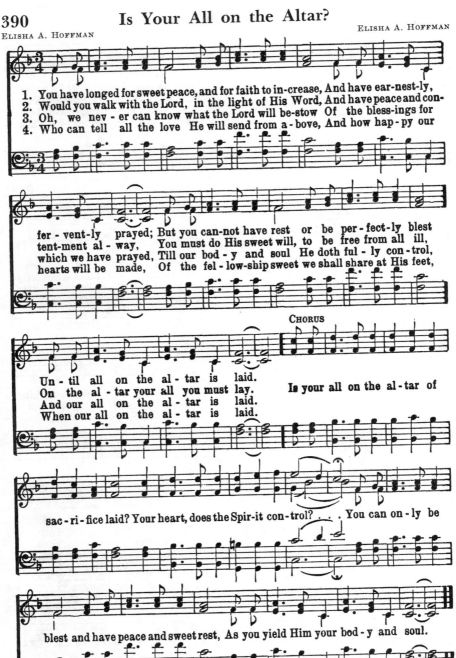

1. You have longed for sweet peace, and for faith to in-crease, And have ear-nest-ly,
2. Would you walk with the Lord, in the light of His Word, And have peace and con-
3. Oh, we nev - er can know what the Lord will be-stow Of the bless-ings for
4. Who can tell all the love He will send from a - bove, And how hap - py our

fer - vent-ly prayed; But you can-not have rest or be per - fect-ly blest
tent-ment al - way, You must do His sweet will, to be free from all ill,
which we have prayed, Till our bod - y and soul He doth ful - ly con - trol,
hearts will be made, Of the fel - low-ship sweet we shall share at His feet,

CHORUS

Un - til all on the al - tar is laid.
On the al - tar your all you must lay.
And our all on the al - tar is laid.
When our all on the al - tar is laid.

Is your all on the al - tar of

sac - ri - fice laid? Your heart, does the Spir-it con-trol? . . . You can on - ly be

blest and have peace and sweet rest, As you yield Him your bod - y and soul.

I Surrender All

Judson W. Van DeVenter

Winfield S. Weeden

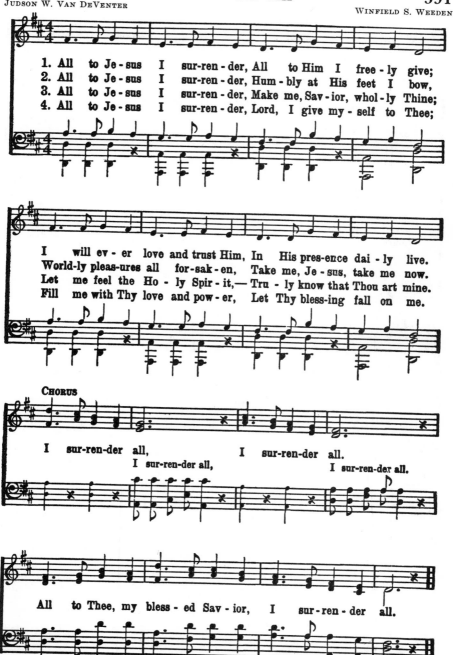

1. All to Je-sus I sur-ren-der, All to Him I free-ly give;
2. All to Je-sus I sur-ren-der, Hum-bly at His feet I bow,
3. All to Je-sus I sur-ren-der, Make me, Sav-ior, whol-ly Thine;
4. All to Je-sus I sur-ren-der, Lord, I give my-self to Thee;

I will ev-er love and trust Him, In His pres-ence dai-ly live.
World-ly pleas-ures all for-sak-en, Take me, Je-sus, take me now.
Let me feel the Ho-ly Spir-it,— Tru-ly know that Thou art mine.
Fill me with Thy love and pow-er, Let Thy bless-ing fall on me.

Chorus

I sur-ren-der all, I sur-ren-der all.
I sur-ren-der all, I sur-ren-der all.

All to Thee, my bless-ed Sav-ior, I sur-ren-der all.

392 Savior, My Heart Is Thine

AUTHOR UNKNOWN
ALT. BY GEORGE C. STEBBINS

GEORGE C. STEBBINS

1. Sav - ior, my heart is Thine. Keep it for me; May ev - 'ry
2. Sav - ior, my will is Thine. Keep it for me; May ev - 'ry
3. Sav - ior, my life is Thine. Keep it for me; May ev - 'ry
4. Sav - ior, my all is Thine. Keep it for me; May all I

thought of mine Glo - ri - fy Thee. Glo - ri - fy Thee,
act of mine Be done for Thee. Be done for Thee,
hour of mine Be lived for Thee. Be lived for Thee,
have, O Lord, Be used for Thee. Be used for Thee,

Glo - ri - fy Thee; May ev - 'ry thought of mine Glo - ri - fy Thee.
Be done for Thee; May ev - 'ry act of mine Be done for Thee.
Be lived for Thee; May ev - 'ry hour of mine Be lived for Thee.
Be used for Thee; May all I have, O Lord, Be used for Thee.

393 Where He Leads Me

E. W. BLANDY

JOHN S. NORRIS

1. I can hear my Sav - ior call-ing, I can hear my Sav - ior call-ing,
2. I'll go with Him thro' the gar - den, I'll go with Him thro' the gar - den,
3. I'll go with Him thro' the judg-ment, I'll go with Him thro' the judg-ment,
4. He will give me grace and glo - ry, He will give me grace and glo - ry,

REF. *Where He leads me I will fol - low, Where He leads me I will fol - low,*

Where He Leads Me

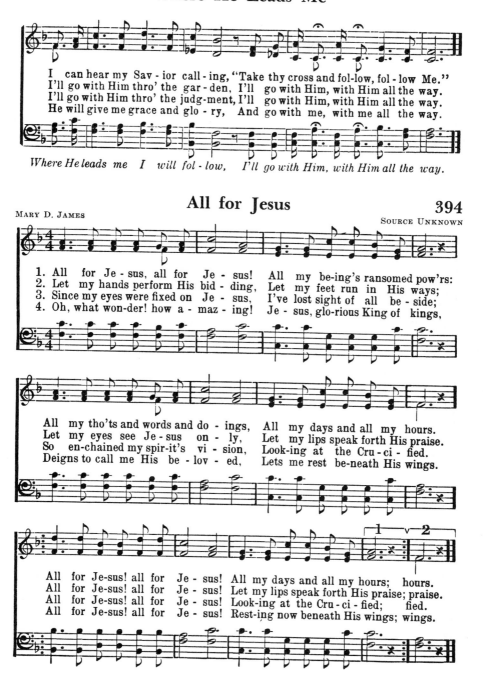

I can hear my Sav - ior call - ing, "Take thy cross and fol - low, fol - low Me."
I'll go with Him thro' the gar - den, I'll go with Him, with Him all the way.
I'll go with Him thro' the judg - ment, I'll go with Him, with Him all the way.
He will give me grace and glo - ry, And go with me, with me all the way.

Where He leads me   I   will fol - low,   I'll go with Him, with Him all the way.

All for Jesus

394

MARY D. JAMES

SOURCE UNKNOWN

1. All for Je - sus, all for Je - sus! All my be - ing's ransomed pow'rs:
2. Let my hands perform His bid - ding, Let my feet run in His ways;
3. Since my eyes were fixed on Je - sus, I've lost sight of all be - side;
4. Oh, what won - der! how a - maz - ing! Je - sus, glo-rious King of kings,

All my tho'ts and words and do - ings, All my days and all my hours.
Let my eyes see Je - sus on - ly, Let my lips speak forth His praise.
So en-chained my spir-it's vi - sion, Look-ing at the Cru - ci - fied.
Deigns to call me His be - lov - ed, Lets me rest be-neath His wings.

1

All for Je - sus! all for Je - sus! All my days and all my hours;
All for Je - sus! all for Je - sus! Let my lips speak forth His praise;
All for Je - sus! all for Je - sus! Look-ing at the Cru - ci - fied;
All for Je - sus! all for Je - sus! Rest-ing now beneath His wings;

2

hours.
praise.
fied.
wings.

395 I Will Follow Thee

JOHNSON OATMAN, JR.

EDWIN O. EXCELL

1. Sav-iour, I will fol-low Thee; Thou art all the world to me;
2. Sav-iour, I will fol-low Thee, Tho' it lead me to the cross;
3. Sav-iour, I will fol-low Thee, Tho' it lead through toil and tears;
4. Sav-iour, I will fol-low Thee Till the toils of life are o'er;

Tho' the way I can-not see, Sav-iour, I will fol-low Thee.
Count-ing all things here but dross, Sav-iour, I will fol-low Thee.
Through the long and wea-ry years, Sav-iour, I will fol-low Thee.
Till I reach the Gold-en Shore, Sav-iour, I will fol-low Thee.

CHORUS

Fol-low Thee, I will fol-low Thee, Fol-low Thee,
Fol-low, I will fol-low Thee, fol-low Thee, Fol-low, I will fol-low

I will fol-low Thee, Fol-low till the day is done,
Thee, fol-low Thee,

Fol-low till the crown is won, Sav-iour, I will fol-low Thee.

I'll Put Jesus First in My Life

JAMES D. MURCH

JAMES D. MURCH

1. The world all a - bout me has now no al - lure: Its pleas-ures bring pain,
2. The Lord Je-sus died my sal - va-tion to win: He went in my stead
3. I know there's a home for the ran-somed and blest, When death is no more,
4. Tho' earth's trib-u - la-tions con-tin-ue each day, Tho' pleas-ures may call,

Its wis-dom is vain; I seek a foun-da-tion that's stead-fast and sure:
To Cal-v'ry and bled; Re-demp-tion im-pels me to give up all sin:
When strug-gle is o'er, For those who love Je-sus and give Him their best:
Tho' e - vil en-thrall, His grace will pro-tect me for - ev-er and aye:

CHORUS

I'll put Je-sus first in my life. In all that I say, In

all that I do, Thro'-out the world of toil and strife, By day and by

night, Thro' trust in His might, I'll put Je-sus first in my life.

397 If Jesus Goes with Me

C. Austin Miles

C. Austin Miles

1. It may be in the val-ley, where countless dangers hide; It may be in the sun-shine that I, in peace, a-bide; But this one thing I know—if it be dark or fair, If Je-sus is with me, I'll go an-y-where!

2. It may be I must car-ry the bless-ed word of life A-cross the burning des-erts to those in sin-ful strife; And tho' it be my lot to bear my col-ors there, If Je-sus goes with me, I'll go an-y-where!

3. But if it be my por-tion to bear my cross at home, While others bear their bur-dens be-yond the bil-low's foam, I'll prove my faith in Him—con-fess His judgments fair, And, if He stays with me, I'll stay an-y-where!

4. It is not mine to ques-tion the judg-ments of my Lord, It is but mine to fol-low the lead-ings of His Word; But if to go or stay, or wheth-er here or there, I'll be, with my Sav-ior, Con-tent an-y-where!

Chorus

If Je-sus goes with me, I'll go.... An-y-where! 'Tis heaven to me, Wher-e'er I may be, If He is there! I count it a priv-i-lege here.. His

399 I'll Go Where You Want Me to Go

CHARLES H. GABRIEL

CARRIE E. ROUNSEFELL

1. It may not be on the mountain's height, Or o - ver the storm - y sea;
2. Per-haps to-day there are lov - ing words Which Jesus would have me speak;
3. There's surely somewhere a low - ly place In earth's harvest-fields so wide,

It may not be at the bat - tle's front My Lord will have need of me;
There may be now, in the paths of sin, Some wand'rer whom I should seek.
Where I may la - bor thro' life's short day For Je - sus, the Cru - ci - fied.

But if by a still, small voice He calls To paths I do not know,
O Sav - ior, if Thou wilt be my Guide, Tho' dark and rug-ged the way,
So, trust-ing my all un - to Thy care, I know Thou lov - est me!

I'll answer, dear Lord, with my hand in Thine, I'll go where you want me to go.
My voice shall ech - o the mes-sage sweet, I'll say what you want me to say.
I'll do Thy will with a heart sin-cere, I'll be what you want me to be.

REFRAIN

I'll go where you want me to go, dear Lord, O'er mountain, or plain, or sea;

I'll Go Where You Want Me to Go

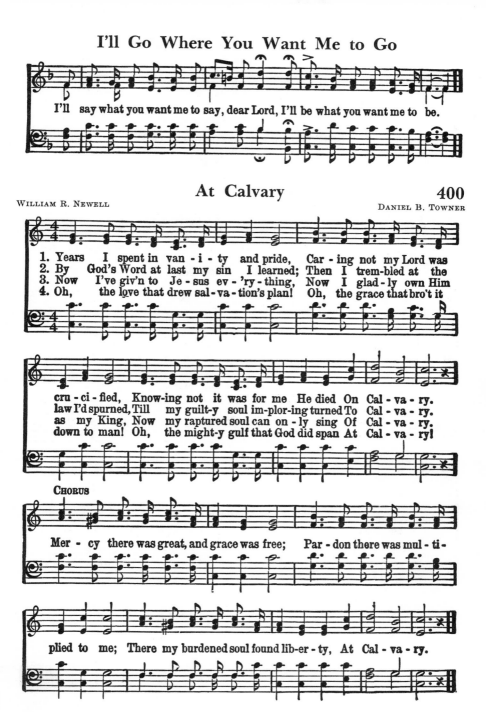

I'll say what you want me to say, dear Lord, I'll be what you want me to be.

At Calvary

400

WILLIAM R. NEWELL

DANIEL B. TOWNER

1. Years I spent in van-i-ty and pride, Car-ing not my Lord was
2. By God's Word at last my sin I learned; Then I trem-bled at the
3. Now I've giv'n to Je-sus ev-'ry-thing, Now I glad-ly own Him
4. Oh, the love that drew sal-va-tion's plan! Oh, the grace that bro't it

cru-ci-fied, Know-ing not it was for me He died On Cal-va-ry.
law I'd spurned, Till my guilt-y soul im-plor-ing turned To Cal-va-ry.
as my King, Now my raptured soul can on-ly sing Of Cal-va-ry.
down to man! Oh, the might-y gulf that God did span At Cal-va-ry!

CHORUS

Mer-cy there was great, and grace was free; Par-don there was mul-ti-

plied to me; There my burdened soul found lib-er-ty, At Cal-va-ry.

401 Where He Leads I'll Follow

WILLIAM A. OGDEN   WILLIAM A. OGDEN

1. Sweet are the prom-is-es, Kind is the word, Dear-er far than
2. Sweet is the ten-der love Je-sus hath shown, Sweet-er far than
3. List to His lov-ing words, "Come un-to Me;" Wea-ry, heav-y-

an-y mes-sage man ev-er heard; Pure was the mind of Christ,
an-y love that mor-tals have known; Kind to the err-ing one,
la-den, there is sweet rest for thee; Trust in His prom-is-es,

Sin-less I see; He the great ex-am-ple is, and pat-tern for me.
Faith-ful is He; He the great ex-am-ple is, and pat-tern for me.
Faith-ful and sure; Lean up-on the Sav-ior, and thy soul is se-cure.

CHORUS

Where . . . . He leads I'll fol - - - low,
Where He leads I'll fol-low, Where He leads I'll fol-low,

Fol - - - low all the way.   Fol-low Je-sus ev-'ry day.
Fol-low all the way, yes, fol-low all the way.

The Way of the Cross Leads Home

402

JESSIE B. POUNDS

CHARLES H. GABRIEL

1. I must needs go home by the way of the cross, There's no oth-er
2. I must needs go on in the blood-sprinkled way, The path that the
3. Then I bid fare-well to the way of the world, To walk in it

way but this; I shall ne'er get sight of the Gates of Light,
Sav-ior trod, If I ev-er climb to the heights sub-lime,
nev-er-more; For my Lord says "Come," and I seek my home,

If the way of the cross I miss.
Where the soul is at home with God.
Where He waits at the o-pen door.

CHORUS.

The way of the cross leads home, The way of the cross leads home; It is
(leads home, leads home;)

sweet to know as I on-ward go, The way of the cross leads home.

403 He Wore a Crown of Thorns

WILLIAM M. RUNYAN

GEORGE S. SCHULER

1. 'Twas God's own Son who came to earth, Who chose to know a low-ly birth;
2. Won-der-ful, Coun-sel-lor was He, Matchless His grace; how could it be
3. Kind were the deeds that crowned each day, Gracious the words His lips would say.
4. Nev-er a-gain His brow shall know Pierc-ings of ag-o-ny and woe;

But, tho' a King of matchless worth, He wore a crown of thorns.
That, at the last, He wore for me That bitter crown of thorns?
While He pur-sued the fate-ful way To wear that crown of thorns.
But 'twas for us that, here be-low, He wore the crown of thorns.

CHORUS.

He wore a crown of thorns that I Might wear a crown of glo-ry!

He laid His heav'n-ly splendors by To bring me love's sweet sto-ry. In

pov-er-ty He walked life's way, In Ol-ive's gar-den bowed to pray;

He Wore a Crown of Thorns

He wore a crown of thorns that I Might wear a crown of glo-ry!

No One Understands Like Jesus 404

JOHN W. PETERSON

JOHN W. PETERSON

1. No one un-der-stands like Je-sus, He's a friend be-yond com-pare;
2. No one un-der-stands like Je-sus, Eve-ry woe He sees and feels;
3. No one un-der-stands like Je-sus, When the foes of life as-sail;
4. No one un-der-stands like Je-sus, When you falt-er on the way;

Meet Him at the throne of mer-cy. He is wait-ing for you there.
Ten-der-ly He whis-pers com-fort. And the bro-ken heart He heals.
You should nev-er be dis-cour-aged, Je-sus cares and will not fail.
Tho' you fail Him, sad-ly fail Him, He will par-don you to-day.

CHORUS

No one un-der-stands like Je-sus. When the days are dark and grim;

No one is so near, so dear as Je-sus, Cast your eve-ry care on Him.

405 Kneel at the Cross

Charles E. Moody

Charles E. Moody
Arr. by William J. Floyd

1. Kneel at the cross, Christ will meet you there, Come while He waits for you;
2. Kneel at the cross, There is room for all Who would His glo-ry share;
3. Kneel at the cross, Give your i-dols up, Look un-to realms a-bove;

List to His voice, Leave with Him your care, And start your life a-new.
Bliss there a-waits, Harm can ne'er be-fall Those who are an-chored there.
Turn not a way To life's spark-ling cup, Trust on-ly in His love.

REFRAIN

Kneel at the cross,
(at the cross,)
Leave ev-ery care,

Kneel at the cross,
(oh kneel)
(at the cross,)

Je-sus will meet you there.
(meet you there.)

Come, Holy Spirit

Lily Hedman Wells

Kenneth H. Wells

406

1. Come, Ho-ly Spi-rit, heav'n-ly Dove, De-scend up-on my
2. Come, Ho-ly Spi-rit, cleans-ing fire, Thou pur-i-fy-ing
3. Come, Ho-ly Spi-rit, migh-ty pow'r I claim the prom-ised

heart; Fill all my soul with per-fect love,
Flame; Burn out the dross of base de-sire,
Word, That grace be mine each pass-ing hour,

Thy won-drous peace im-part.
And cleanse in Je-sus' name.
To wit-ness for my Lord.

CHORUS

Come, Ho-ly Spir-it, fill me now, My spir-it yearns for Thee; With faith be-fore Thy throne I bow, And claim Thy Gift for me.

407

Near the Cross

FANNY J. CROSBY

WILLIAM H. DOANE

1. Je - sus, keep me near the cross, There a pre-cious foun - tain
2. Near the cross, a trem-bling soul, Love and mer - cy found me;
3. Near the cross! O Lamb of God, Bring its scenes be - fore me;
4. Near the cross I'll watch and wait, Hop - ing, trust-ing ev - er,

Free to all— a heal - ing stream, Flows from Cal - v'ry's moun - tain.
There the Bright and Morn - ing Star Sheds its beams a - round me.
Help me walk from day to day, With its shad - ows o'er me.
Till I reach the gold - en strand, Just be - yond the riv - er.

CHORUS

In the cross, in the cross, Be my glo - ry ev - er;

Till my rap - tured soul shall find Rest be - yond the riv - er.

408

In the Cross of Christ

JOHN BOWRING

ITHAMAR CONKEY

1. In the cross of Christ I glo - ry, Tow'r-ing o'er the wrecks of time;
2. When the woes of life o'er-take me. Hopes de-ceive. and fears an - noy,
3. When the sun of bliss is beam-ing Light and love up - on my way,
4. Bane and bless-ing, pain and pleas-ure, By the cross are sanc - ti - fied;

In the Cross of Christ

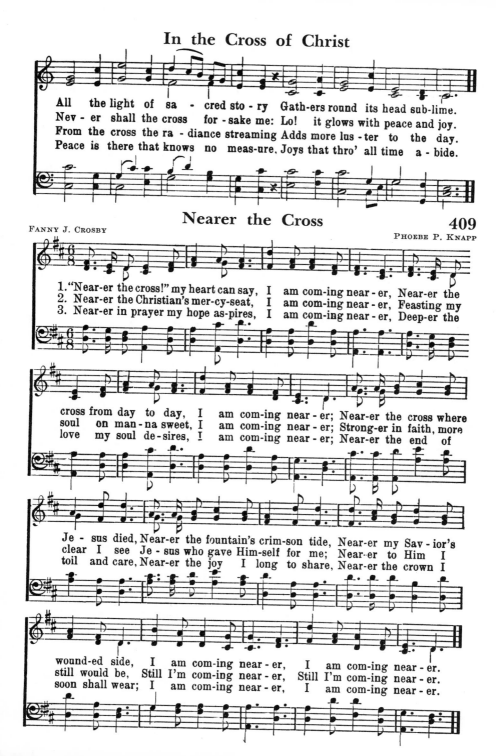

All the light of sa - cred sto - ry Gath-ers round its head sub-lime.
Nev - er shall the cross for - sake me: Lo! it glows with peace and joy.
From the cross the ra - diance streaming Adds more lus - ter to the day.
Peace is there that knows no meas-ure, Joys that thro' all time a - bide.

Nearer the Cross

409

FANNY J. CROSBY

PHOEBE P. KNAPP

1. "Near-er the cross!" my heart can say, I am com-ing near - er, Near-er the
2. Near-er the Christian's mer-cy-seat, I am com-ing near - er, Feasting my
3. Near-er in prayer my hope as-pires, I am com-ing near - er, Deep-er the

cross from day to day, I am com-ing near - er; Near-er the cross where
soul on man-na sweet, I am com-ing near - er; Strong-er in faith, more
love my soul de-sires, I am com-ing near - er; Near-er the end of

Je - sus died, Near-er the fountain's crim-son tide, Near-er my Sav - ior's
clear I see Je - sus who gave Him-self for me; Near-er to Him I
toil and care, Near-er the joy I long to share, Near-er the crown I

wound-ed side, I am com-ing near - er, I am com-ing near - er.
still would be, Still I'm com-ing near - er, Still I'm com-ing near - er.
soon shall wear; I am com-ing near - er, I am com-ing near - er.

410 Ten Thousand Angels

RAY OVERHOLT   RAY OVERHOLT

Slowly, with much feeling

1. They bound the hands of Je-sus in the gar-den where He prayed; They
2. Up - on His pre-cious head they placed a crown of thorns; They
3. When they nailed Him to the cross, His moth-er stood near by; He
4. To the howl-ing mob He yield-ed; He did not for mer-cy cry. The

led Him thro' the streets in shame. They spat up-on the Sav-iour so
laughed and said, "Be-hold the King". They struck Him and they cursed Him and
said, "Wom-an, be-hold thy son!" He cried, "I thirst for wa-ter," but they
cross of shame He took a-lone. And when He cried, "It's fin-ished," He

pure and free from sin; They said, "Cru-ci-fy Him; He's to blame."
mocked His ho-ly name. All a-lone He suf-fered ev-'ry-thing.
gave Him none to drink. Then the sin-ful work of man was done.
gave Him-self to die; Sal - va-tion's won-drous plan was done.

CHORUS   *Faster*

He could have called ten thou-sand an-gels To de-stroy the

world and set Him free. He could have called

the world

Ten Thousand Angels

rall.

ten thou-sand an - gels, But He died a - lone, for you and me.

a-lone,

Jesus Only, Let Me See

411

Oswald J. Smith

Daniel B. Towner

1. For sal - va - tion full and free, Pur-chased once on Cal - va - ry,
2. He my guide from day to day, As I jour-ney on life's way;
3. May my mod - el ev - er be Christ the Lord, and none save He,
4. He shall reign from shore to shore, His the glo - ry ev - er-more—

Christ a - lone shall be my plea— Je - sus! Je - sus on - ly.
Close be-side Him let me stay— Je - sus! Je - sus on - ly.
That the world may see in me Je - sus! Je - sus on - ly.
Heav'n and earth shall bow be-fore Je - sus! Je - sus on - ly.

CHORUS

Je - sus on - ly, let me see, Je - sus on - ly, none save He,

Then my song shall ev - er be— Je - sus! Je - sus on - ly!

412 We Would See Jesus

ANNA B. WARNER

FELIX MENDELSSOHN-BARTHOLDY

1. We would see Je - sus, for the shad-ows length-en A - cross this lit - tle land-scape of our life; We would see Je - sus, our weak faith to strength-en For the last wea - ri - ness, the fi - nal strife.

2. We would see Je - sus, the great rock foun-da - tion, Where-on our feet were set by sov-'reign grace; Not life, nor death, with all their ag - i - ta - tion, Can thence re - move us, if we see His face.

3. We would see Je - sus; oth - er lights are pal - ing, Which for long years we have re-joiced to see; The bless-ings of our pil - grim-age are fail - ing; We would not mourn them, for we go to Thee.

4. We would see Je - sus; this is all we're need - ing; Strength, joy, and will - ing-ness come with the sight; We would see Je - sus, dy - ing, ris - en, plead - ing; Then wel-come, day! and fare-well, mor - tal night!

413 When I Survey the Wondrous Cross

ISAAC WATTS

ARR. BY LOWELL MASON

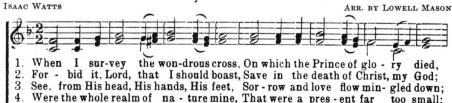

1. When I sur-vey the won-drous cross, On which the Prince of glo - ry died,

2. For - bid it, Lord, that I should boast, Save in the death of Christ, my God;

3. See, from His head, His hands, His feet, Sor - row and love flow min- gled down;

4. Were the whole realm of na - ture mine, That were a pres - ent far too small;

When I Survey the Wondrous Cross

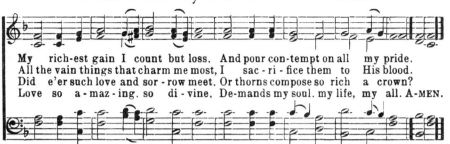

My rich-est gain I count but loss, And pour con-tempt on all my pride.
All the vain things that charm me most, I sac-ri-fice them to His blood.
Did e'er such love and sor-row meet, Or thorns compose so rich a crown?
Love so a-maz-ing, so di-vine, De-mands my soul, my life, my all. A-MEN.

Dear Lord and Father of Mankind   414

JOHN G. WHITTIER

FREDERICK C. MAKER

1. Dear Lord and Fa-ther of man-kind, For-give our fool-ish
2. In sim-ple trust like theirs who heard, Be-side the Syr-ian
3. Drop Thy still dews of qui-et-ness, Till all our striv-ings
4. Breathe through the heats of our de-sire Thy cool-ness and Thy

ways! Re-clothe us in our right-ful mind; In pur-er
sea The gra-cious call-ing of the Lord, Let us like
cease; Take from our souls the strain and stress, And let our
balm; Let sense be dumb, let flesh re-tire; Speak through the

lives Thy serv-ice find, In deep-er rev-'rence, praise.
them, with-out a word, Rise up and fol-low Thee.
or-dered lives con-fess The beau-ty of Thy peace.
earth-quake, wind, and fire, O still small voice of calm! A-MEN.

415 All Glory, Laud and Honor

THEODULPH OF ORLEANS
TR. BY JOHN M. NEALE

MELCHIOR TESCHNER

1. All glo-ry, laud and hon-or To Thee, Re-deem-er, King,
2. Thou art the King of Is-rael, Thou Da-vid's roy-al Son,
3. Thou didst ac-cept their prais-es; Ac-cept the prayers we bring,

To Whom the lips of chil-dren Made sweet ho-san-nas ring!
Who in the Lord's name com-est, The King and bless-ed One!
Who in all good de-light-est, Thou good and gra-cious King!

The peo-ple of the He-brews With palms be-fore Thee went;
To Thee, be-fore Thy pas-sion They sang their hymns of praise;
All glo-ry, laud and hon-or To Thee, Re-deem-er, King,

Our praise and prayer and an-thems Be-fore Thee we pre-sent.
To Thee, now high ex-alt-ed, Our mel-o-dy we raise.
To Whom the lips of chil-dren Made sweet ho-san-nas ring! A-MEN.

Christ Arose!

ROBERT LOWRY

ROBERT LOWRY

1. Low in the grave He lay— Je-sus my Sav-ior! Wait-ing the com-ing day—
2. Vain-ly they watch His bed—Je-sus my Sav-ior! Vain-ly they seal the dead—
3. Death cannot keep his prey—Je-sus my Sav-ior! He tore the bars a-way—

REFRAIN *Faster*

Je-sus my Lord! Up from the grave He a-rose,(He a-rose,)With a

might-y tri-umph o'er His foes; (He a-rose!)He a-rose a Vic-tor from the

dark do-main, And He lives for-ev-er with His saints to reign. He a-

rose! He a-rose! Hal-le-lu-jah! Christ a-rose!

He a-rose! He a-rose!

417 Christ the Lord Is Risen Today

CHARLES WESLEY   ARR. FROM "LYRA DAVIDICA"

1. Christ the Lord is ris'n to - day, Al - - le - lu - ia!
2. Lives a - gain our glo - rious King: Al - - le - lu - ia!
3. Love's re - deem - ing work is done, Al - - le - lu - ia!
4. Soar we now, where Christ has led, Al - - le - lu - ia!

Sons of men and an - gels say: Al - - - le - lu - ia!
Where, O death, is now thy sting? Al - - - le - lu - ia!
Fought the fight, the bat - tle won; Al - - - le - lu - ia!
Fol - l'wing our ex - alt - ed Head; Al - - - le - lu - ia!

Raise your joys and tri - umphs high, Al - - - le - lu - ia!
Dy - ing once, He all doth save: Al - - - le - lu - ia!
Death in vain for - bids Him rise; Al - - - le - lu - ia!
Made like Him, like Him we rise; Al - - - le - lu - ia!

Sing, ye heav'ns, and earth re - ply. Al - - - le - lu - ia!
Where thy vic - to - ry, O grave? Al - - - le - lu - ia!
Christ has o - pened Par - a - dise. Al - - - le - lu - ia!
Ours the cross, the grave, the skies. Al - - - le - lu - ia!

Come, Ye Faithful, Raise the Strain 418

JOHN OF DAMASCUS
TR. BY JOHN M. NEALE

ARTHUR S. SULLIVAN

1. Come, ye faith-ful, raise the strain Of tri - um-phant glad - ness;
2. 'Tis the Spring of souls to - day; Christ hath burst His pris - on,
3. Now the queen of sea-sons, bright With the day of splen - dor,
4. Al - le - lu - ia now to Thee, Christ, our King im - mor - tal,

God hath brought His Is - ra - el In - to joy from sad - ness.
And from three day's sleep in death As a sun hath ris - en.
With the roy - al feast of feasts, Comes its joy to ren - der;
Who hast passed the gates of death And the tomb's sealed por - tal;

Loosed from Pha-raoh's bit - ter yoke Ja - cob's sons and daugh-ters,
All the Win - ter of our sins, Long and dark, is fly - ing
Comes to glad Je - ru - sa - lem, Who with true af - fec - tion
Who, though nev - er door un - close, In th' as - sem - bly stand-ing,

Led them with un-mois-tened foot Through the Red Sea wa - ters.
From His light, to whom we give Laud and praise un - dy - ing.
Wel-comes in un-wea-ried strains Je - sus' res - ur - rec - tion.
Breath-est on Thy friends the peace Past all un-der-stand-ing. A-MEN.

419 I Know That My Redeemer Liveth

JESSIE B. POUNDS   JAMES H. FILLMORE

1. I know that my Redeemer liv-eth, And on the earth a-gain shall stand;
2. I know His promise never fail-eth, The word He speaks, it can-not die;
3. I know my mansion He prepareth, That where He is there I may be;

I know e-ter-nal life He giv-eth, That grace and pow'r are in His hand.
Tho' cruel death my flesh assaileth, Yet I shall see .... Him by and by.
O wondrous tho't, for me He careth, And He at last. . . . will come for me.

CHORUS

I know, I know........ that Je-sus liv-eth, And on the
earth...... a-gain shall stand; I know, I know......
that life He giv-eth, That grace and pow'r...... are in His hand.

Day Is Dying in the West

420

MARY A. LATHBURY

WILLIAM F. SHERWIN

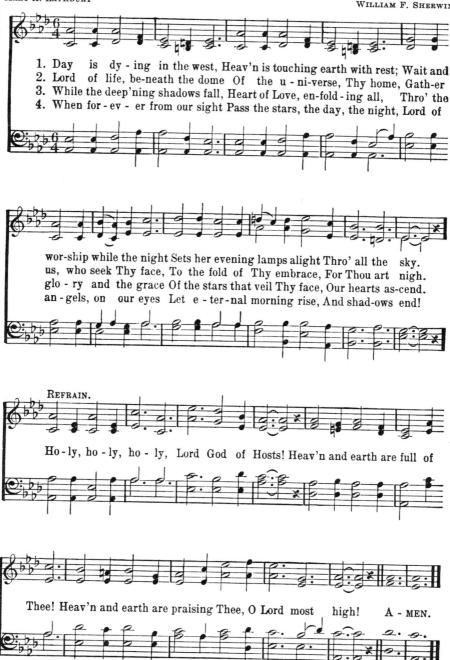

1. Day is dy-ing in the west, Heav'n is touching earth with rest; Wait and
2. Lord of life, be-neath the dome Of the u-ni-verse, Thy home, Gath-er
3. While the deep'ning shadows fall, Heart of Love, en-fold-ing all, Thro' the
4. When for-ev-er from our sight Pass the stars, the day, the night, Lord of

wor-ship while the night Sets her evening lamps alight Thro' all the sky.
us, who seek Thy face, To the fold of Thy embrace, For Thou art nigh.
glo-ry and the grace Of the stars that veil Thy face, Our hearts as-cend.
an-gels, on our eyes Let e-ter-nal morning rise, And shad-ows end!

REFRAIN.

Ho-ly, ho-ly, ho-ly, Lord God of Hosts! Heav'n and earth are full of

Thee! Heav'n and earth are praising Thee, O Lord most high! A-MEN.

Now the Day Is Over

SABINE BARING-GOULD

JOSEPH BARNBY

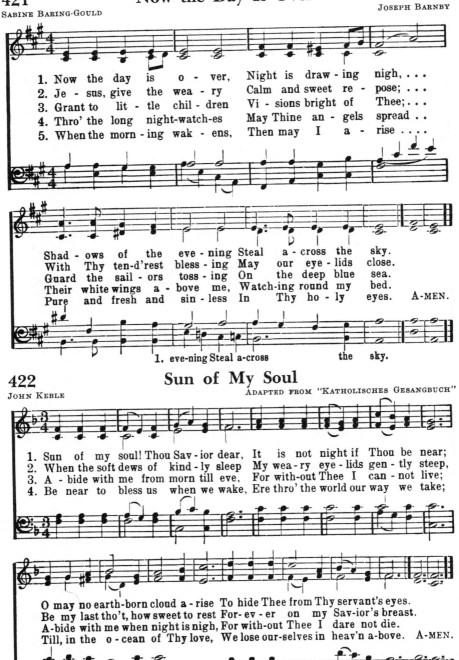

1. Now the day is o - ver, Night is draw - ing nigh, ...
2. Je - sus, give the wea - ry Calm and sweet re - pose; ...
3. Grant to lit - tle chil - dren Vi - sions bright of Thee; ...
4. Thro' the long night-watch-es May Thine an - gels spread ..
5. When the morn - ing wak - ens, Then may I a - rise ....

Shad - ows of the eve - ning Steal a - cross the sky.
With Thy ten-d'rest bless - ing May our eye - lids close.
Guard the sail - ors toss - ing On the deep blue sea.
Their white wings a - bove me, Watch-ing round my bed.
Pure and fresh and sin - less In Thy ho - ly eyes. A - MEN.

1. eve-ning Steal a-cross the sky.

422

Sun of My Soul

JOHN KEBLE

ADAPTED FROM "KATHOLISCHES GESANGBUCH"

1. Sun of my soul! Thou Sav - ior dear, It is not night if Thou be near;
2. When the soft dews of kind - ly sleep My wea - ry eye - lids gen - tly steep,
3. A - bide with me from morn till eve, For with-out Thee I can - not live;
4. Be near to bless us when we wake, Ere thro' the world our way we take;

O may no earth-born cloud a - rise To hide Thee from Thy servant's eyes.
Be my last tho't, how sweet to rest For - ev - er on my Sav - ior's breast.
A-bide with me when night is nigh, For with-out Thee I dare not die.
Till, in the o - cean of Thy love, We lose our-selves in heav'n a-bove. A - MEN.

Faith of Our Fathers

423

FREDERICK W. FABER

HENRI F. HEMY
ALT. BY JAMES G. WALTON

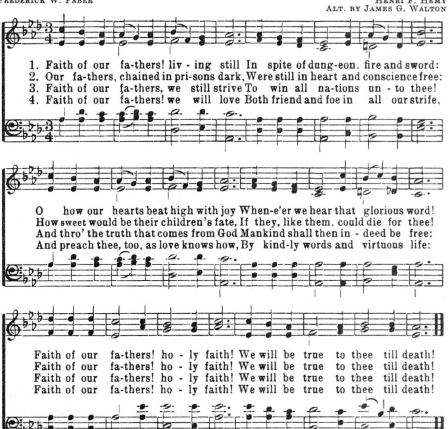

1. Faith of our fa-thers! liv - ing still In spite of dung-eon, fire and sword:
2. Our fa-thers, chained in pri-sons dark, Were still in heart and conscience free:
3. Faith of our fa-thers, we still strive To win all na-tions un - to thee!
4. Faith of our fa-thers! we will love Both friend and foe in all our strife,

O how our hearts beat high with joy When-e'er we hear that glorious word!
How sweet would be their children's fate, If they, like them, could die for thee!
And thro' the truth that comes from God Mankind shall then in - deed be free:
And preach thee, too, as love knows how, By kind-ly words and virtuous life:

Faith of our fa-thers! ho - ly faith! We will be true to thee till death!
Faith of our fa-thers! ho - ly faith! We will be true to thee till death!
Faith of our fa-thers! ho - ly faith! We will be true to thee till death!
Faith of our fa-thers! ho - ly faith! We will be true to thee till death!

Faith of Our Mothers

424

TUNE-ABOVE

1 Faith of our mothers, living still
In cradle song and bedtime prayer;
In nursery lore and fireside love,
Thy presence still pervades the air:
Faith of our mothers, living faith!
We will be true to thee till death.

2 Faith of our mothers, loving faith,
Fount of our childhood's trust and grace,
Oh, may thy consecration prove
Source of a finer, nobler race:
Faith of our mothers, living faith,
We will be true to thee till death.

3 Faith of our mothers, guiding faith,
For youthful longing, youthful doubt,
How blurred our vision, blind our way,
Thy providential care without:
Faith of our mothers, guiding faith,
We will be true to thee till death.

4 Faith of our mothers, Christian faith,
In truth beyond our stumbling creeds,
Still serve the home and save the Church,
And breathe thy spirit thro' our deeds:
Faith of our mothers, Christian faith!
We will be true to thee till death.

Words by A. B. Patten

425   Faith Is the Victory!

JOHN H. YATES   IRA D. SANKEY

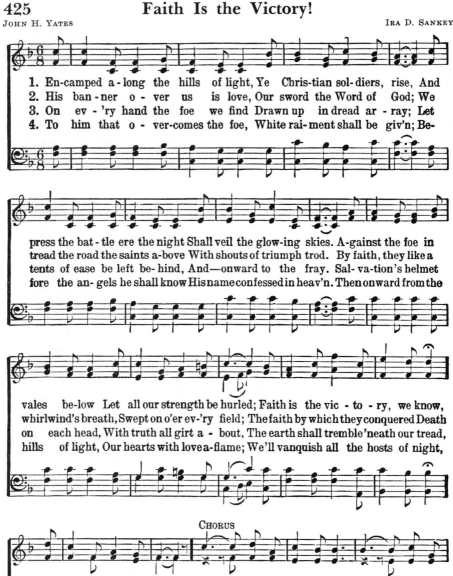

1. En-camped a-long the hills of light, Ye Chris-tian sol-diers, rise, And
2. His ban-ner o-ver us is love, Our sword the Word of God; We
3. On ev-'ry hand the foe we find Drawn up in dread ar-ray; Let
4. To him that o-ver-comes the foe, White rai-ment shall be giv'n; Be-

press the bat-tle ere the night Shall veil the glow-ing skies. A-gainst the foe in
tread the road the saints a-bove With shouts of triumph trod. By faith, they like a
tents of ease be left be-hind, And—onward to the fray. Sal-va-tion's helmet
fore the an-gels he shall know His name confessed in heav'n. Then onward from the

vales be-low Let all our strength be hurled; Faith is the vic-to-ry, we know,
whirlwind's breath, Swept on o'er ev-'ry field; The faith by which they conquered Death
on each head, With truth all girt a-bout, The earth shall tremble 'neath our tread,
hills of light, Our hearts with love a-flame; We'll vanquish all the hosts of night,

CHORUS

That o-ver-comes the world.
Is still our shin-ing shield.   Faith is the vic-to-ry! Faith is the
And ech-o with our shout.
In Je-sus' conqu'ring name.   Faith is the vic-to-ry! Faith is the

Faith Is the Victory!

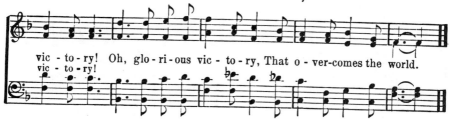

vic - to - ry! Oh, glo - ri - ous vic - to - ry, That o - ver-comes the world.
vic - to - ry!

Beneath the Cross of Jesus

426

ELIZABETH C. CLEPHANE

FREDERICK C. MAKER

1. Be - neath the cross of Je - sus I fain would take my stand,
2. Up - on that cross of Je - sus Mine eye at times can see
3. I take, O cross thy shad - ow For my a - bid - ing - place;

The shad - ow of a might - y Rock With - in a wea - ry land;
The ver - y dy - ing form of One Who suf-fered there for me;
I ask no oth - er sun - shine than The sun - shine of His face;

A home with - in the wil - der - ness, A rest up - on the way,
And from my smit - ten heart with tears Two won - ders I con - fess,
Con - tent to let the world go by, To know no gain nor loss,

From the burn-ing of the noon-day heat, And the bur-den of the day.
The won - ders of His glo-rious love, And my own worth-less-ness.
My sin - ful self my on - ly shame, My glo - ry all the cross.

427 The Touch of His Hand on Mine

JESSIE B. POUNDS   HENRY P. MORTON

1. There are days so dark that I seek in vain For the face of my
2. There are times, when tired of the toil-some road, That for ways of the
3. When the way is dim, and I can-not see Thro' the mist of His
4. In the last sad hour, as I stand a-lone Where the pow-ers of

Friend Di-vine; But tho' dark-ness hide, He is there to guide
world I pine; But He draws me back to the up-ward track
wise de-sign, How my glad heart yearns and my faith re-turns
death com-bine, While the dark waves roll He will guide my soul

CHORUS.

By the touch of His hand on mine. Oh, the touch of His hand on

mine, Oh, the touch of His hand on mine! There is grace and
on mine, on mine!

pow'r, in the try-ing hour, In the touch of His hand on mine. A-MEN.

In the Garden

C. Austin Miles

428

C. Austin Miles

1. I come to the gar-den a-lone, While the dew is still on the
2. He speaks, and the sound of His voice Is so sweet the birds hush their
3. I'd stay in the gar-den with Him Tho' the night a-round me be

ros - es, And the voice I hear, Fall-ing on my ear, The
sing - ing, And the mel - o - dy That He gave to me, With-
fall - ing, But He bids me go; Thro' the voice of woe His

Son of God dis - clos - es.
in my heart is ring - ing.
voice to me is call - ing.

Chorus

And He walks with me, and He
talks with me, And He tells me I am His own; And the
joy we share as we tar - ry there, None oth - er has ev - er known.

429 O Master, Let Me Walk with Thee

WASHINGTON GLADDEN

H. PERCY SMITH

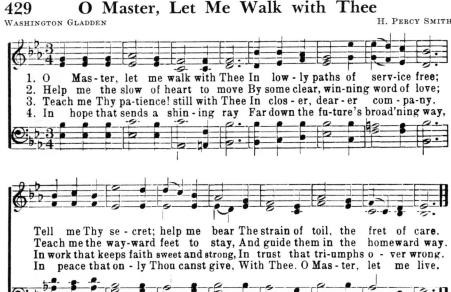

1. O Mas-ter, let me walk with Thee In low-ly paths of serv-ice free;
2. Help me the slow of heart to move By some clear, win-ning word of love;
3. Teach me Thy pa-tience! still with Thee In clos-er, dear-er com-pa-ny,
4. In hope that sends a shin-ing ray Far down the fu-ture's broad'ning way,

Tell me Thy se-cret; help me bear The strain of toil, the fret of care.
Teach me the way-ward feet to stay, And guide them in the homeward way.
In work that keeps faith sweet and strong, In trust that tri-umphs o-ver wrong.
In peace that on-ly Thou canst give, With Thee, O Mas-ter, let me live.

430 Blest Be the Tie That Binds

JOHN FAWCETT

HANS G. NÄGELI
ARR. BY LOWELL MASON

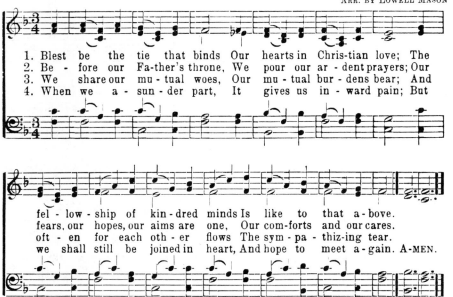

1. Blest be the tie that binds Our hearts in Chris-tian love; The
2. Be-fore our Fa-ther's throne, We pour our ar-dent prayers; Our
3. We share our mu-tual woes, Our mu-tual bur-dens bear; And
4. When we a-sun-der part, It gives us in-ward pain; But

fel-low-ship of kin-dred minds Is like to that a-bove.
fears, our hopes, our aims are one, Our com-forts and our cares.
oft-en for each oth-er flows The sym-pa-thiz-ing tear.
we shall still be joined in heart, And hope to meet a-gain. A-MEN.

Follow On

W. O. Cushing

Robert Lowry

1. Down in the val-ley with my Sav-iour I would go, Where the flowers are
2. Down in the val-ley with my Sav-iour I would go, Where the storms are
3. Down in the val-ley, or up-on the moun-tain steep, Close be-side my

bloom-ing and the sweet wa-ters flow; Ev-ery-where He leads me I would
sweep-ing and the dark wa-ters flow; With His hand to lead me I will
Sav-iour would my soul ev-er keep; He will lead me safe-ly in the

fol-low, fol-low on, Walk-ing in His foot-steps till the crown be won.
nev-er, nev-er fear, Dan-ger can-not fright me if my Lord is near.
path that He has trod, Up to where they gath-er on the hills of God.

REFRAIN

Fol-low! fol-low! I would follow Je-sus! Anywhere, everywhere, I would follow on!

Fol-low! fol-low! I would follow Jesus! Everywhere He leads me I would follow on!

432 According to Thy Gracious Word

JAMES MONTGOMERY

HENRY W. GREATOREX'S COLLECTION

1. Ac - cord - ing to Thy gra-cious word, In meek hu - mil - i - ty,
2. Thy bod - y, bro - ken for my sake, My bread from heaven shall be;
3. When to the cross I turn my eyes, And rest on Cal - va - ry,
4. Re - mem - ber Thee, and all Thy pains, And all Thy love to me:
5. And when these fail - ing lips grow dumb, And mind and mem-ory flee,

This will I do, my dy - ing Lord, I will re - mem - ber Thee.
Thy tes - ta - men-tal cup I take, And thus re - mem - ber Thee.
O Lamb of God, my sac - ri - fice, I must re - mem - ber Thee.
Yea, while I breathe, a pulse re - mains Will I re - mem - ber Thee.
When Thou shalt in Thy King-dom come, Je - sus, re - mem - ber me.

433 Bread of Heaven

JOSEPH CONDER

XAVIER SCHNYDER

1. Bread of heav'n, on Thee we feed, For Thy flesh is meat in - deed;
2. Vine of heav'n, Thy blood sup-plies This blest cup of sac - ri - fice;
3. Day by day, with strength supplied Thro' the life of Him who died,

Ev - er let our souls be fed With this true and liv - ing bread.
Lord, Thy wounds our heal - ing give, To Thy cross we look and live.
Lord of life, O let us be Root - ed, graft - ed, built on Thee!

Communion Hymn

434

CHARLES McMILLAN

J. C. BLAKER

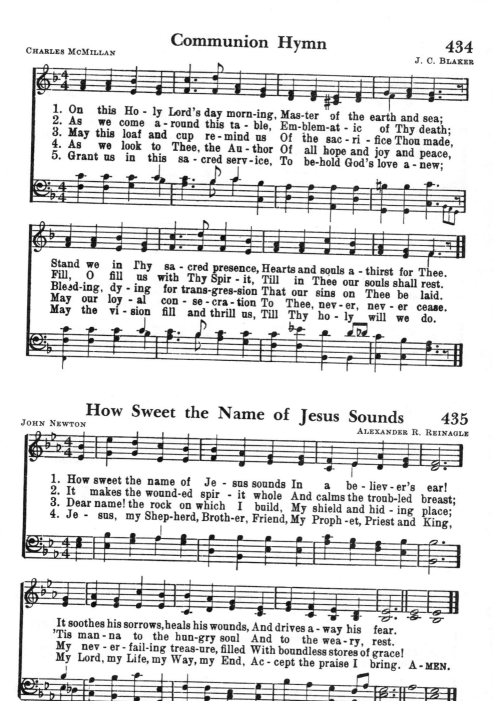

1. On this Ho-ly Lord's day morn-ing, Mas-ter of the earth and sea;
2. As we come a-round this ta-ble, Em-blem-at-ic of Thy death;
3. May this loaf and cup re-mind us Of the sac-ri-fice Thou made,
4. As we look to Thee, the Au-thor Of all hope and joy and peace,
5. Grant us in this sa-cred serv-ice, To be-hold God's love a-new;

Stand we in Thy sa-cred presence, Hearts and souls a-thirst for Thee.
Fill, O fill us with Thy Spir-it, Till in Thee our souls shall rest.
Bleed-ing, dy-ing for trans-gres-sion That our sins on Thee be laid.
May our loy-al con-se-cra-tion To Thee, nev-er, nev-er cease.
May the vi-sion fill and thrill us, Till Thy ho-ly will we do.

How Sweet the Name of Jesus Sounds

435

JOHN NEWTON

ALEXANDER R. REINAGLE

1. How sweet the name of Je-sus sounds In a be-liev-er's ear!
2. It makes the wound-ed spir-it whole And calms the troub-led breast;
3. Dear name! the rock on which I build, My shield and hid-ing place;
4. Je-sus, my Shep-herd, Broth-er, Friend, My Proph-et, Priest and King,

It soothes his sorrows, heals his wounds, And drives a-way his fear.
'Tis man-na to the hun-gry soul And to the wea-ry, rest.
My nev-er-fail-ing treas-ure, filled With boundless stores of grace!
My Lord, my Life, my Way, my End, Ac-cept the praise I bring. A-MEN.

436 Here, O My Lord, I See Thee Face to Face

HORATIUS BONAR

FELIX MENDELSSOHN-BARTHOLDY

1. Here, O my Lord, I see Thee face to face; Here would I touch and han-dle things un-seen; Here grasp with firm-er hand th' e-ter-nal grace, And all my wea-ri-ness up-on Thee lean.

2. Here would I feed up-on the bread of God; Here drink with Thee the roy-al wine of heav'n; Here would I lay a-side each earth-ly load, Here taste a-fresh the calm of sin for-giv'n.

3. Too soon we rise; the sym-bols dis-ap-pear; The feast, tho' not the love, is passed and gone; The bread and wine re-move, but Thou art here— Near-er than ev-er—still my Shield and Sun.

4. Feast aft-er feast thus comes and pass-es by; Yet, pass-ing, points to the glad feast a-bove—Giv-ing sweet fore-taste of the fes-tal joy, The Lamb's great bri-dal feast of bliss and love.

437 Fling Out the Banner! Let It Float

GEORGE W. DOANE

JOHN B. CALKIN

1. Fling out the ban-ner, let it float Sky-ward and sea-ward, high and wide;

2. Fling out the ban-ner, heathen lands Shall see from far the glo-rious sight,

3. Fling out the ban-ner, sin-sick souls That sink and per-ish in the strife.

4. Fling out the ban-ner, let it float Sky-ward and sea-ward, high and wide,

Fling Out the Banner! Let It Float

The sun that lights its shining folds, The cross on which the Sav - ior died.
And nations, crowding to be born, Bap-tize their spir - its in its light.
Shall touch in faith its ra-diant hem, And spring im-mor-tal in - to life.
Our glo-ry on - ly in the cross; Our on - ly hope, the Cru - ci - fied.

Hail to the Brightness 438

Thomas Hastings

Lowell Mason

1. Hail to the bright-ness of Zi - on's glad morn-ing! Joy to the
2. Hail to the bright-ness of Zi - on's glad morn-ing, Long by the
3. Lo, in the des - ert rich flow-ers are spring-ing, Streams ev - er
4. See, from all lands, from the isles of the o - cean, Praise to Je -

lands that in dark-ness have lain! Hushed be the ac - cents of
proph - ets of Is - rael fore-told! Hail to the mil - lions from
co - pious are glid - ing a - long; Loud from the moun-tain-tops
ho - vah as-cend-ing on high; Fallen are the en - gines of

sor-row and mourn-ing, Zi - on in tri-umph be - gins her mild reign.
bond-age re - turn-ing! Gen - tiles and Jews the blest vi - sion be - hold.
ech - oes are ring-ing, Wastes rise in ver-dure and min - gle in song.
war and com - mo-tion, Shouts of sal - va - tion are rend-ing the sky.

439 This Do in Remembrance of Me

HELEN E. FROMM

HELEN E. FROMM

1. The trial of the cross was ap-proach-ing With its bit-ter-ness, sor-row and
2. Then take of the bread to re-mem-ber That His bod-y was bro-ken for
3. The Sav-iour now liv-eth in glo-ry, Tri-um-phant o'er death and o'er
4. The Son of God gave to His chil-dren This to-ken in mem-'ry of

pain, When there in the up-per room, Je-sus Spoke
you; And drink of the cup to re-mem-ber His
sin; Un-til He shall come for His dear ones, Do
Him; Come, take of the bread of life free-ly, And

CHORUS

with His dis-ci-ples a-gain.
blood that was shed for you too. This do in re-mem-brance of
this in re-mem-brance of Him. Do this in re-mem-brance of
let His blood cleanse you from sin.

Me, This do in re-mem-brance of Me; The wine and the bread speak of
Him, Do this in re-mem-brance of Him; The wine and the bread speak of

blood that was shed; This do in re-mem-brance of Me.
blood that was shed; Do this in re-mem-brance of Him.

Macedonia

ANNE ORTLUND

440

HENRY S. CUTLER

1. The vis-ion of a dy-ing world Is vast be-fore our eyes;
2. The sav-age hugs his god of stone And fears de-scent of night;
3. To-day, as un-der-stand-ing's bounds Are stretch'd on ev-ery hand,
4. The warn-ing bell of judg-ment tolls, A-bove us looms the cross;

We feel the heart-beat of its need, We hear its fee-ble cries:
The cit-y dwell-er cring-es lone A-mid the gar-ish light:
O, clothe Thy Word in bright, new sounds, And speed it o'er the land;
A-round are ev-er-dy-ing souls—How great, how great the loss!

Lord Je-sus Christ, re-vive Thy church In this, her cru-cial hour!
Lord Je-sus Christ, a-rouse Thy church To see their mute dis-tress!
Lord Je-sus Christ, em-pow-er us To preach by ev-ery means!
O Lord, con-strain and move Thy church The glad news to im-part!

Lord Je-sus Christ, a-wake Thy church With Spir-it-giv-en pow'r.
Lord Je-sus Christ, e-quip Thy church With love and ten-der-ness.
Lord Je-sus Christ, em-bold-en us In near and dis-tant scenes.
And Lord, as Thou dost stir Thy church, Be-gin with-in my heart.

Go Ye into All the World

441

JAMES McGRANAHAN

JAMES McGRANAHAN

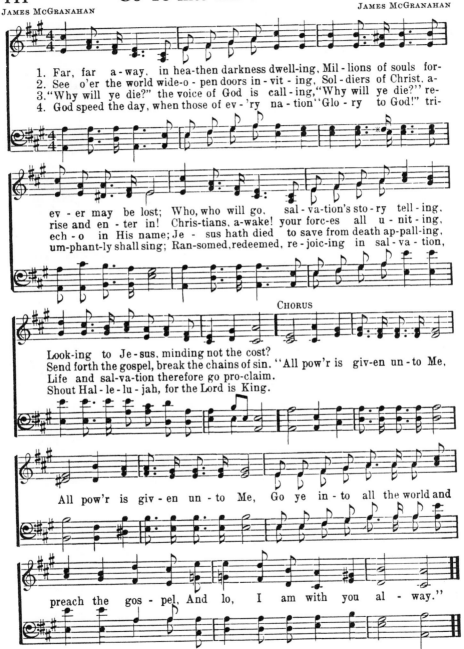

1. Far, far a - way, in hea-then darkness dwell-ing, Mil - lions of souls for-
2. See o'er the world wide-o - pen doors in - vit - ing, Sol - diers of Christ, a-
3. "Why will ye die?" the voice of God is call-ing, "Why will ye die?" re-
4. God speed the day, when those of ev - 'ry na - tion "Glo - ry to God!" tri-

ev - er may be lost; Who, who will go, sal - va-tion's sto - ry tell - ing,
rise and en - ter in! Chris-tians, a-wake! your forc-es all u - nit - ing,
ech - o in His name; Je - sus hath died to save from death ap-pall-ing,
um-phant-ly shall sing; Ran-somed, redeemed, re - joic-ing in sal - va - tion,

CHORUS

Look-ing to Je - sus, minding not the cost?
Send forth the gospel, break the chains of sin. "All pow'r is giv-en un-to Me,
Life and sal-va-tion therefore go pro-claim.
Shout Hal - le - lu - jah, for the Lord is King.

All pow'r is giv-en un-to Me, Go ye in-to all the world and

preach the gos - pel, And lo, I am with you al - way."

So Send I You

E. MARGARET CLARKSON

JOHN W. PETERSON

1. So send I you to la-bor un-re-ward-ed, To serve un-
2. So send I you to bind the bruised and bro-ken, O'er wand'ring
3. So send I you to lone-li-ness and long-ing, With heart a-
4. So send I you to leave your life's am-bi-tion, To die to
5. So send I you to hearts made hard by hat-red, To eyes made

paid, un-loved, un-sought, un-known, To bear re-buke, to suf-fer
souls to work, to weep, to wake, To bear the bur-dens of a
hung'ring for the loved and known, For-sak-ing home and kin-dred,
dear de-sire, self-will re-sign, To la-bor long, and love where
blind be-cause they will not see, To spend, tho' it be blood, to

scorn and scoff-ing— So send I you to toil for Me a-lone.
world a-wea-ry— So send I you to suf-fer for My sake.
friend and dear one— So send I you to know My love a-lone.
men re-vile you— So send I you to lose your life in Mine.
spend and spare not— So send I you to taste of Cal-va-ry.

*CHORUS

"As the Fa-ther hath sent me, So send I you."

*Effective if sung only after the last verse.

443 From Greenland's Icy Mountains

REGINALD HEBER

LOWELL MASON

1. From Green-land's i - cy moun-tains, From In - dia's cor - al strand;
2. What tho' the spi - cy breez - es Blow soft o'er Cey-lon's isle;
3. Shall we, whose souls are light - ed With wis-dom from on high,
4. Waft, waft, ye winds, His sto - ry, And you, ye wa - ters, roll,

Where Af - ric's sun - ny foun - tains Roll down their gold - en sand:
Though ev - 'ry pros - pect pleas - es, And on - ly man is vile?
Shall we to men be - night - ed The lamp of life de - ny?
Till, like a sea of glo - ry, It spreads from pole to pole:

From man-y an an-cient riv - er, From man-y a palm - y plain,
In vain with lav - ish kind - ness The gifts of God are strown;
Sal - va - tion! O sal - va - tion! The joy - ful sound pro - claim,
Till o'er our ran-somed na - ture The Lamb for sin - ners slain,

They call us to de - liv - er Their land from er - ror's chain.
The hea-then in his blind - ness Bows down to wood and stone.
Till earth's re-mot - est na - tion Has learned Mes-si - ah's name.
Re - deem-er, King, Cre - a - tor, In bliss re - turns to reign. A-MEN.

Bringing In the Sheaves

KNOWLES SHAW

444

GEORGE A. MINOR

1. Sow - ing in the morn - ing, sow-ing seeds of kind - ness, Sow-ing in the
2. Sow - ing in the sun - shine, sow-ing in the shad - ows, Fear-ing nei - ther
3. Go - ing forth with weep-ing, sow-ing for the Mas - ter, Tho' the loss sus-

noon - tide and the dew - y eve; Wait-ing for the har - vest,
clouds nor win - ter's chill - ing breeze; By and by the har - vest,
tained our spir - it oft - en grieves; When our weep-ing's o - ver,

and the time of reap-ing, We shall come re - joic - ing, bring-ing in the sheaves.
and the la - bor end - ed, We shall come re - joic - ing, bring-ing in the sheaves.
He will bid us wel-come, We shall come re - joic - ing, bring-ing in the sheaves.

CHORUS

Bring-ing in the sheaves, bring-ing in the sheaves, We shall come re-joic-
Bring-ing in the sheaves, bring-ing in the sheaves, We shall come re-joic-

1
ing, bring - ing in the sheaves;

2
ing, bring - ing in the sheaves.

445   Jesus Saves

PRISCILLA J. OWENS

WILLIAM J. KIRKPATRICK

1. We have heard the joy - ful sound: Je - sus saves! Je - sus saves!
2. Waft it on the roll - ing tide; Je - sus saves! Je - sus saves!
3. Sing a - bove the bat - tle strife, Je - sus saves! Je - sus saves!
4. Give the winds a might - y voice, Je - sus saves! Je - sus saves!

Spread the ti - dings all a - round: Je - sus saves! Je - sus saves!
Tell to sin - ners far and wide: Je - sus saves! Je - sus saves!
By His death and end - less life, Je - sus saves! Je - sus saves!
Let the na - tions now re - joice,— Je - sus saves! Je - sus saves!

Bear the news to ev - 'ry land, Climb the steeps and cross the waves;
Sing, ye is - lands of the sea; Ech - o back, ye o - cean caves;
Sing it soft - ly thro' the gloom, When the heart for mer - cy craves;
Shout sal - va - tion full and free; High - est hills and deep - est caves;

On - ward!—'tis our Lord's com - mand; Je - sus saves! Je - sus saves!
Earth shall keep her ju - bi - lee: Je - sus saves! Je - sus saves!
Sing in tri - umph o'er the tomb,— Je - sus saves! Je - sus saves!
This our song of vic - to - ry,— Je - sus saves! Je - sus saves!

O Zion, Haste

446

MARY A. THOMSON

JAMES WALCH

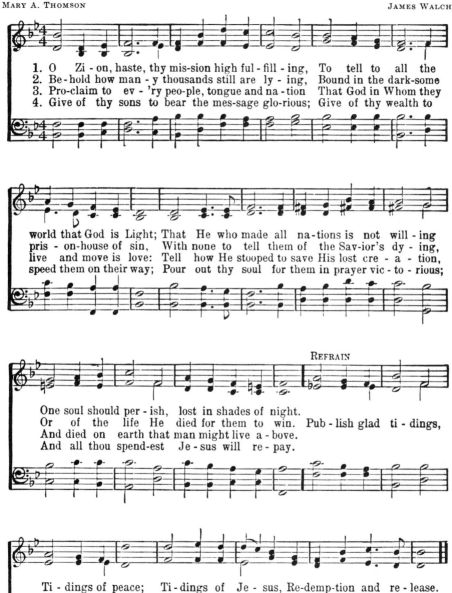

1. O Zi - on, haste, thy mis-sion high ful - fill - ing, To tell to all the
2. Be - hold how man - y thousands still are ly - ing, Bound in the dark-some
3. Pro-claim to ev - 'ry peo-ple, tongue and na - tion That God in Whom they
4. Give of thy sons to bear the mes-sage glo-rious; Give of thy wealth to

world that God is Light; That He who made all na-tions is not will - ing
pris - on-house of sin, With none to tell them of the Sav-ior's dy - ing,
live and move is love: Tell how He stooped to save His lost cre - a - tion,
speed them on their way; Pour out thy soul for them in prayer vic - to - rious;

REFRAIN

One soul should per - ish, lost in shades of night.
Or of the life He died for them to win. Pub - lish glad ti - dings,
And died on earth that man might live a - bove.
And all thou spend-est Je - sus will re - pay.

Ti - dings of peace; Ti - dings of Je - sus, Re-demp-tion and re - lease.

447 Send the Light

CHARLES H. GABRIEL   CHARLES H. GABRIEL

1. There's a call comes ring-ing o'er the rest-less wave, "Send the light! ...
2. We have heard the Mac - e - do-nian call to - day, "Send the light! ...
3. Let us pray that grace may ev-'ry-where a-bound; Send the light! ...
4. Let us not grow wea-ry in the work of love, Send the light! ...

Send the light!

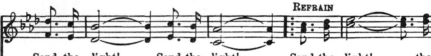

Send the light!"   There are souls to res-cue, there are souls to save,
Send the light!"   And a gold-en of-f'ring at the cross we lay,
Send the light!   And a Christ-like spir - it ev - 'ry-where be found,
Send the light!   Let us gath-er jew - els for a crown a - bove,

Send the light!

REFRAIN

Send the light! ... Send the light! ... Send the light! ... the
Send the light!   Send the light!   Send the light!

1

bless - ed gos - pel light; Let it shine ... from shore to
the bless - ed gos - pel light; Let it shine

2

shore! .... shine ... for - ev - er-more.
from shore to shore! Let it shine   for - ev - er-more.

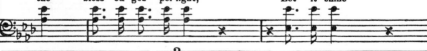

The Regions Beyond

ALBERT B. SIMPSON

MARGARET M. SIMPSON

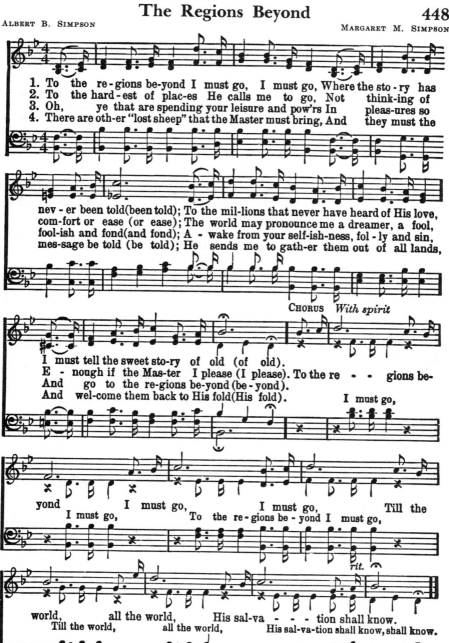

1. To the re-gions be-yond I must go, I must go, Where the sto-ry has
2. To the hard-est of plac-es He calls me to go, Not think-ing of
3. Oh, ye that are spending your leisure and pow'rs In pleas-ures so
4. There are oth-er "lost sheep" that the Master must bring, And they must the

nev-er been told(been told); To the mil-lions that never have heard of His love,
com-fort or ease (or ease); The world may pronounce me a dreamer, a fool,
fool-ish and fond(and fond); A-wake from your self-ish-ness, fol-ly and sin,
mes-sage be told (be told); He sends me to gath-er them out of all lands,

CHORUS *With spirit*

I must tell the sweet sto-ry of old (of old).
E-nough if the Mas-ter I please (I please). To the re - - gions be-
And go to the re-gions be-yond(be-yond).
And wel-come them back to His fold(His fold).

I must go,

yond I must go, I must go, Till the
I must go, To the re-gions be-yond I must go,

rit.

world, all the world, His sal-va - - - tion shall know.
Till the world, all the world, His sal-va-tion shall know, shall know.

449 We've a Story to Tell to the Nations

H. ERNEST NICHOL   H. ERNEST NICHOL

1. We've a sto-ry to tell to the na-tions That shall turn their hearts
2. We've a song to be sung to the na-tions That shall lift their hearts
3. We've a mes-sage to give to the na-tions, That the Lord who reign-
4. We've a Sav-ior to show to the na-tions Who the path of sor-

1. That shall turn

to the right, A sto-ry of truth and mer-cy, A
to the Lord, A song that shall con-quer e-vil And
eth a-bove Hath sent us His Son to save us, And
row hath trod, That all of the world's great peo-ples Might

their hearts to the right,

sto-ry of peace and light, A sto-ry of peace and light.
shat-ter the spear and sword, And shat-ter the spear and sword.
show us that God is love, And show us that God is love.
come to the truth of God, Might come to the truth of God.

A sto-ry of peace and light.

CHORUS

For the darkness shall turn to dawn-ing, And the dawn-ing to noonday bright,

rall.

And Christ's great kingdom shall come to earth, The kingdom of love and light.

O Beautiful for Spacious Skies 450

KATHERINE L. BATES

SAMUEL A. WARD

1. O beau - ti - ful for spa-cious skies, For am - ber waves of grain,
2. O beau - ti - ful for pil - grim feet, Whose stern, im-pas-sioned stress
3. O beau - ti - ful for he-roes proved In lib - er - at - ing strife,
4. O beau - ti - ful for pa-triot dream That sees be - yond the years

For pur - ple moun-tain maj - es - ties A - bove the fruit - ed plain!
A thor-ough-fare for free - dom beat A - cross the wil - der - ness!
Who more than self their coun-try loved, And mer - cy more than life!
Thine al - a - bas - ter cit - ies gleam, Undimmed by hu - man tears!

A - mer - i - ca! A - mer - i - ca! God shed His grace on thee,
A - mer - i - ca! A - mer - i - ca! God mend thine ev - 'ry flaw,
A - mer - i - ca! A - mer - i - ca! May God thy gold re - fine,
A - mer - i - ca! A - mer - i - ca! God shed His grace on thee,

And crown thy good with broth - er-hood From sea to shin - ing sea!
Con - firm thy soul in self - con-trol, Thy lib - er - ty in law!
Till all suc - cess be no - ble-ness And ev - 'ry gain di - vine!
And crown thy good with broth - er-hood From sea to shin - ing sea!

451   The Star-Spangled Banner

Francis Scott Key   Author Unknown

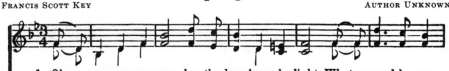

1. Oh,   say, can you see, by the dawn's ear-ly light, What so proud-ly we
2. On the shore, dim-ly seen thro' the mists of the deep, Where the foe's haughty
3. And where is that band, who so vaunt-ing-ly swore That the hav-oc of
4. Oh,   thus be it ev-er when free-men shall stand Be-tween their loved

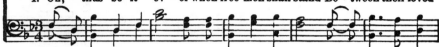

hailed at the twilight's last gleaming? Whose broad stripes and bright stars, thro' the
host in dread si-lence re-pos-es, What is that which the breeze, o'er the
war and the bat-tle's con-fu-sion, A   home and a coun-try should
homes and the war's des-o-la-tion; Blest with vic-t'ry and peace, may the

per-il-ous fight, O'er the ramparts we watched, were so gal-lant-ly stream-ing?
tow-er-ing steep, As   it fit-ful-ly blows, half conceals, half dis-clos-es?
leave us no more? Their   blood has washed out their foul footsteps' pol-lu-tion;
Heav'n-rescued land Praise the Pow'r that hath made and preserved us a na-tion!

And the rock-ets' red glare, the bombs bursting in air,   Gave proof thro' the
Now it catch-es the gleam of the morning's first beam, In full glo-ry re-
No   ref-uge could save the   hire-ling and slave From the ter-ror of
Then con-quer we must, when our cause it is just;   And this be our

The Star-Spangled Banner

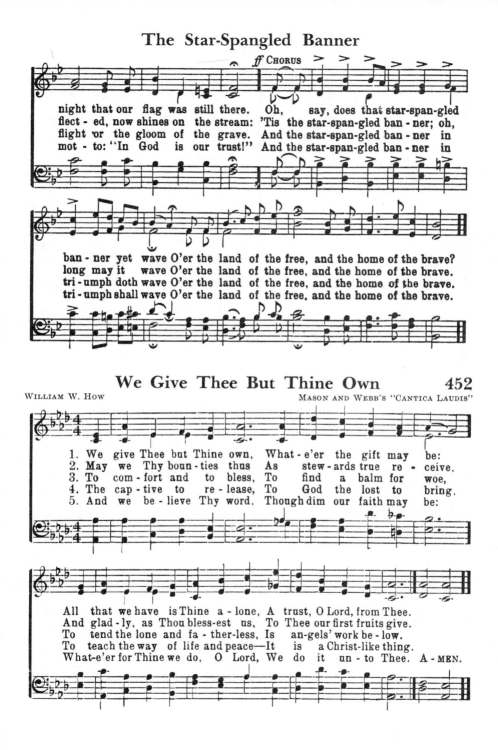

ff CHORUS

night that our flag was still there. Oh, say, does that star-span-gled
flect - ed, now shines on the stream: 'Tis the star-span-gled ban - ner; oh,
flight or the gloom of the grave. And the star-span-gled ban - ner in
mot - to: "In God is our trust!" And the star-span-gled ban - ner in

ban - ner yet wave O'er the land of the free, and the home of the brave?
long may it wave O'er the land of the free, and the home of the brave.
tri - umph doth wave O'er the land of the free, and the home of the brave.
tri - umph shall wave O'er the land of the free, and the home of the brave.

We Give Thee But Thine Own   452

WILLIAM W. HOW   MASON AND WEBB'S "CANTICA LAUDIS"

1. We give Thee but Thine own, What - e'er the gift may be:
2. May we Thy boun - ties thus As stew - ards true re - ceive,
3. To com - fort and to bless, To find a balm for woe,
4. The cap - tive to re - lease, To God the lost to bring,
5. And we be - lieve Thy word, Though dim our faith may be:

All that we have is Thine a - lone, A trust, O Lord, from Thee.
And glad - ly, as Thou bless-est us, To Thee our first fruits give.
To tend the lone and fa - ther-less, Is an-gels' work be - low.
To teach the way of life and peace—It is a Christ-like thing.
What-e'er for Thine we do, O Lord, We do it un - to Thee. A - MEN.

453 Battle Hymn of the Republic

JULIA WARD HOWE   WILLIAM STEFFE

1. Mine eyes have seen the glo-ry of the com-ing of the Lord; He is
2. I have seen Him in the watch-fires of a hun-dred circling camps; They have
3. He has sound-ed forth the trumpet that shall nev-er sound re-treat; He is
4. In the beau-ty of the lil-ies Christ was born a-cross the sea, With a

tram-pling out the vintage where the grapes of wrath are stored; He hath loosed the
build-ed Him an al-tar in the eve-ning dews and damps; I can read His
sift-ing out the hearts of men be-fore His judg-ment seat. O be swift, my
glo-ry in His bos-om that trans-fig-ures you and me; As He died to

fate-ful light-ning of His ter-ri-ble swift sword; His truth is march-ing on.
righteous sen-tence by the dim and flar-ing lamps; His day is march-ing on.
soul, to an-swer Him! be ju-bi-lant, my feet! Our God is march-ing on.
make men ho-ly, let us die to make men free; While God is march-ing on.

CHORUS

Glo-ry! glory, hal-le-lu-jah! Glory! glory, hal-le-lu-jah! His truth is marching on.
Glo-ry! glory, hal-le-lu-jah! Glory! glory, hal-le-lu-jah! His day is march-ing on.
Glo-ry! glory, hal-le-lu-jah! Glory! glory, hal-le-lu-jah! Our God is marching on.
Glo-ry! glory, hal-le-lu-jah! Glory! glory, hal-le-lu-jah! While God is marching on.

God of Our Fathers, Whose Almighty Hand 454

Daniel O. Roberts

George W. Warren

Trumpets, before each verse.

1. God of our fa - thers, whose al - might - y
2. Thy love di - vine hath led us in the
3. From war's a - larms, from dead - ly pes - ti -
4. Re - fresh Thy peo - ple on their toil - some

hand   Leads forth in beau - ty all the star - ry band
past,   In this free land by Thee our lot is cast;
lence,   Be Thy strong arm our ev - er strong de-fense;
way,   Lead us from night to nev - er - end - ing day;

Of shin - ing worlds in splen - dor thro' the skies,
Be Thou our rul - er, guard - ian, guide and stay,
Thy true re - lig - ion in our hearts in - crease,
Fill all our lives with love and grace di - vine,

Our grate - ful songs be - fore Thy throne a - rise.
Thy word our law, Thy paths our cho - sen way.
Thy boun - teous good - ness nour - ish us in peace.
And glo - ry, laud, and praise be ev - er Thine.

My Country, 'Tis of Thee

Samuel F. Smith

Author Unknown

1. My coun-try, 'tis of thee, Sweet land of lib-er-ty,
2. My na-tive coun-try, thee, Land of the no-ble, free,
3. Let mu-sic swell the breeze, And ring from all the trees
4. Our fa-thers' God, to Thee, Au-thor of lib-er-ty,

Of thee I sing: Land where my fa-thers died, Land of the
Thy name I love: I love thy rocks and rills, Thy woods and
Sweet free-dom's song: Let mor-tal tongues a-wake; Let all that
To Thee we sing: Long may our land be bright With free-dom's

pil-grim's pride, From ev-'ry moun-tain side Let free-dom ring!
tem-pled hills; My heart with rap-ture thrills Like that a-bove.
breathe par-take; Let rocks their si-lence break, The sound pro-long.
ho-ly light; Pro-tect us by Thy might, Great God, our King!

O for a Thousand Tongues to Sing

Charles Wesley

Carl G. Glaser
Arr. by Lowell Mason

1. O for a thou-sand tongues to sing My great Re-deem-er's praise,
2. My gra-cious Mas-ter and my God, As-sist me to pro-claim,
3. Je-sus! the name that charms our fears, That bids our sor-rows cease;
4. He breaks the pow'r of can-celed sin, He sets the pris-'ner free;
5. Hear Him, ye deaf; His praise, ye dumb, Your loosened tongues em-ploy;

O for a Thousand Tongues to Sing

The glo-ries of my God and King, The tri-umphs of His grace.
To spread thro' all the earth a-broad, The hon-ors of Thy name.
'Tis mu-sic in the sin-ner's ears, 'Tis life, and health, and peace.
His blood can make the foul-est clean; His blood a-vailed for me.
Ye blind, be-hold your Sav-ior come; And leap, ye lame, for joy.

For the Beauty of the Earth 457

FOLLIOTT S. PIERPOINT

ARR. FROM CONRAD KOCHER

1. For the beau-ty of the earth, For the glo-ry of the skies,
2. For the won-der of each hour Of the day and of the night,
3. For the joy of hu-man love, Broth-er, sis-ter, par-ent, child,
4. For Thy Church that ev-er-more Lift-eth ho-ly hands a-bove,

For the love which from our birth O-ver and a-round us lies:
Hill and vale and tree and flower, Sun and moon and stars of light:
Friends on earth, and friends a-bove, For all gen-tle thoughts and mild:
Of-fering up on ev-ery shore Her pure sac-ri-fice of love:

Christ our God, to Thee we raise This our hymn of grate-ful praise.
Christ our God, to Thee we raise This our hymn of grate-ful praise.
Christ our God, to Thee we raise This our hymn of grate-ful praise.
Christ our God, to Thee we raise This our hymn of grate-ful praise.

458 This Is My Father's World

MALTBIE D. BABCOCK

FRANKLIN L. SHEPPARD

1. This is my Fa-ther's world, And to my lis-t'ning ears, All na-ture sings, and round me rings The mu-sic of the spheres.

2. This is my Fa-ther's world, The birds their car-ols raise, The morn-ing light, the lil-y white, De-clare their Ma-ker's praise.

3. This is my Fa-ther's world, O let me ne'er for-get That though the wrong seems oft so strong, God is the Rul-er yet.

This is my Fa-ther's world, I rest me in the thought Of rocks and trees, of . . skies and seas—His hand the won-ders wrought.

This is my Fa-ther's world, He shines in all that's fair; In the rus-tling grass I . . hear Him pass, He speaks to me ev-'ry-where.

This is my Fa-ther's world, The bat-tle is not done, Je-sus who died shall be sat-is-fied, And earth and heav'n be one. A-MEN.

Stepping in the Light

ELIZA E. HEWITT

WILLIAM J. KIRKPATRICK

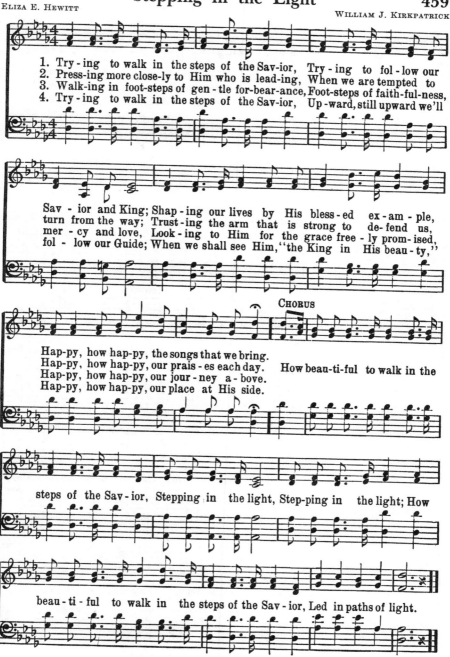

1. Try-ing to walk in the steps of the Sav-ior, Try-ing to fol-low our
2. Press-ing more close-ly to Him who is lead-ing, When we are tempted to
3. Walk-ing in foot-steps of gen-tle for-bear-ance, Foot-steps of faith-ful-ness,
4. Try-ing to walk in the steps of the Sav-ior, Up-ward, still upward we'll

Sav-ior and King; Shap-ing our lives by His bless-ed ex-am-ple,
turn from the way; Trust-ing the arm that is strong to de-fend us,
mer-cy and love, Look-ing to Him for the grace free-ly prom-ised,
fol-low our Guide; When we shall see Him, "the King in His beau-ty,"

CHORUS

Hap-py, how hap-py, the songs that we bring.
Hap-py, how hap-py, our prais-es each day. How beau-ti-ful to walk in the
Hap-py, how hap-py, our jour-ney a-bove.
Hap-py, how hap-py, our place at His side.

steps of the Sav-ior, Stepping in the light, Step-ping in the light; How

beau-ti-ful to walk in the steps of the Sav-ior, Led in paths of light.

460 Room at the Cross for You

IRA F. STANPHILL

IRA F. STANPHILL

1. The cross up-on which Je-sus died Is a shel-ter in which we can
2. Tho' mil-lions have found Him a friend, And have turned from the sins they have
3. The hand of my Sav-iour is strong, And the love of my Sav-iour is

hide, And its grace so free is suf - fi-cient for me, And
sinned, The Sav - iour still waits to o - pen the gate And
long; Through sun-shine or rain, through loss or in gain, The

CHORUS

deep is its foun-tain, as wide as the sea.
wel-come a sin-ner be - fore it's too late. There's room at the cross for
blood flows from Cal-v'ry to cleanse ev-'ry stain.

you, There's room at the cross for you; Tho' mil-lions have come, There's

still room for one, Yes, there's room at the cross for you.

O Perfect Love

461

DOROTHY F. GURNEY

JOSEPH BARNBY

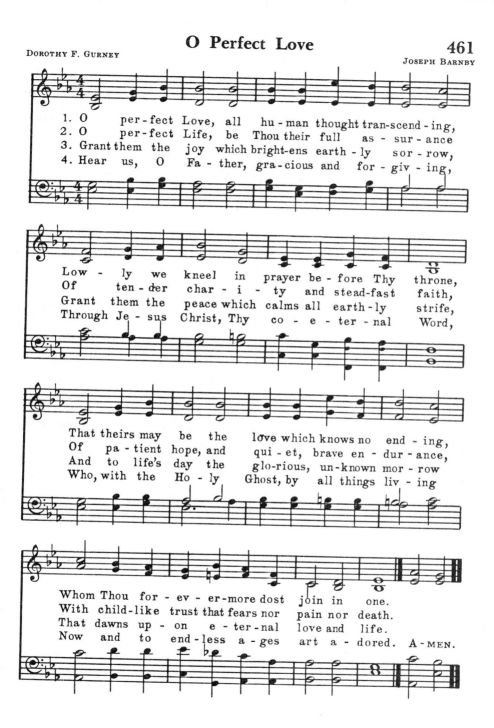

1. O per-fect Love, all hu-man thought tran-scend-ing,
2. O per-fect Life, be Thou their full as-sur-ance
3. Grant them the joy which bright-ens earth-ly sor-row,
4. Hear us, O Fa-ther, gra-cious and for-giv-ing,

Low-ly we kneel in prayer be-fore Thy throne,
Of ten-der char-i-ty and stead-fast faith,
Grant them the peace which calms all earth-ly strife,
Through Je-sus Christ, Thy co-e-ter-nal Word,

That theirs may be the love which knows no end-ing,
Of pa-tient hope, and qui-et, brave en-dur-ance,
And to life's day the glo-rious, un-known mor-row
Who, with the Ho-ly Ghost, by all things liv-ing

Whom Thou for-ev-er-more dost join in one.
With child-like trust that fears nor pain nor death.
That dawns up-on e-ter-nal love and life.
Now and to end-less a-ges art a-dored. A-MEN.

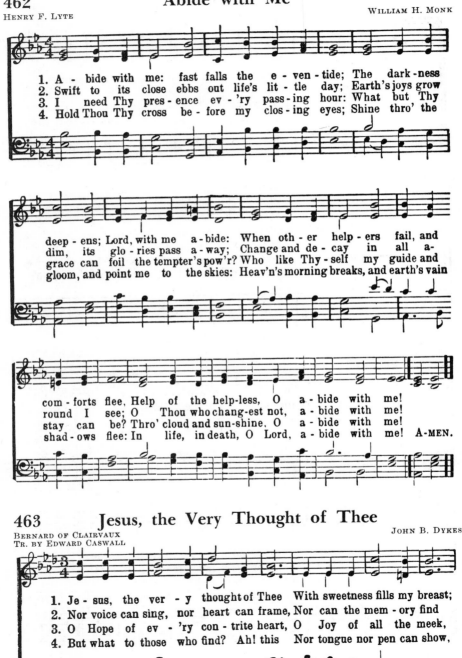

462   **Abide with Me**

HENRY F. LYTE

WILLIAM H. MONK

1. A - bide with me: fast falls the e - ven - tide; The dark - ness
2. Swift to its close ebbs out life's lit - tle day; Earth's joys grow
3. I need Thy pres - ence ev - 'ry pass - ing hour: What but Thy
4. Hold Thou Thy cross be - fore my clos - ing eyes; Shine thro' the

deep - ens; Lord, with me a - bide: When oth - er help - ers fail, and
dim, its glo - ries pass a - way; Change and de - cay in all a -
grace can foil the tempter's pow'r? Who like Thy - self my guide and
gloom, and point me to the skies: Heav'n's morning breaks, and earth's vain

com - forts flee, Help of the help-less, O a - bide with me!
round I see; O Thou who chang-est not, a - bide with me!
stay can be? Thro' cloud and sun-shine, O a - bide with me!
shad - ows flee: In life, in death, O Lord, a - bide with me! A-MEN.

463   **Jesus, the Very Thought of Thee**

BERNARD OF CLAIRVAUX
TR. BY EDWARD CASWALL

JOHN B. DYKES

1. Je - sus, the ver - y thought of Thee With sweetness fills my breast;
2. Nor voice can sing, nor heart can frame, Nor can the mem - ory find
3. O Hope of ev - 'ry con - trite heart, O Joy of all the meek,
4. But what to those who find? Ah! this Nor tongue nor pen can show,

Jesus, the Very Thought of Thee

But sweet-er far Thy face to see, And in Thy pres-ence rest.
A sweet-er sound than Thy blest name, O Sav-ior of man-kind!
To those who fall, how kind Thou art! How good to those who seek!
The love of Je-sus, what it is None but His loved ones know.

Near to the Heart of God   464

CLELAND B. MCAFEE   CLELAND B. MCAFEE

1. There is a place of qui-et rest, Near to the heart of God,
2. There is a place of com-fort sweet, Near to the heart of God,
3. There is a place of full re-lease, Near to the heart of God,

A place where sin can-not mo-lest, Near to the heart of God.
A place where we our Sav-ior meet, Near to the heart of God.
A place where all is joy and peace, Near to the heart of God.

REFRAIN

O Je-sus, blest Re-deem-er, Sent from the heart of God,

Hold us, who wait be-fore Thee, Near to the heart of God.

465   I Am His, and He Is Mine

GEORGE W. ROBINSON   JAMES MOUNTAIN

1. Loved with ev - er - last-ing love, Led by grace that love to know;
2. Heav'n a - bove is soft-er blue, Earth a - round is sweet-er green!
3. Things that once were wild a - larms Can-not now dis - turb my rest;
4. His for - ev - er, on - ly His; Who the Lord and me shall part?

Spir - it, breath-ing from a - bove, Thou hast taught me it is so!
Some-thing lives in ev - 'ry hue Christ-less eyes have nev-er seen:
Closed in ev - er - last - ing arms, Pil - lowed on the lov-ing breast.
Ah, with what a rest of bliss Christ can fill the lov-ing heart!

Oh, this full and per - fect peace! Oh, this trans - port all di - vine!
Birds with glad - der songs o'er - flow, Flow'rs with deep-er beau-ties shine,
Oh, to lie for - ev - er here, Doubt and care and self re - sign,
Heav'n and earth may fade and flee, First-born light in gloom de - cline,

In a love which can-not cease, I am His and He is mine.
Since I know, as now I know, I am His and He is mine.
While He whis-pers in my ear— I am His and He is mine.
But while God' and I shall be, I am His and He is mine.

A Mighty Fortress Is Our God

MARTIN LUTHER
TR. BY FREDERICK H. HEDGE

MARTIN LUTHER

1. A might-y for-tress is our God, A bul-wark nev-er fail - ing;
2. Did we in our own strength confide, Our striv-ing would be los - ing;
3. And tho' this world, with dev-ils filled, Should threaten to un-do us;
4. That word a-bove all earthly pow'rs—No thanks to them—a-bid - eth:

Our help-er He, a-mid the flood Of mor-tal ills pre-vail - ing.
Were not the right Man on our side, The Man of God's own choos - ing.
We will not fear, for God hath willed His truth to tri-umph through us.
The Spir-it and the gifts are ours Thro' Him who with us sid - eth.

For still our an-cient foe Doth seek to work us woe; His craft and pow'r are
Dost ask who that may be? Christ Je-sus, it is He; Lord Sabaoth is His
The prince of darkness grim—We tremble not for him; His rage we can en-
Let goods and kin-dred go, This mor-tal life al - so; The bod-y they may

great, And, armed with cru-el hate, On earth is not his e - qual.
name, From age to age the same, And He must win the bat - tle.
dure, For lo! his doom is sure, One lit-tle word shall fell him.
kill: God's truth a-bid-eth still, His king-dom is for-ev - er.

467 O God, Our Help in Ages Past

ISAAC WATTS

WILLIAM CROFT

1. O God, our help in a-ges past, Our hope for years to come,
2. Un-der the shad-ow of Thy throne Still may we dwell se-cure;
3. Be-fore the hills in or-der stood, Or earth re-ceived her frame,
4. Time, like an ev-er-roll-ing stream, Bears all its sons a-way;
5. O God, our help in a-ges past, Our hope for years to come,

Our shel-ter from the storm-y blast, And our e-ter-nal home!
Suf-fi-cient is Thine arm a-lone, And our de-fense is sure.
From ev-er-last-ing Thou art God, To end-less years the same.
They fly, for-got-ten, as a dream Dies at the ope-ning day.
Be Thou our guide while life shall last, And our e-ter-nal home. A-MEN.

468 There's a Wideness in God's Mercy

FREDERICK W. FABER

LIZZIE S. TOURJÉE

1. There's a wide-ness in God's mer-cy, Like the wide-ness of the sea;
2. There is wel-come for the sin-ner, And more grac-es for the good;
3. For the love of God is broad-er, Than the meas-ure of man's mind;
4. If our love were but more sim-ple, We should take Him at His Word,

There's a kind-ness in His jus-tice, Which is more than lib-er-ty.
There is mer-cy with the Sav-ior; There is heal-ing in His blood.
And the heart of the E-ter-nal Is most won-der-ful-ly kind.
And our lives would be all sun-shine In the sweet-ness of our Lord.

Grace Greater Than Our Sin

JULIA H. JOHNSTON

DANIEL B. TOWNER

1. Mar - vel-ous grace of our lov - ing Lord, Grace that ex - ceeds our
2. Sin and de - spair like the sea waves cold, Threat-en the soul with
3. Dark is the stain that we can - not hide, What can a - vail to
4. Mar - vel-ous, in - fi - nite, match-less grace, Free - ly be - stowed on

sin and our guilt, Yon - der on Cal - va - ry's mount out - poured,
in - fi - nite loss; Grace that is great - er, yes, grace un - told,
wash it a - way? Look! there is flow - ing a crim - son tide,
all who be - lieve; You that are long - ing to see His face,

CHORUS

There where the blood of the Lamb was spilt.
Points to the Ref - uge, the Might - y Cross. Grace, grace,
Whit - er than snow you may be to - day.
Will you this mo - ment His grace re - ceive? Mar - vel - ous grace,

God's grace, Grace that will par-don and cleanse with-in; Grace,
In - fi - nite grace, Mar - vel-ous

grace, God's grace, Grace that is great-er than all our sin.
grace, In - fi - nite grace,

470 Wonderful Grace of Jesus

HALDOR LILLENAS

HALDOR LILLENAS

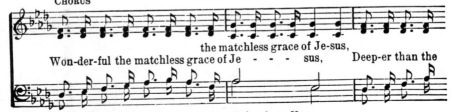

1. Won - der - ful grace of Je - sus, Great - er than all my sin; . .
2. Won - der - ful grace of Je - sus, Reach-ing to all the lost, . .
3. Won - der - ful grace of Je - sus, Reach-ing the most de - filed, . .

How shall my tongue de - scribe it, Where shall its praise be - gin? . . .
By it I have been pardoned, Saved to the ut - ter - most, . . .
By its trans-form-ing pow - er, Mak - ing him God's dear child, . .

Tak - ing a - way my bur - den, Set - ting my spir - it free; . . .
Chains have been torn a - sun - der, Giv - ing me lib - er - ty; . . .
Pur - chas-ing peace and heav - en, For all e - ter - ni - ty; . . .

For the won - der - ful grace of Je - sus reach - es me.
For the won - der - ful grace of Je - sus reach - es me.
And the won - der - ful grace of Je - sus reach - es me.

CHORUS

the matchless grace of Je-sus,
Won-der-ful the matchless grace of Je - - - sus, Deep-er than the

Wonderful Grace of Jesus

471 Saved by Grace

FANNY J. CROSBY

GEORGE C. STEBBINS
ARR. BY SEYMOUR SWETS

1. Some day the sil - ver cord will break, And I no more as now shall sing;
2. Some day my earth - ly house will fall, I can-not tell how soon 'twill be;
3. Some day, when fades the gold-en sun Be-neath the ro - sy -tint-ed west,
4. Some day: till then I'll watch and wait, My lamp all trimmed and burning bright,

But oh, the joy when I shall wake With-in the pal-ace of the King!
But this I know—my All in All Has now a place in heav'n for me.
My blessed Lord will say, "Well done!" And I shall en - ter in - to rest.
That when my Sav - ior opes the gate, My soul to Him may take its flight.

REFRAIN

And I shall see Him face to face, And tell the sto-ry—Saved by grace;
shall see to face,

And I shall see Him face to face, And tell the sto-ry—Saved by grace.
shall see to face,

rit.

All the Way My Savior Leads Me

FANNY J. CROSBY

ROBERT LOWRY

472

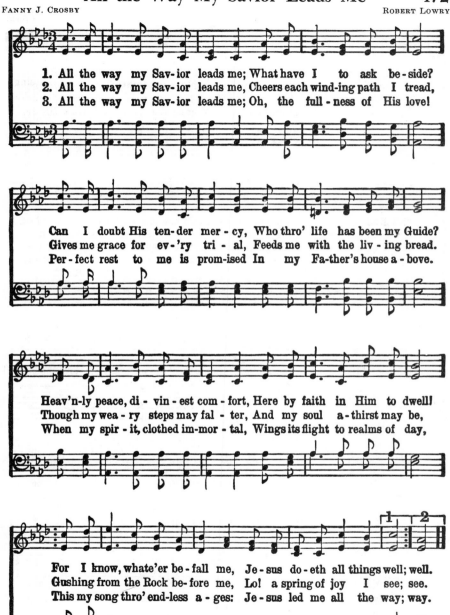

1. All the way my Sav-ior leads me; What have I to ask be-side?
2. All the way my Sav-ior leads me, Cheers each wind-ing path I tread,
3. All the way my Sav-ior leads me; Oh, the full-ness of His love!

Can I doubt His ten-der mer-cy, Who thro' life has been my Guide?
Gives me grace for ev-'ry tri-al, Feeds me with the liv-ing bread.
Per-fect rest to me is prom-ised In my Fa-ther's house a-bove.

Heav'n-ly peace, di-vin-est com-fort, Here by faith in Him to dwell!
Though my wea-ry steps may fal-ter, And my soul a-thirst may be,
When my spir-it, clothed im-mor-tal, Wings its flight to realms of day,

For I know, whate'er be-fall me, Je-sus do-eth all things well; well.
Gushing from the Rock be-fore me, Lo! a spring of joy I see; see.
This my song thro' end-less a-ges: Je-sus led me all the way; way.

473 God Leads Us Along

G. A. Young

G. A. Young

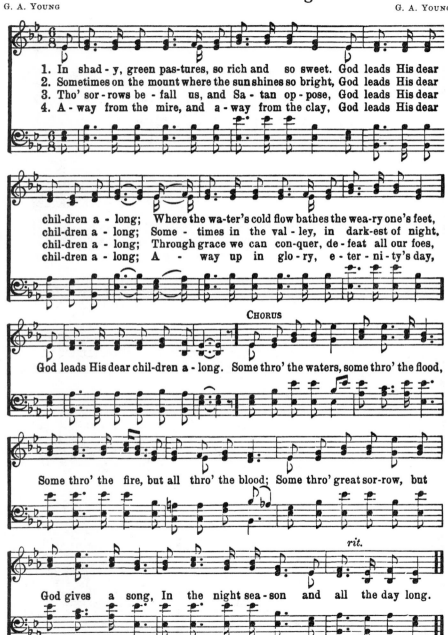

1. In shad - y, green pas-tures, so rich and so sweet, God leads His dear
2. Sometimes on the mount where the sun shines so bright, God leads His dear
3. Tho' sor - rows be - fall us, and Sa - tan op - pose, God leads His dear
4. A - way from the mire, and a - way from the clay, God leads His dear

chil-dren a - long; Where the wa-ter's cold flow bathes the wea-ry one's feet,
chil-dren a - long; Some - times in the val - ley, in dark-est of night,
chil-dren a - long; Through grace we can con-quer, de - feat all our foes,
chil-dren a - long; A - way up in glo - ry, e - ter - ni - ty's day,

CHORUS

God leads His dear chil-dren a - long. Some thro' the waters, some thro' the flood,

Some thro' the fire, but all thro' the blood; Some thro' great sor-row, but

rit.

God gives a song, In the night sea - son and all the day long.

What God Hath Promised

ANNIE JOHNSON FLINT

474

WILLIAM M. RUNYAN

1. God hath not prom-ised skies al-ways blue, Flow-er-strewn path-ways
2. God hath not prom-ised we shall not know Toil and temp-ta-tion,
3. God hath not prom-ised smooth roads and wide, Swift, eas-y trav-el,

all our lives through; God hath not prom-ised sun with-out rain,
trou-ble and woe; He hath not told us we shall not bear
need-ing no guide; Nev-er a moun-tain rock-y and steep,

CHORUS

Joy with-out sor-row, peace with-out pain.
Man-y a bur-den, man-y a care. But God hath prom-ised
Nev-er a riv-er tur-bid and deep.

strength for the day, Rest for the la-bor, light for the way, Grace for the

tri-als, help from a-bove, Un-fail-ing sym-pa-thy, un-dy-ing love.

475 Guide Me, O Thou Great Jehovah

WILLIAM WILLIAMS

THOMAS HASTINGS

1. Guide me, O Thou great Je - ho - vah, Pil - grim thro' this bar - ren
2. O - pen now the crys - tal foun - tain Whence the heal - ing wa - ters
3. When I tread the verge of Jor - dan, Bid my anx - ious fears sub -

land; I am weak, but Thou art might - y, Hold me with Thy pow'r - ful
flow; Let the fi - er - y, cloud - y pil - lar Lead me all my jour - ney
side; Bear me thro' the swell - ing cur - rent, Land me safe on Ca - naan's

hand: Bread of Heav - en, Feed me till I want no more;
thro': Strong De - liv - 'rer, Be Thou still my Strength and Shield;
side: Songs of prais - es I will ev - er give to Thee;

Bread of Heav - en, Feed me till I want no more.
Strong De - liv - 'rer, Be Thou still my Strength and Shield.
Songs of prais - es I will ev - er give to Thee. A - MEN.

Songs of Praises

WILLIAM WILLIAMS
GIPSY SMITH, 4

JOHN HUGHES
ARR. BY E. EDWIN YOUNG

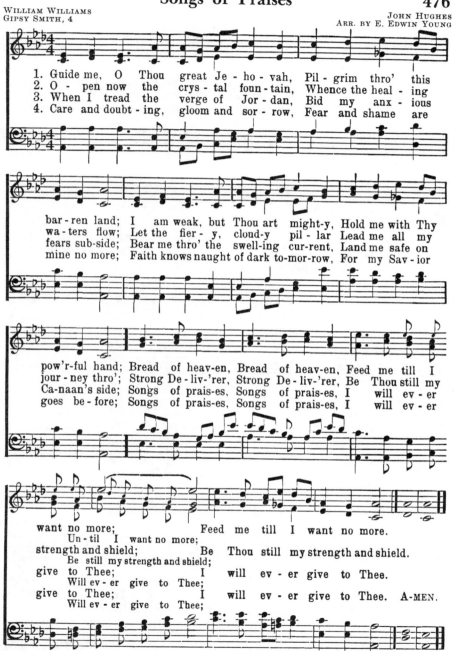

1. Guide me, O Thou great Je - ho - vah, Pil - grim thro' this
2. O - pen now the crys - tal foun - tain, Whence the heal - ing
3. When I tread the verge of Jor - dan, Bid my anx - ious
4. Care and doubt - ing, gloom and sor - row, Fear and shame are

bar - ren land; I am weak, but Thou art might - y, Hold me with Thy
wa - ters flow; Let the fier - y, cloud - y pil - lar Lead me all my
fears sub - side; Bear me thro' the swell - ing cur - rent, Land me safe on
mine no more; Faith knows naught of dark to - mor - row, For my Sav - ior

pow'r - ful hand; Bread of heav - en, Bread of heav - en, Feed me till I
jour - ney thro'; Strong De - liv - 'rer, Strong De - liv - 'rer, Be Thou still my
Ca - naan's side; Songs of prais - es, Songs of prais - es, I will ev - er
goes be - fore; Songs of prais - es, Songs of prais - es, I will ev - er

want no more; Feed me till I want no more.
Un - til I want no more;
strength and shield; Be Thou still my strength and shield.
Be still my strength and shield;
give to Thee; I will ev - er give to Thee.
Will ev - er give to Thee;
give to Thee; I will ev - er give to Thee. A-MEN.
Will ev - er give to Thee;

477

Jesus, Savior, Pilot Me

EDWARD HOPPER

JOHN E. GOULD

1. Je - sus, Sav - ior, pi - lot me O - ver life's tem - pes-tuous sea;
2. As   a moth - er   stills her child, Thou canst hush the   o - cean wild;
3. When at last I   near the shore, And the fear - ful break-ers roar

Un-known waves be - fore me   roll, Hid - ing rock and treacherous shoal;
Boisterous waves o - bey Thy   will When Thou say'st to them "Be still!"
'Twixt me and the peace-ful rest, Then, while lean-ing on Thy breast,

Chart and com - pass came from Thee: Je - sus, Sav - ior, pi - lot me.
Won-drous Sov-'reign of   the   sea, Je - sus, Sav - ior, pi - lot me.
May   I hear Thee say   to   me, "Fear not, I   will pi - lot thee."

478

I Need Thee Every Hour

ANNIE S. HAWKS

ROBERT LOWRY

1. I need Thee ev-'ry hour, Most gra - cious Lord; No ten - der voice like
2. I need Thee ev-'ry hour, Stay Thou near by; Temp-ta-tions lose their
3. I need Thee ev-'ry hour, In   joy or   pain; Come quick-ly and a-
4. I need Thee ev-'ry hour, Most Ho - ly One; O make me Thine in-

I Need Thee Every Hour

CHORUS

Thine Can peace af - ford.
pow'r When Thou art nigh.
bide, Or life is vain.
deed, Thou bless-ed Son!

I need Thee, O I need Thee; Ev-'ry hour I need Thee! O bless me now, my Sav - ior, I come to Thee!

I Am Not Skilled to Understand

DORA GREENWELL

479

WILLIAM J. KIRKPATRICK

1. I am not skilled to un-der-stand What God hath willed, what God hath planned;
2. I take Him at His word indeed: "Christ died for sin - ners," this I read;
3. That He should leave His place on high And come for sin - ful man to die,
4. Yea, liv - ing, dy - ing, let me bring My strength, my sol-ace from this spring:

I on - ly know at His right hand Is One who is my Sav-iour!
For in my heart I find a need Of Him to be my Sav-iour!
You count it strange? so once did I, Be - fore I knew my Sav-iour!
That He who lives to be my King Once died to be my Sav-iour!

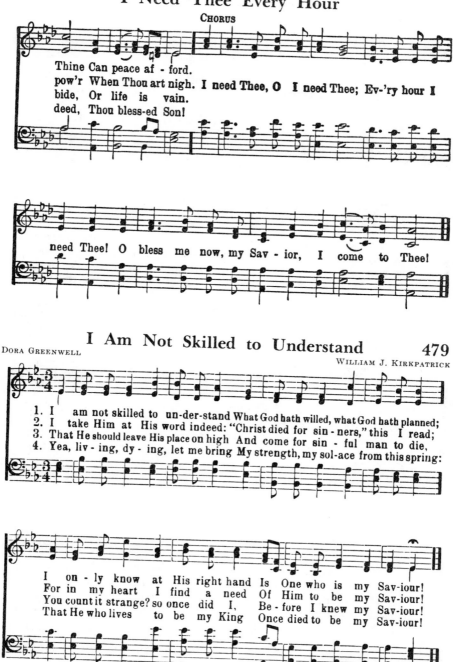

480   Savior, Like a Shepherd Lead Us

WILLIAM B. BRADBURY

"HYMNS FOR THE YOUNG"
ASC. TO DOROTHY A. THRUPP

1. Sav-ior, like a shep-herd lead us, Much we need Thy ten-der care;
2. We are Thine; do Thou be-friend us, Be the Guardian of our way;
3. Thou hast promised to re-ceive us, Poor and sin-ful though we be;
4. Ear-ly let us seek Thy fa-vor; Ear-ly let us do Thy will;

In Thy pleas-ant pas-tures feed us, For our use Thy folds pre-pare:
Keep Thy flock, from sin de-fend us, Seek us when we go a-stray:
Thou hast mer-cy to re-lieve us, Grace to cleanse, and pow'r to free:
Bless-ed Lord and on-ly Sav-ior, With Thy love our bos-oms fill:

Bless-ed Je-sus, Bless-ed Je-sus, Thou hast bought us, Thine we are;
Bless-ed Je-sus, Bless-ed Je-sus, Hear, O hear us when we pray;
Bless-ed Je-sus, Bless-ed Je-sus, Ear-ly let us turn to Thee;
Bless-ed Je-sus, Bless-ed Je-sus, Thou hast loved us, love us still;

Bless-ed Je-sus, Bless-ed Je-sus, Thou hast bought us, Thine we are.
Bless-ed Je-sus, Bless-ed Je-sus, Hear, O hear us when we pray.
Bless-ed Je-sus, Bless-ed Je-sus, Ear-ly let us turn to Thee.
Bless-ed Je-sus, Bless-ed Je-sus, Thou hast loved us, love us still.

Beulah Land

EDGAR P. STITES

JOHN R. SWENEY

1. I've reached the land of corn and wine, And all its rich-es free-ly mine;
2. My Sav-ior comes and walks with me, And sweet com-mun-ion here have we;
3. A sweet per-fume up-on the breeze Is borne from ev-er-ver-nal trees,
4. The zeph-yrs seem to float to me, Sweet sounds of Heaven's mel-o-dy,

Here shines undimmed one bliss-ful day, For all my night has passed a-way.
He gen-tly leads me by His hand, For this is Heav-en's bor-der-land.
And flow'rs, that nev-er-fad-ing grow, Where streams of life for-ev-er flow.
As an-gels with the white-robed throng Join in the sweet Re-demp-tion song.

CHORUS

O Beu-lah Land, sweet Beu-lah Land, As on thy high-est mount I stand,

I look a-way a-cross the sea, Where mansions are pre-pared for me, And

view the shin-ing glo-ry-shore,—My Heav'n, my home for-ev-er-more!

482 Sooner or Later

Lulu W. Koch

Wilbur E. Nelson

1. Soon-er or lat-er the skies will be bright, Tears will be all wiped a-
2. Soon-er or lat-er, our Lord knows the hour, He'll send His be-lov-ed
3. Soon-er or lat-er, yes, soon-er for some, Darkness will all then be

way; Soon-er or lat-er, then com-eth the light, Night will be
Son; Soon-er or lat-er, in His might and pow'r, Our bat-tles
past; Soon-er or lat-er our Sav-iour will come, With Him will

CHORUS

turned in-to day. (glad day.)
all will be won. (be won.) Soon-er or lat-er cares will have flown,
your lot be cast? (be cast?)

Sun-shine and glad-ness we'll see; Soon-er or lat-er God
we'll see;

call-eth His own, With Him for-ev-er to be. (to be.)

He the Pearly Gates Will Open

FRED BLOM
TR. BY NATHANIEL CARLSON

ELSIE AHLWÉN

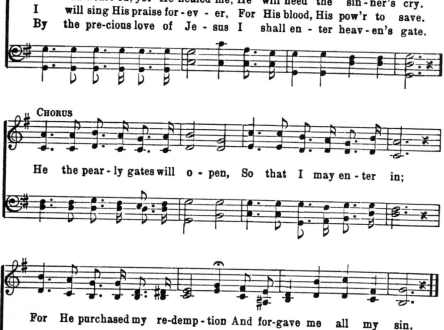

1. Love Di-vine, so great and won-drous, Deep and might-y, pure, sub-lime!
2. Like a dove when hunt-ed, frightened, As a wound-ed fawn was I;
3. Love Di-vine, so great and won-drous, All my sins He then for-gave!
4. In life's e-ven-tide, at twi-light, At His door I'll knock and wait;

Com-ing from the heart of Je-sus, Just the same thro' tests of time.
Bro-ken-heart-ed, yet He healed me, He will heed the sin-ner's cry.
I will sing His praise for-ev-er, For His blood, His pow'r to save.
By the pre-cious love of Je-sus I shall en-ter heav-en's gate.

CHORUS

He the pear-ly gates will o-pen, So that I may en-ter in;

For He purchased my re-demp-tion And for-gave me all my sin.

484   He'll Understand and Say "Well Done"

LUCY E. CAMPBELL

LUCY E. CAMPBELL
ARR. BY WILLIAM J. FLOYD

1. If when you give the best of your ser-vice, Tell-ing the world that the Sav-iour is come; Be not dis-mayed when men don't be-lieve you, He un-der-stands; He'll say, "Well done."

2. Mis-un-der-stood, the Sav-iour of sin-ners Hung on the cross; He was God's on-ly Son; Oh! hear Him call His Fa-ther in heav-en, "Let not my will, but Thine be done."

3. If when this life of la-bor is end-ed, And the re-ward of the race you have run; Oh! take the sweet rest pre-pared for faith-ful, Will be His blest and fi-nal, "Well done."

4. But if you try and fail in your try-ing, Hands sore and scarred from the work you've be-gun; Take up your cross, run quick-ly to meet Him, He'll un-der-stand; He'll say, "Well done."

CHORUS

Oh when I come to the end of my jour-ney, Wea-ry of life and the bat-tle is won; Car-rying the staff and the

He'll Understand and Say "Well Done"

cross of re-demp-tion, He'll un-der-stand and say, "Well done."

Just a Closer Walk with Thee 485

Author Unknown

Arr. by William J. Floyd

1. I am weak but Thou art strong; (art strong;) Je-sus, keep me from all wrong;
2. Thro' this world of toil and snares, (and snares,) If I fal-ter Lord, who cares?
3. When my fee-ble life is o'er, (is o'er,) Time for me will be no more;

I'll be sat-is-fied as long (just as long) As I walk, let me walk close to Thee.
Who with me my bur-den shares (bur-den shares) None but Thee, dear Lord, none but Thee.
Guide me gent-ly, safe-ly o'er (safe-ly o'er) To Thy king-dom shore, to Thy shore.

REFRAIN

Just a clos-er walk with Thee, (with Thee) Grant it, Je-sus, is my plea,

Dai-ly walk-ing close to Thee, (to Thee,) Let it be, dear Lord, let it be.

Copyright © 1964 by Hope Publishing Co. International copyright secured. All rights reserved

486 Beyond the Sunset

VIRGIL P. BROCK

BLANCHE K. BROCK

1. Be-yond the sun-set, O bliss-ful morn-ing, When with our
2. Be-yond the sun-set no clouds will gath-er, No storms will
3. Be-yond the sun-set a hand will guide me To God, the
4. Be-yond the sun-set, O glad re-un-ion, With our dear

Sav-iour heav'n is be-gun. Earth's toiling end-ed, O glorious
threat-en, no fears an-noy; O day of glad-ness, O day un-
Fa-ther, whom I a-dore; His glorious pres-ence, His words of
loved ones who've gone be-fore; In that fair homeland we'll know no

dawn-ing; Be-yond the sun-set, when day is done.
end-ing, Be-yond the sun-set, e-ter-nal joy!
wel-come, Will be my por-tion on that fair shore.
par-ting, Bey-ond the sun-set for ev-er-more!

487 Amazing Grace

JOHN NEWTON

EARLY AMERICAN MELODY
ARR. BY EDWIN O. EXCELL

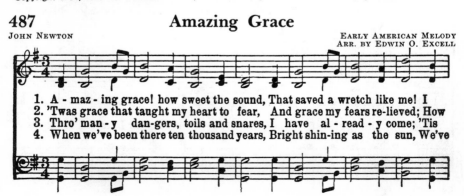

1. A-maz-ing grace! how sweet the sound, That saved a wretch like me! I
2. 'Twas grace that taught my heart to fear, And grace my fears re-lieved; How
3. Thro' man-y dan-gers, toils and snares, I have al-read-y come; 'Tis
4. When we've been there ten thousand years, Bright shin-ing as the sun, We've

Amazing Grace

once was lost, but now am found, Was blind, but now I see.
pre - cious did that grace ap - pear The hour I first be-lieved!
grace hath bro't me safe thus far And grace will lead me home.
no less days to sing God's praise Than when we first be - gun.

I Shall Be Like Him

488

W. A. SPENCER

W. A. SPENCER

1. When I shall reach the more ex-cel-lent glo-ry, And all my tri-als are passed,
2. We shall not wait till the glo - ri-ous dawning Breaks on the vi-sion so fair,
3. More and more like Him, repeat the blest story, O - ver and o - ver a-gain,

I shall be like Him, O won-der-ful sto-ry! I shall be like Him at last.
Now we may welcome the heav-en-ly morning, Now we His image may bear.
Changed by His Spirit from glo-ry to glo-ry, I shall be sat - is - fied then.

CHORUS

I shall be like Him, I shall be like Him, And in His beau-ty shall shine,

I shall be like Him, wondrously like Him, Je-sus, my Sav-iour di - vine.

489 · Peace, Perfect Peace

EDWARD H. BICKERSTETH

GEORGE T. CALDBECK
ARR. BY CHARLES J. VINCENT

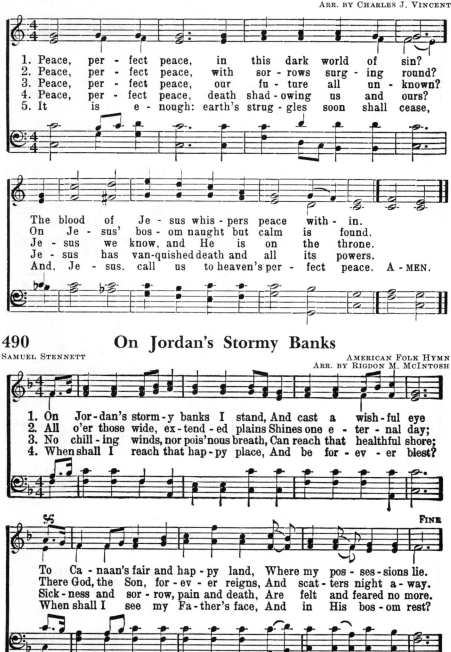

1. Peace, per-fect peace, in this dark world of sin?
2. Peace, per-fect peace, with sor-rows surg-ing round?
3. Peace, per-fect peace, our fu-ture all un-known?
4. Peace, per-fect peace, death shad-owing us and ours?
5. It is e-nough: earth's strug-gles soon shall cease,

The blood of Je-sus whis-pers peace with-in.
On Je-sus' bos-om naught but calm is found.
Je-sus we know, and He is on the throne.
Je-sus has van-quished death and all its powers.
And, Je-sus, call us to heaven's per-fect peace. A-MEN.

490 · On Jordan's Stormy Banks

SAMUEL STENNETT

AMERICAN FOLK HYMN
ARR. BY RIGDON M. McINTOSH

1. On Jor-dan's storm-y banks I stand, And cast a wish-ful eye
2. All o'er those wide, ex-tend-ed plains Shines one e-ter-nal day;
3. No chill-ing winds, nor pois'nous breath, Can reach that healthful shore;
4. When shall I reach that hap-py place, And be for-ev-er blest?

Fine

To Ca-naan's fair and hap-py land, Where my pos-ses-sions lie.
There God, the Son, for-ev-er reigns, And scat-ters night a-way.
Sick-ness and sor-row, pain and death, Are felt and feared no more.
When shall I see my Fa-ther's face, And in His bos-om rest?

D.S.—*O who will come and go with me? I am bound for the prom-ised land.*

On Jordan's Stormy Banks

REFRAIN

D. S.

I am bound for the promised land, . . . I am bound for the promised land;

prom-ised land,

Shall We Gather at the River? 491

ROBERT LOWRY

ROBERT LOWRY

1. Shall we gath-er at the riv-er, Where bright an-gel feet have trod;
2. On the bos-om of the riv-er, Where the Sav-ior-King we own,
3. Ere we reach the shin-ing riv-er, Lay we ev-'ry bur-den down;
4. Soon we'll reach the shin-ing riv-er, Soon our pil-grim-age will cease;

With its crys-tal tide for-ev-er Flow-ing by the throne of God?
We shall meet, and sor-row nev-er,'Neath the glo-ry of the throne.
Grace our spir-its will de-liv-er, And pro-vide a robe and crown.
Soon our hap-py hearts will quiv-er With the mel-o-dy of peace.

CHORUS

p

Yes, we'll gath-er at the riv-er, The beau-ti-ful, the beau-ti-ful riv-er,

Gath-er with the saints at the riv-er That flows by the throne of God.

492   No Night There

John R. Clements   Hart P. Danks

1. In the land of fade-less day Lies the "cit-y four-square,"
2. All the gates of pearl are made, In the "cit-y four-square,"
3. And the gates shall nev-er close To the "cit-y four-square,"
4. There they need no sun-shine bright, In that "cit-y four-square,"

It shall nev-er pass a-way, And there is "no night there."
All the streets with gold are laid, And there is "no night there."
There life's crys-tal riv-er flows, And there is "no night there."
For the Lamb is all the light, And there is "no night there."

Chorus

mf

God shall "wipe a-way all tears;" There's no death, no pain, nor fears;

f   *dim.*   *mf*

And they count not time by years, For there is "no night there."
And they count not time by years, by years, For there is "no night..... there."

Face to Face

493

CARRIE E. BRECK

GRANT C. TULLAR

1. Face to face with Christ, my Sav - ior, Face to face—what will it be?
2. On - ly faint - ly now I see Him, With the dark-ling veil be-tween,
3. What re-joic-ing in His pres-ence, When are ban-ished grief and pain;
4. Face to face! O bliss-ful mo-ment! Face to face—to see and know;

When with rap-ture I be-hold Him, Je - sus Christ who died for me.
But a bless-ed day is com-ing, When His glo - ry shall be seen.
When the crook-ed ways are straightened, And the dark things shall be plain.
Face to face with my Re-deem - er, Je - sus Christ who loves me so.

CHORUS

Face to face I shall be - hold Him, Far be-yond the star - ry sky;

Face to face in all His glo - ry, I shall see Him by and by!

O That Will Be Glory

Charles H. Gabriel

Charles H. Gabriel

1. When all my la-bors and tri-als are o'er, And I am safe on that
2. When, by the gift of His in-fi-nite grace, I am ac-cord-ed in
3. Friends will be there I have loved long a-go; Joy like a riv-er a-

beau-ti-ful shore, Just to be near the dear Lord I a-dore,
Heav-en a place, Just to be there and to look on His face,
round me will flow; Yet, just a smile from my Sav-ior, I know,

rit. CHORUS. *Faster*

Will thro' the a-ges be glo-ry for me. . . . O that will be
O . . . . . . that will

glo-ry for me, Glo-ry for me, glo-ry for me; When by His grace
be glo-ry for me, Glo-ry for me, glo-ry for me; . . . . . .

rit. > > > >

I shall look on His face, That will be glo-ry, be glo-ry for me.

Some Golden Daybreak

Carl A. Blackmore

Carl A. Blackmore

1. Some glo-rious morn-ing sor - row will cease, Some glo-rious morn-ing
2. Sad hearts will glad - den, all shall be bright, Good-bye for - ev - er
3. Oh, what a meet - ing, there in the skies, No tears nor cry - ing

all will be peace; Heart-aches all end - ed, school-days all done,
to earth's dark night; Changed in a mo - ment, like Him to be,
shall dim our eyes; Loved ones u - nit - ed e - ter - nal - ly,

rit.

Chorus

Heav - en will o - pen— Je - sus will come.
Oh, glo-rious day-break, Je - sus I'll see, Some gold - en day-break
Oh, what a day-break that morn will be.

Je - sus will come; Some gold-en day-break, bat-tles all won, He'll shout the

vic - t'ry, break thro' the blue, Some gold-en day-break, for me, for you.

496   Some Time We'll Understand

MAXWELL N. CORNELIUS   JAMES McGRANAHAN

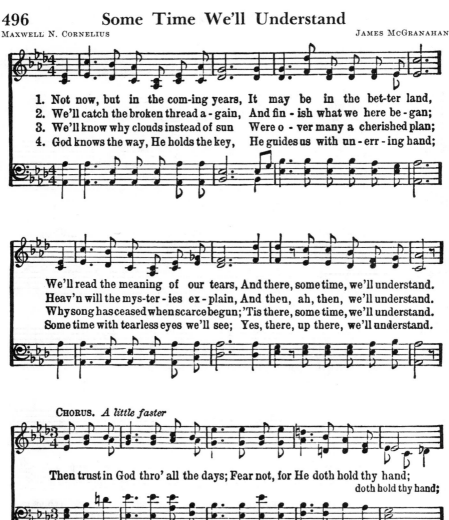

1. Not now, but in the com-ing years, It may be in the bet-ter land,
2. We'll catch the broken thread a - gain, And fin - ish what we here be - gan;
3. We'll know why clouds instead of sun Were o - ver many a cherished plan;
4. God knows the way, He holds the key, He guides us with un - err - ing hand;

We'll read the meaning of our tears, And there, some time, we'll understand.
Heav'n will the mys-ter-ies ex-plain, And then, ah, then, we'll understand.
Why song has ceased when scarce begun; 'Tis there, some time, we'll understand.
Some time with tearless eyes we'll see; Yes, there, up there, we'll understand.

CHORUS. *A little faster*

Then trust in God thro' all the days; Fear not, for He doth hold thy hand;
doth hold thy hand;

A tempo   *cres.*   *ad lib.*

Though dark thy way, still sing and praise, Some time, some time, we'll understand.

Sweet By and By

497

SANFORD F. BENNETT

JOSEPH P. WEBSTER

1. There's a land that is fair-er than day, And by faith we can see it a-far; For the Fa-ther waits o-ver the way, To pre-pare us a dwell-ing-place there.

2. We shall sing on that beau-ti-ful shore The mel-o-di-ous songs of the blest, And our spir-its shall sor-row no more, Not a sigh for the bless-ing of rest.

3. To our boun-ti-ful Fa-ther a-bove, We will of-fer our trib-ute of praise, For the glo-ri-ous gift of His love, And the bless-ings that hal-low our days.

CHORUS

In the sweet by and by, We shall meet on that beau-ti-ful shore; In the sweet by and by, We shall meet on that beau-ti-ful shore.

We Shall See the King Some Day

LEWIS E. JONES

LEWIS E. JONES

1. Tho' the way we jour-ney may be oft-en drear, We shall see the
2. Aft-er pain and an-guish, aft-er toil and care, We shall see the
3. Aft-er foes are con-quered, aft-er bat-tles won, We shall see the
4. There with all the loved ones who have gone be-fore, We shall see the

King some day (some day); On that bless-ed morn-ing clouds will dis-ap-pear;
King some day (some day); Thro' the end-less a - ges joy and blessings share,
King some day (some day); Aft - er strife is o - ver, aft-er set of sun,
King some day (some day); Sor - row past for-ev - er on that peace-ful shore,

CHORUS

We shall see the King some day. We shall see the King some day (some day),

We will shout and sing some day (some day); Gath-ered round the throne,

When He shall call His own, We shall see the King some day.

Accepted in the Beloved

CIVILLA D. MARTIN

WENDELL P. LOVELESS

1. "In the Be-lov-ed" ac-cept-ed am I, Ris-en, as-cend-ed, and
2. "In the Be-lov-ed"—how safe my re-treat, In the Be-lov-ed ac-
3. "In the Be-lov-ed" I went to the tree, There, in His Per-son, by

seat-ed on high; Saved from all sin thro' His in-fi-nite grace,
count-ed com-plete; "Who can con-demn me?" In Him I am free,
faith I may see In-fi-nite wrath roll-ing o-ver His head,

CHORUS

With the re-deemed ones ac-cord-ed a place.
Sav-ior and Keep-er for-ev-er is He. "In the Be-lov-ed," God's
In-fi-nite grace, for He died in my stead.

mar-vel-ous grace Calls me to dwell in this won-der-ful place; God sees my

Sav-ior and then He sees me "In the Be-lov-ed," ac-cept-ed and free.

500 When the Roll Is Called Up Yonder

James M. Black

James M. Black

1. When the trumpet of the Lord shall sound, and time shall be no more, And the
2. On that bright and cloudless morning when the dead in Christ shall rise, And the
3. Let us la-bor for the Mas-ter from the dawn till set-ting sun, Let us

morning breaks, e-ter-nal, bright and fair; When the saved of earth shall gather
glo-ry of His res-ur-rec-tion share; When His cho-sen ones shall gather
talk of all His wondrous love and care; Then when all of life is o-ver,

o-ver on the oth-er shore, And the roll is called up yon-der, I'll be there.
to their home beyond the skies, And the roll is called up yon-der, I'll be there.
and our work on earth is done, And the roll is called up yon-der, I'll be there.

CHORUS.

When the roll . . . . . . is called up yon - - - - der, When the
When the roll is called up yon-der, I'll be there,

roll . . . . is called up yon - - der, When the roll . . . . is called up
When the roll is called up yon-der, I'll be there, When the roll is called up

When the Roll Is Called Up Yonder

yon - der, When the roll is called up yon - der, I'll be there.

When We All Get to Heaven

501

ELIZA E. HEWITT

EMILY D. WILSON

1. Sing the won-drous love of Je - sus, Sing His mer-cy and His grace;
2. While we walk the pil - grim pathway, Clouds will o - ver-spread the sky;
3. Let us then be true and faith-ful, Trust-ing, serv-ing ev - 'ry day;
4. On - ward to the prize be - fore us! Soon His beau-ty we'll be - hold;

In the man-sions bright and blessed, He'll pre-pare for us a place.
But when trav'ling days are o - ver, Not a shad-ow, not a sigh.
Just one glimpse of Him in glo - ry Will the toils of life re - pay.
Soon the pearl - y gates will o - pen, We shall tread the streets of gold.

for us a place.

CHORUS

When we all get to heaven, What a day of re-joicing that will be!
When we all What a day of re-joicing that will be!

When we all see Je-sus, We'll sing and shout the vic-to-ry.........
When we all and shout the vic-to-ry.

502   Where the Gates Swing Outward Never

CHARLES H. GABRIEL   CHARLES H. GABRIEL

1. Just a few more days to be filled with praise, And to tell the
2. Just a few more years with their toil and tears, And the jour - ney
3. Tho' the hills be steep and the val - leys deep, With no flow'rs my
4. What a joy 'twill be when I wake to see Him for whom my

old, old sto - ry; Then, when twi - light falls, and my Sav - ior calls,
will be end - ed; Then I'll be with Him, where the tide of time
way a - dorn - ing; Tho' the night be lone and my rest a stone,
heart is burn - ing! Nev - er - more to sigh, nev - er - more to die—

CHORUS

I shall go to Him in glo - ry.
With e - ter - ni - ty is blend - ed. I'll ex-change my cross for a
Joy a - waits me in the morn - ing.
For that day my heart is yearn - ing.

star - ry crown, Where the gates swing out-ward nev - er; At His feet I'll

lay ev - 'ry bur - den down, And with Je - sus reign for - ev - er.

Will There Be Any Stars?

Eliza E. Hewitt

John R. Sweney

1. I am think-ing to-day of that beau-ti-ful land I shall reach when the
2. In the strength of the Lord let me la-bor and pray, Let me watch as a
3. Oh, what joy it will be when His face I be-hold, Liv-ing gems at His

sun go-eth down; When thro' wonderful grace by my Sav-ior I stand, Will there
win-ner of souls; That bright stars may be mine in the glo-ri-ous day, When His
feet to lay down; It would sweeten my bliss in the cit-y of gold, Should there

be an-y stars in my crown?
praise like the sea-bil-low rolls. Will there be an-y stars, an-y stars in my
be an-y stars in my crown.

CHORUS.

crown When at evening the sun go-eth down? . . . When I wake with the blest
go-eth down?

In the mansions of rest, Will there be an-y stars in my crown? . . A-MEN.
an-y stars in my crown?

504   When We See Christ

ESTHER K. RUSTHOI   ESTHER K. RUSTHOI

1. Oft - times the day seems long, our tri - als hard to bear,
2. Some - times the sky looks dark with not a ray of light,
3. Life's day will soon be o'er, all storms for - ev - er past,

We're tempt - ed to com - plain, To mur - mur and de - spair;
We're tossed and driv - en on, No hu - man help in sight;
We'll cross the great di - vide To glo - ry — safe at last;

But Christ will soon ap - pear To catch His Bride a - way,
But there is one in heav'n Who knows our deep - est care,
We'll share the joys of heav'n—A harp, a home, a crown,

All tears for - ev - er o - ver In God's e - ter - nal day.
Let Je - sus solve your prob - lem, Just go to Him in pray'r.
The tempt - er will be ban - ished, We'll lay our bur - den down.

CHORUS

It will be worth it all when we see Je - sus, Life's trials will

When We See Christ

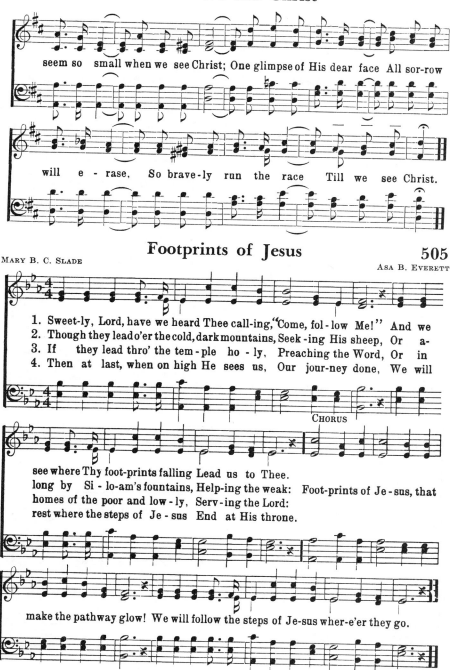

seem so small when we see Christ; One glimpse of His dear face All sor-row will e - rase, So brave-ly run the race Till we see Christ.

Footprints of Jesus

505

MARY B. C. SLADE

ASA B. EVERETT

1. Sweet-ly, Lord, have we heard Thee call-ing, "Come, fol-low Me!" And we
2. Though they lead o'er the cold, dark mountains, Seek-ing His sheep, Or a-
3. If they lead thro' the tem-ple ho - ly, Preaching the Word, Or in
4. Then at last, when on high He sees us, Our jour-ney done, We will

CHORUS

see where Thy foot-prints falling Lead us to Thee.
long by Si - lo-am's fountains, Help-ing the weak: Foot-prints of Je - sus, that
homes of the poor and low - ly, Serv-ing the Lord:
rest where the steps of Je - sus End at His throne.

make the pathway glow! We will follow the steps of Je-sus wher-e'er they go.

506 I Won't Have to Cross Jordan Alone

Thomas Ramsey

Charles E. Durham

1. When I come to the riv-er at end-ing of day, When the last winds of
2. Of-ten-times I'm for-sak-en, and wea-ry and sad, When it seems that my
3. Tho' the bil-lows of sor-row and trouble may sweep, Christ the Sav-iour will

1. When the last

sor-row have blown; There'll be some-bod-y wait-ing to show me the way,
friends have all gone; There is one tho't that cheers me and makes my heart glad,
care for His own; Till the end of the jour-ney, my soul He will keep,
winds of sor-row have blown;

CHORUS

I won't have to cross Jor-dan a-lone. I won't have to cross Jor-dan a-
I won't have to cross Jor-dan a-

lone. . . . Je-sus died for my sins to a-tone; When the
Jor-dan a-lone,

Solo ad lib.

PARTS

dark-ness I see, He'll be waiting for me, I won't have to cross Jordan a-lone.

Hum

Hum

Jerusalem the Golden

BERNARD OF CLUNY
TR. BY JOHN M. NEALE

ALEXANDER EWING

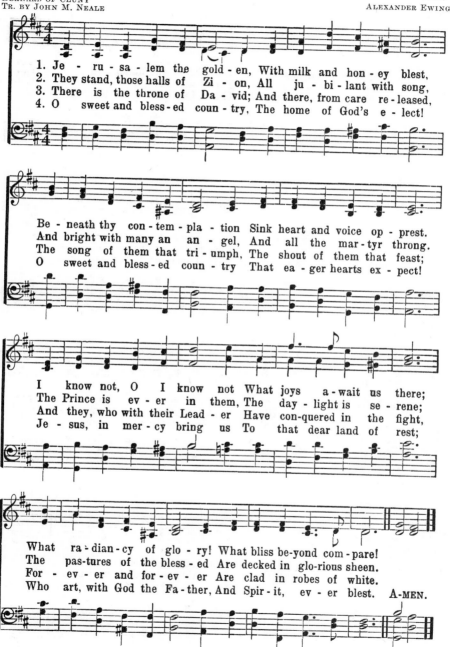

1. Je - ru - sa - lem the gold - en, With milk and hon - ey blest,
2. They stand, those halls of Zi - on, All ju - bi - lant with song,
3. There is the throne of Da - vid; And there, from care re - leased,
4. O sweet and bless - ed coun - try, The home of God's e - lect!

Be - neath thy con - tem - pla - tion Sink heart and voice op - prest.
And bright with many an an - gel, And all the mar - tyr throng.
The song of them that tri - umph, The shout of them that feast;
O sweet and bless - ed coun - try That ea - ger hearts ex - pect!

I know not, O I know not What joys a - wait us there;
The Prince is ev - er in them, The day - light is se - rene;
And they, who with their Lead - er Have con-quered in the fight,
Je - sus, in mer - cy bring us To that dear land of rest;

What ra - dian-cy of glo - ry! What bliss be-yond com - pare!
The pas-tures of the bless - ed Are decked in glo-rious sheen.
For - ev - er and for - ev - er Are clad in robes of white.
Who art, with God the Fa - ther, And Spir - it, ev - er blest. A-MEN.

508 Now Thank We All Our God

MARTIN RINKART
TR. BY CATHERINE WINKWORTH

JOHANN CRÜGER
HAR. BY FELIX MENDELSSOHN-BARTHOLDY

1. Now thank we all our God, With heart and hands and voic - es,
2. O may this boun-teous God, Thro' all our life be near us,
3. All praise and thanks to God The Fa - ther now be giv - en,

Who won-drous things hath done. In whom His world re - joic - es;
With ev - er joy - ful hearts. And bless - ed peace to cheer us;
The Son and Him who reigns With Them in high - est heav - en;

Who from our moth - er's arms Hath blessed us on our way
And keep us in His grace, And guide us when per - plexed,
The one e - ter - nal God, Whom earth and heaven a - dore;

With count-less gifts of love, And still is ours to - day.
And free us from all ills In this world and the next.
For thus it was, is now, And shall be ev - er - more. A-MEN.

Come, Ye Thankful People, Come

509

HENRY ALFORD

GEORGE J. ELVEY

1. Come, ye thank-ful peo-ple, come, Raise the song of har-vest-home:
2. All the world is God's own field, Fruit un-to His praise to yield;
3. For the Lord our God shall come, And shall take His har-vest home;
4. E-ven so, Lord, quick-ly come To Thy fi-nal har-vest-home;

All is safe-ly gath-ered in, Ere the win-ter storms be-gin;
Wheat and tares to-geth-er sown, Un-to joy or sor-row grown;
From His field shall in that day All of-fenc-es purge a-way;
Gath-er Thou Thy peo-ple in, Free from sor-row, free from sin;

God, our Ma-ker, doth pro-vide For our wants to be sup-plied:
First the blade, and then the ear, Then the full corn shall ap-pear:
Give His an-gels charge at last In the fire the tares to cast;
There, for-ev-er pu-ri-fied, In Thy pres-ence to a-bide:

Come to God's own tem-ple, come, Raise the song of har-vest-home.
Lord of har-vest, grant that we Wholesome grain and pure may be.
But the fruit-ful ears to store In His gar-ner ev-er-more.
Come, with all Thine an-gels, come, Raise the glo-rious har-vest-home.

510 The Children's Friend Is Jesus

ROBERT HARKNESS

ROBERT HARKNESS

1. The children's Friend is Je-sus, He calls them to His side; He gave His life a-
2. The children's Friend is Je-sus, He loves their joys to share, He knows their lit-tle
3. The children's Friend is Je-sus, There's no one else so true; He keeps all those who

CHORUS

ran-som, Heav'n's gate too o-pen wide.
sor-rows, He longs each one to bear. The children's Friend is Je-sus, Je-sus.
trust Him, As no one else can do.

Je-sus; His life He gave their souls to save, The children's Friend is He.

511 Jewels

WILLIAM O. CUSHING

GEORGE F. ROOT

1. When He com-eth, when He com-eth To make up His jew-els, All His
2. He will gath-er, He will gath-er The gems for His king-dom; All the
3. Lit-tle chil-dren, lit-tle chil-dren, Who love their Re-deem-er, Are the

jew-els, pre-cious jew-els, His loved and His own:
pure ones, all the bright ones, His loved and His own.
jew-els, pre-cious jew-els, His loved and His own.

Jewels

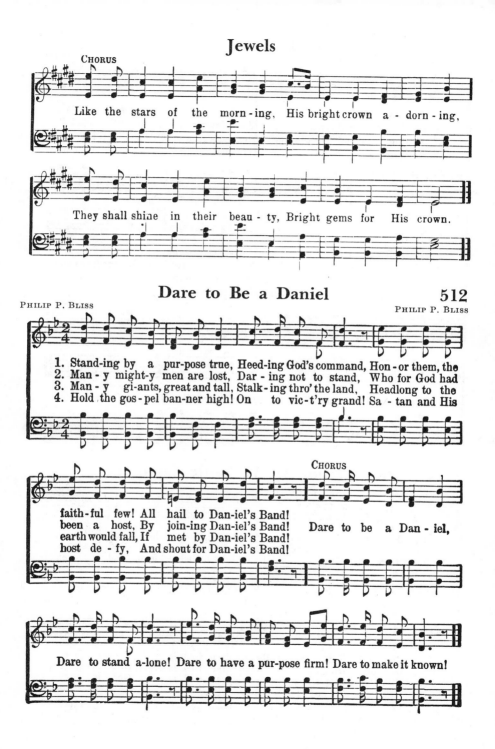

Chorus

Like the stars of the morn-ing, His bright crown a-dorn-ing,

They shall shine in their beau-ty, Bright gems for His crown.

Dare to Be a Daniel

512

Philip P. Bliss

Philip P. Bliss

1. Stand-ing by a pur-pose true, Heed-ing God's command, Hon-or them, the
2. Man-y might-y men are lost, Dar-ing not to stand, Who for God had
3. Man-y gi-ants, great and tall, Stalk-ing thro' the land, Headlong to the
4. Hold the gos-pel ban-ner high! On to vic-t'ry grand! Sa-tan and His

faith-ful few! All hail to Dan-iel's Band!
been a host, By join-ing Dan-iel's Band!
earth would fall, If met by Dan-iel's Band!
host de-fy, And shout for Dan-iel's Band!

Chorus

Dare to be a Dan-iel,

Dare to stand a-lone! Dare to have a pur-pose firm! Dare to make it known!

513   Jesus Loves Me

ANNA B. WARNER, ALT.

WILLIAM B. BRADBURY

1. Je - sus loves me! this I know, For the Bi - ble tells me so; Lit - tle
2. Je - sus loves me! loves me still, Tho' I'm ver - y weak and ill; That I
3. Je - sus loves me! He who died, Heaven's gate to o - pen wide; He will
4. Je - sus loves me! He will stay Close be - side me all the way; Thou hast

CHORUS

ones to Him be - long; They are weak, but He is strong.
might from sin be free, Bled and died up - on the tree. Yes, Je - sus loves me!
wash a - way my sin, Let His lit - tle child come in.
bled and died for me, I will hence-forth live for Thee.

Yes Je - sus loves me! Yes, Je - sus loves me! The Bi - ble tells me so.

514   Praise Him, All Ye Little Children

AUTHOR UNKNOWN

AUTHOR UNKNOWN

1. Praise Him, praise Him, all ye lit - tle chil - dren, God is love, God is love;
2. Love Him, love Him, all ye lit - tle chil - dren, God is love, God is love;
3. Thank Him, thank Him, all ye lit - tle chil - dren, God is love, God is love;

Praise Him, praise Him, all ye lit - tle chil - dren, God is love, God is love.
Love Him, love Him, all ye lit - tle chil - dren, God is love, God is love.
Thank Him, thank Him, all ye lit - tle chil - dren, God is love, God is love.

I'll Be a Sunbeam

NELLIE TALBOT

EDWIN O. EXCELL

515

1. Je-sus wants me for a sun-beam, To shine for Him each day;
2. Je-sus wants me to be lov-ing, And kind to all I see;
3. I will ask Je-sus to help me To keep my heart from sin,
4. I'll be a sun-beam for Je-sus; I can if I but try;

In ev-'ry way try to please Him, At home, at school, at play.
Showing how pleasant and hap-py His lit-tle one can be.
Ev-er re-flect-ing His good-ness, And al-ways shine for Him.
Serv-ing Him mo-ment by mo-ment, Then live with Him on high.

CHORUS

A sun-beam, a sun-beam, Je-sus wants me for a sun-beam; A
sun-beam, a sun-beam, I'll be a sun-beam for Him.

516 Count Your Blessings

JOHNSON OATMAN, JR.

EDWIN O. EXCELL

1. When up-on life's bil-lows you are tem-pest-tossed, When you are dis-
2. Are you ev-er bur-dened with a load of care? Does the cross seem
3. When you look at oth-ers with their lands and gold, Think that Christ has
4. So, a-mid the con-flict, whether great or small, Do not be dis-

cour-aged, think-ing all is lost, Count your man-y bless-ings, name them
heav-y you are called to bear? Count your man-y bless-ings, ev-'ry
prom-ised you His wealth un-told; Count your man-y bless-ings, mon-ey
cour-aged, God is o-ver all; Count your man-y bless-ings, an-gels

one by one, And it will sur-prise you what the Lord hath done.
doubt will fly, And you will be sing-ing as the days go by.
can-not buy Your re-ward in heav-en, nor your home on high.
will at-tend, Help and com-fort give you to your jour-ney's end.

CHORUS.

Count your bless-ings, Name them one by one; Count your
Count your man-y bless-ings, Name them one by one; Count your man-y

bless-ings, See what God hath done; Count your bless-ings,
bless-ings, See what God hath done; Count your man-y bless-ings,

Count Your Blessings

Name them one by one; Count your man-y blessings, See what God hath done.

What a Friend We Have in Jesus 517

JOSEPH SCRIVEN
CHARLES C. CONVERSE

1. What a Friend we have in Je - sus, All our sins and griefs to bear!
2. Have we tri - als and temp - ta - tions? Is there troub-le an - y - where?
3. Are we weak and heav-y - la - den, Cumbered with a load of care?—

What a priv - i - lege to car - ry Ev - 'ry-thing to God in prayer!
We should nev-er be dis - cour-aged, Take it to the Lord in prayer.
Pre - cious Sav-ior, still our ref - uge,—Take it to the Lord in prayer.

O what peace we oft - en for - feit, O what need-less pain we bear,
Can we find a friend so faith - ful Who will all our sor-rows share?
Do thy friends despise, for-sake thee? Take it to the Lord in prayer;

All be-cause we do not car - ry Ev - 'ry-thing to God in prayer!
Je - sus knows our ev - 'ry weak - ness, Take it to the Lord in prayer.
In His arms He'll take and shield thee, Thou wilt find a sol - ace there.

518 All Hail, Immanuel!

D. R. VAN SICKLE

CHARLES H. GABRIEL

1. All hail to Thee, Im-man-u-el, We cast . . . our crowns be-fore Thee;
2. All hail to Thee, Im-man-u-el, The ran - somed hosts surround Thee;
3. All hail to Thee, Im-man-u-el, Our ris - - en King and Sav-ior!

Let ev - 'ry heart o - bey Thy will, And ev - - - 'ry voice a-
And earth-ly mon-archs clam - or forth Their Sov - - 'reign King to
Thy foes are van-quished, and Thou art Om - nip - - o-tent for-

dore Thee. In praise to Thee, our Sav - ior King, The vi - brant
crown Thee. While those re-deemed in a - ges gone, As - sem - bled
ev - er. Death, sin and hell no lon - ger reign, And Sa - tan's

chords of Heav - en ring, And ech - o back the might-y strain:
round the great white throne, Break forth in - to im - mor - tal song:
pow'r is burst in twain; E - ter - nal glo - ry to Thy Name:

All hail! all hail! All hail! all hail! Im-man-u - el!
All hail! all hail!

All Hail, Immanuel!

SCRIPTURE READINGS

The text used for the readings is the King James Version. The readings are arranged, generally, as follows: God the Father, life of Christ, the Holy Spirit, the church, and the Christian life. An Index to Scripture Readings is on page 498.

519   GOD THE CREATOR

In the beginning God created the heaven and the earth.

And the earth was without form, and void; and darkness was upon the face of the deep.

And the Spirit of God moved upon the face of the waters. And God said, Let there be light: and there was light.

And God saw the light, that it was good: and God divided the light from the darkness.

And God called the light Day, and the darkness he called Night.

And the evening and the morning were the first day.   —Genesis 1:1-5.

By the word of the Lord were the heavens made; and all the host of them by the breath of his mouth.

He gathereth the waters of the sea together as an heap: he layeth up the depth in storehouses.

Let all the earth fear the Lord: let all the inhabitants of the world stand in awe of him.

For he spake, and it was done; he commanded, and it stood fast.
—Psalm 33:6-9.

Let us come before his presence with thanksgiving, and make a joyful noise unto him with psalms.

For the Lord is a great God, and a great King above all gods.

In his hand are the deep places of the earth: the strength of the hills is his also.

The sea is his, and he made it: and his hands formed the dry land.

O come, let us worship and bow down: let us kneel before the Lord our maker.

For he is our God; and we are the people of his pasture, and the sheep of his hand.   —Psalm 95:2-7.

520   GOD'S OMNISCIENCE

O Lord, thou hast searched me, and known me.

Thou knowest my downsitting and mine uprising, thou understandest my thought afar off.

Thou compassest my path and my lying down, and art acquainted with all my ways.

For there is not a word in my tongue, but, lo, O Lord, thou knowest it altogether.

Thou hast beset me behind and before, and laid thine hand upon me.

Such knowledge is too wonderful for me; it is high, I cannot attain unto it.

Whither shall I go from thy spirit? or whither shall I flee from thy presence?

If I ascend up into heaven, thou art there: if I make my bed in hell, behold, thou art there.

If I take the wings of the morning, and dwell in the uttermost parts of the sea;

Even there shall thy hand lead me, and thy right hand shall hold me.

If I say, Surely the darkness shall cover me; even the night shall be light about me.

Yea, the darkness hideth not from thee; but the night shineth as the

day: the darkness and the light are both alike to thee.

I will praise thee; for I am fearfully and wonderfully made: marvellous are thy works; and that my soul knoweth right well.

Search me, O God, and know my heart: try me, and know my thoughts: and see if there be any wicked way in me, and lead me in the way everlasting.
—Psalm 139:1-12, 14, 23, 24.

521 GOD'S CARE

I will lift up mine eyes unto the hills, from whence cometh my help.

My help cometh from the Lord, which made heaven and earth.

He will not suffer thy foot to be moved: he that keepeth thee will not slumber.

Behold, he that keepeth Israel shall neither slumber nor sleep.

The Lord is thy keeper: the Lord is thy shade upon thy right hand.

The sun shall not smite thee by day, nor the moon by night.

The Lord shall preserve thee from all evil: he shall preserve thy soul.

The Lord shall preserve thy going out and thy coming in from this time forth, and even for evermore.
—Psalm 121.

522 THE SHEPHERD PSALM

The Lord is my shepherd; I shall not want.

He maketh me to lie down in green pastures: he leadeth me beside the still waters.

He restoreth my soul: he leadeth me in the paths of righteousness for his name's sake.

Yea, though I walk through the valley of the shadow of death, I will fear no evil:

For thou art with me; thy rod and thy staff they comfort me.

Thou preparest a table before me in the presence of mine enemies:

Thou anointest my head with oil; my cup runneth over.

Surely goodness and mercy shall follow me all the days of my life: and I will dwell in the house of the Lord for ever. —Psalm 23.

523 DIVINE PROVIDENCE

I will bless the Lord at all times: his praise shall continually be in my mouth.

My soul shall make her boast in the Lord: the humble shall hear thereof, and be glad.

O magnify the Lord with me, and let us exalt his name together.

I sought the Lord, and he heard me, and delivered me from all my fears.

They looked unto him, and were lightened: and their faces were not ashamed.

This poor man cried, and the Lord heard him, and saved him out of all his troubles.

The angel of the Lord encampeth round about them that fear him, and delivereth them.

O taste and see that the Lord is good: blessed is the man that trusteth in him.

O fear the Lord, ye his saints: for there is no want to them that fear him.

The young lions do lack, and suffer hunger: but they that seek the Lord shall not want any good thing.

The righteous cry, and the Lord heareth, and delivereth them out of all their troubles.

The Lord is nigh unto them that

(over)

are of a broken heart; and saveth such as be of a contrite spirit.

Many are the afflictions of the righteous: but the Lord delivereth him out of them all.

The Lord redeemeth the soul of his servants: and none of them that trust in him shall be desolate.
—Psalm 34:1-10, 17-19, 22.

524 GOD'S COMMANDMENTS

I am the Lord thy God, which have brought thee out of the land of Egypt, out of the house of bondage. Thou shalt have no other gods before me.

Thou shalt not make unto thee any graven image, or any likeness of any thing that is in heaven above, or that is in the earth beneath, or that is in the water under the earth: thou shalt not bow down thyself to them, nor serve them:

Thou shalt not take the name of the Lord thy God in vain;

For the Lord will not hold him guiltless that taketh his name in vain.

Remember the sabbath day, to keep it holy. For in six days the Lord made heaven and earth, the sea, and all that in them is, and rested the seventh day:

Wherefore the Lord blessed the sabbath day, and hallowed it.

Honour thy father and thy mother: that thy days may be long upon the land which the Lord thy God giveth thee.

Thou shalt not kill.

Thou shalt not commit adultery.

Thou shalt not steal.

Thou shalt not bear false witness against thy neighbour.

Thou shalt not covet thy neighbour's house, thou shalt not covet thy neighbour's wife, nor his manservant, nor his maidservant, nor his ox, nor his ass, nor any thing that is thy neighbour's.
—Exodus 20:2-5, 7, 8, 11-17.

Thou shalt love the Lord thy God with all thy heart, and with all thy soul, and with all thy mind. This is the first and great commandment.

And the second is like unto it, Thou shalt love thy neighbour as thyself. On these two commandments hang all the law and the prophets. —Matthew 22:37-40.

525 WORSHIP OF GOD

O sing unto the Lord a new song: sing unto the Lord, all the earth.

Sing unto the Lord, bless his name; shew forth his salvation from day to day.

Declare his glory among the heathen, his wonders among all people.

For the Lord is great, and greatly to be praised: he is to be feared above all gods.

For all the gods of the nations are idols: but the Lord made the heavens.

Honour and majesty are before him: strength and beauty are in his sanctuary.

Give unto the Lord, O ye kindreds of the people, give unto the Lord glory and strength.

Give unto the Lord the glory due unto his name: bring an offering, and come into his courts.

O worship the Lord in the beauty of holiness: fear before him, all the earth.

Say among the heathen that the Lord reigneth: the world also shall be established that it shall not be moved: he shall judge the people righteously.

Let the heavens rejoice, and let the earth be glad;

Let the sea roar, and the fulness thereof. Let the field be joyful, and all that is therein:

Then shall all the trees of the wood rejoice before the Lord: for he cometh, for he cometh to judge the earth:

He shall judge the world with righteousness, and the people with his truth. —Psalm 96.

526 THANKSGIVING TO GOD

Bless the Lord, O my soul: and all that is within me, bless his holy name.

Bless the Lord, O my soul, and forget not all his benefits:

Who forgiveth all thine iniquities; who healeth all thy diseases;

Who redeemeth thy life from destruction; who crowneth thee with lovingkindness and tender mercies;

Who satisfieth thy mouth with good things; so that thy youth is renewed like the eagle's.

The Lord executeth righteousness and judgment for all that are oppressed.

He made known his ways unto Moses, his acts unto the children of Israel.

The Lord is merciful and gracious, slow to anger, and plenteous in mercy.

He will not always chide: neither will he keep his anger for ever.

He hath not dealt with us after our sins; nor rewarded us according to our iniquities.

For as the heaven is high above the earth, so great is his mercy toward them that fear him.

As far as the east is from the west, so far hath he removed our transgressions from us.

Like as a father pitieth his children, so the Lord pitieth them that fear him.

Bless the Lord, all his works in all places of his dominion: bless the Lord, O my soul. —Psalm 103:1-13, 22.

527 OBEDIENCE TO GOD

Thou hast commanded us to keep thy precepts diligently.

O that my ways were directed to keep thy statutes!

Then shall I not be ashamed, when I have respect unto all thy commandments.

I will praise thee with uprightness of heart, when I shall have learned thy righteous judgments.

I will keep thy statutes: O forsake me not utterly.

Wherewithal shall a young man cleanse his way? by taking heed thereto according to thy word.

With my whole heart have I sought thee: O let me not wander from thy commandments.

Thy word have I hid in mine heart, that I might not sin against thee.

Blessed art thou, O Lord: teach me thy statutes.

With my lips have I declared all the judgments of thy mouth.

I have rejoiced in the way of thy testimonies, as much as in all riches.

I will meditate in thy precepts, and have respect unto thy ways.

I will delight myself in thy statutes: I will not forget thy word.

Deal bountifully with thy servant, that I may live, and keep thy word.

Open thou mine eyes, that I may behold wondrous things out of thy law. —Psalm 119:4-18.

528 THE INCARNATE CHRIST

In the beginning was the Word, and the Word was with God, and the Word was God.

The same was in the beginning with God.

All things were made by him; and without him was not any thing made that was made.

In him was life; and the life was the light of men.

And the light shineth in darkness; and the darkness comprehended it not.

There was a man sent from God, whose name was John.

The same came for a witness, to bear witness of the Light, that all men through him might believe.

He was not that Light, but was sent to bear witness of that Light.

That was the true Light, which lighteth every man that cometh into the world.

He was in the world, and the world was made by him, and the world knew him not.

He came unto his own, and his own received him not.

But as many as received him, to them gave he power to become the sons of God, even to them that believe on his name:

Which were born, not of blood, nor of the will of the flesh, nor of the will of man, but of God.

And the Word was made flesh, and dwelt among us, (and we beheld his glory, the glory as of the only begotten of the Father,) full of grace and truth. —John 1:1-14.

For God so loved the world, that he gave his only begotten Son, that whosoever believeth in him should not perish, but have everlasting life.

For God sent not his Son into the world to condemn the world; but that the world through him might be saved. —John 3:16, 17.

529 THE SAVIOUR'S ADVENT

And there were in the same country shepherds abiding in the field, keeping watch over their flock by night.

And, lo, the angel of the Lord came upon them, and the glory of the Lord shone round about them: and they were sore afraid.

And the angel said unto them, Fear not: for, behold, I bring you good tidings of great joy, which shall be to all people.

For unto you is born this day in the city of David a Saviour, which is Christ the Lord.

And this shall be a sign unto you; Ye shall find the babe wrapped in swaddling clothes, lying in a manger.

And suddenly there was with the angel a multitude of the heavenly host praising God, and saying,

Glory to God in the highest, and on earth peace, good will toward men.

And it came to pass, as the angels were gone away from them into heaven, the shepherds said one to another,

Let us now go even unto Bethlehem, and see this thing which is come to pass, which the Lord hath made known unto us.

And they came with haste, and found Mary, and Joseph, and the babe lying in a manger.

And when they had seen it, they made known abroad the saying which was told them concerning this child.

And all they that heard it wondered at those things which were told them by the shepherds.

But Mary kept all these things, and pondered them in her heart.

And the shepherds returned, glorifying and praising God for all the things that they had heard and seen, as it was told unto them.
—Luke 2:8-20.

530 ADORATION OF THE MAGI

Now when Jesus was born in Bethlehem of Judaea in the days of Herod the king, behold, there came wise men from the east to Jerusalem, saying,

Where is he that is born King of the Jews? for we have seen his star in the east, and are come to worship him.

When Herod the king had heard these things, he was troubled, and all Jerusalem with him.

And when he had gathered all the chief priests and scribes of the people together, he demanded of them where Christ should be born.

And they said unto him, In Bethlehem of Judaea: for thus it is written by the prophet,

And thou Bethlehem, in the land of Juda, art not the least among the princes of Juda: for out of thee shall come a Governor, that shall rule my people Israel.

Then Herod, when he had privily called the wise men, enquired of them diligently what time the star appeared. And he sent them to Bethlehem, and said,

Go and search diligently for the young child; and when ye have found him, bring me word again,

that I may come and worship him also.

When they had heard the king, they departed; and, lo, the star, which they saw in the east, went before them, till it came and stood over where the young child was.

When they saw the star, they rejoiced with exceeding great joy. And when they were come into the house, they saw the young child with Mary his mother, and fell down, and worshipped him:

And when they had opened their treasures, they presented unto him gifts; gold, and frankincense, and myrrh.

And being warned of God in a dream that they should not return to Herod, they departed into their own country another way. —Matthew 2:1-12.

531 BAPTISM OF JESUS

In those days came John the Baptist, preaching in the wilderness of Judaea, and saying,

Repent ye: for the kingdom of heaven is at hand.

For this is he that was spoken of by the prophet Esaias, saying, The voice of one crying in the wilderness, Prepare ye the way of the Lord, make his paths straight.

And the same John had his raiment of camel's hair, and a leathern girdle about his loins; and his meat was locusts and wild honey.

Then went out to him Jerusalem, and all Judaea, and all the region round about Jordan, and were baptized of him in Jordan, confessing their sins.

But when he saw many of the Pharisees and Sadducees come to his baptism, he said unto them,

O generation of vipers, who hath warned you to flee from the wrath

(over)

to come? Bring forth therefore fruits meet for repentance:

I indeed baptize you with water unto repentance: but he that cometh after me is mightier than I, whose shoes I am not worthy to bear: he shall baptize you with the Holy Ghost, and with fire:

Then cometh Jesus from Galilee to Jordan unto John, to be baptized of him.

But John forbad him, saying, I have need to be baptized of thee, and comest thou to me?

And Jesus answering said unto him, Suffer it to be so now: for thus it becometh us to fulfil all righteousness. Then he suffered him.

And Jesus, when he was baptized, went up straightway out of the water:

And, lo, the heavens were opened unto him, and he saw the Spirit of God descending like a dove, and lighting upon him:

And lo a voice from heaven, saying, This is my beloved Son, in whom I am well pleased.
—Matthew 3:1-8, 11, 13-17.

532 THE LAMB OF GOD

Who hath believed our report? and to whom is the arm of the Lord revealed?

For he shall grow up before him as a tender plant, and as a root out of a dry ground: he hath no form nor comeliness; and when we shall see him, there is no beauty that we should desire him.

He is despised and rejected of men; a man of sorrows, and acquainted with grief: and we hid as it were our faces from him; he was despised, and we esteemed him not.

Surely he hath borne our griefs, and carried our sorrows: yet we did esteem him stricken, smitten of God, and afflicted.

But he was wounded for our transgressions, he was bruised for our iniquities: the chastisement of our peace was upon him; and with his stripes we are healed.

All we like sheep have gone astray; we have turned every one to his own way; and the Lord hath laid on him the iniquity of us all.

He was oppressed, and he was afflicted, yet he opened not his mouth: he is brought as a lamb to the slaughter, and as a sheep before her shearers is dumb, so he openeth not his mouth.

He was taken from prison and from judgment: and who shall declare his generation? for he was cut off out of the land of the living: for the transgression of my people was he stricken.

And he made his grave with the wicked, and with the rich in his death; because he had done no violence, neither was any deceit in his mouth.

Yet it pleased the Lord to bruise him; he hath put him to grief: when thou shalt make his soul an offering for sin, he shall see his seed, he shall prolong his days, and the pleasure of the Lord shall prosper in his hand.

He shall see of the travail of his soul, and shall be satisfied: by his knowledge shall my righteous servant justify many; for he shall bear their iniquities.

Therefore will I divide him a portion with the great, and he shall divide the spoil with the strong; because he hath poured out his soul unto death: and he was numbered with the transgressors; and he bare the sin of many, and made intercession for the transgressors. —Isaiah 53.

533 THE LAST SUPPER

And the disciples did as Jesus had appointed them; and they made ready the passover.

Now when the even was come, he sat down with the twelve.

And as they did eat, he said, Verily I say unto you, that one of you shall betray me.

And they were exceeding sorrowful, and began every one of them to say unto him, Lord, is it I?

And he answered and said, He that dippeth his hand with me in the dish, the same shall betray me.

The Son of man goeth as it is written of him: but woe unto that man by whom the Son of man is betrayed! it had been good for that man if he had not been born.

Then Judas, which betrayed him, answered and said, Master, is it I? He said unto him, Thou hast said.

And as they were eating, Jesus took bread, and blessed it, and brake it, and gave it to the disciples, and said, Take, eat; this is my body.

And he took the cup, and gave thanks, and gave it to them, saying, Drink ye all of it; for this is my blood of the new testament, which is shed for many for the remission of sins.

But I say unto you, I will not drink henceforth of this fruit of the vine, until that day when I drink it new with you in my Father's kingdom.
—Matthew 26:19-29.

534 THE TRIUMPHAL ENTRY

And when they came nigh to Jerusalem, unto Bethphage and Bethany, at the mount of Olives, he sendeth forth two of his disciples, and saith unto them,

Go your way into the village over against you: and as soon as ye be entered into it, ye shall find a colt tied, whereon never man sat; loose him, and bring him.

And if any man say unto you, Why do ye this? say ye that the Lord hath need of him; and straightway he will send him hither.

And they went their way, and found the colt tied by the door without in a place where two ways met; and they loose him.

And certain of them that stood there said unto them, What do ye, loosing the colt?

And they said unto them even as Jesus had commanded: and they let them go.

And they brought the colt to Jesus, and cast their garments on him; and he sat upon him.

And many spread their garments in the way: and others cut down branches off the trees, and strawed them in the way.

And they that went before, and they that followed, cried, saying, Hosanna; Blessed is he that cometh in the name of the Lord:

Blessed be the kingdom of our father David, that cometh in the name of the Lord: Hosanna in the highest. And Jesus entered into Jerusalem, and into the temple.
—Mark 11:1-11.

And when he was come into Jerusalem, all the city was moved, saying, Who is this?

And the multitude said, This is Jesus the prophet of Nazareth of Galilee.
—Matthew 21:10, 11.

535 CRUCIFIXION OF CHRIST

Then delivered he him therefore unto them to be crucified. And they took Jesus, and led him away.

(over)

And he bearing his cross went forth into a place called the place of a skull, which is called in the Hebrew Golgotha:

Where they crucified him, and two other with him, on either side one, and Jesus in the midst.

And Pilate wrote a title, and put it on the cross. And the writing was, JESUS OF NAZARETH THE KING OF THE JEWS.

Then the soldiers, when they had crucified Jesus, took his garments, and made four parts, to every soldier a part; and also his coat: now the coat was without seam, woven from the top throughout.

They said therefore among themselves, Let us not rend it, but cast lots for it, whose it shall be: . . . These things therefore the soldiers did.

Now there stood by the cross of Jesus his mother, and his mother's sister, Mary the wife of Cleophas, and Mary Magdalene.

When Jesus therefore saw his mother, and the disciple standing by, whom he loved, he saith unto his mother, Woman, behold thy son!

Then saith he to the disciple, Behold thy mother! And from that hour that disciple took her unto his own home.

After this, Jesus knowing that all things were now accomplished, that the scripture might be fulfilled, saith, I thirst.

Now there was set a vessel full of vinegar: and they filled a spunge with vinegar, and put it upon hyssop, and put it to his mouth.

When Jesus therefore had received the vinegar, he said, It is finished: and he bowed his head, and gave up the ghost.
—John 19:16-19, 23-30.

536   THE RISEN LORD

In the end of the sabbath, as it began to dawn toward the first day of the week, came Mary Magdalene and the other Mary to see the sepulchre.

And, behold, there was a great earthquake: for the angel of the Lord descended from heaven, and came and rolled back the stone from the door, and sat upon it.

And the angel answered and said unto the women, Fear not ye: for I know that ye seek Jesus, which was crucified.

He is not here: for he is risen, as he said. Come, see the place where the Lord lay.

And go quickly, and tell his disciples that he is risen from the dead; and, behold, he goeth before you into Galilee; there shall ye see him: lo, I have told you.

And they departed quickly from the sepulchre with fear and great joy; and did run to bring his disciples word.

And as they went to tell his disciples, behold, Jesus met them, saying, All hail. And they came and held him by the feet, and worshipped him.

Then said Jesus unto them, Be not afraid: go tell my brethren that they go into Galilee, and there shall they see me.   —Matthew 28:1, 2, 5-10.

Then the same day at evening, being the first day of the week, when the doors were shut where the disciples were assembled for fear of the Jews, came Jesus and stood in the midst, and saith unto them, Peace be unto you.

And when he had so said, he shewed unto them his hands and his side. Then were the disciples glad, when they saw the Lord.
—John 20:19, 20.

537 THE GREAT COMMISSION

Then the eleven disciples went away into Galilee, into a mountain where Jesus had appointed them.

And when they saw him, they worshipped him: but some doubted.

And Jesus came and spake unto them, saying, All power is given unto me in heaven and in earth.

Go ye therefore, and teach all nations, baptizing them in the name of the Father, and of the Son, and of the Holy Ghost:

Teaching them to observe all things whatsoever I have commanded you: and, lo, I am with you alway, even unto the end of the world. —Matthew 28:16-20.

[Jesus] said unto them, Thus it is written, and thus it behoved Christ to suffer, and to rise from the dead the third day:

And that repentance and remission of sins should be preached in his name among all nations, beginning at Jerusalem.

And ye are witnesses of these things.

And, behold, I send the promise of my Father upon you: but tarry ye in the city of Jerusalem, until ye be endued with power from on high. —Luke 24:46-49.

They asked of him, saying, Lord, wilt thou at this time restore again the kingdom to Israel?

And he said unto them, It is not for you to know the times or the seasons, which the Father hath put in his own power.

But ye shall receive power, after that the Holy Ghost is come upon you:

And ye shall be witnesses unto me both in Jerusalem, and in all Judaea, and in Samaria, and unto the uttermost part of the earth.

And when he had spoken these things, while they beheld, he was taken up; and a cloud received him out of their sight. —Acts 1:6-9.

538 THE BEATITUDES

And seeing the multitudes, he went up into the mountain: and when he was set, his disciples came unto him:

And he opened his mouth, and taught them, saying,

Blessed are the poor in spirit: for theirs is the kingdom of heaven.

Blessed are they that mourn: for they shall be comforted.

Blessed are the meek: for they shall inherit the earth.

Blessed are they which do hunger and thirst after righteousness: for they shall be filled.

Blessed are the merciful: for they shall obtain mercy.

Blessed are the pure in heart: for they shall see God.

Blessed are the peacemakers: for they shall be called the children of God.

Blessed are they which are persecuted for righteousness' sake: for theirs is the kingdom of heaven.

Blessed are ye, when men shall revile you, and persecute you, and shall say all manner of evil against you falsely, for my sake.

Rejoice, and be exceeding glad: for great is your reward in heaven: for so persecuted they the prophets which were before you.

Ye are the light of the world.

Let your light so shine before men, that they may see your good works, and glorify your Father which is in heaven. —Matthew 5:1-12, 14, 16.

539   THE VINE AND BRANCHES

I am the true vine, and my Father is the husbandman.

Every branch in me that beareth not fruit he taketh away: and every branch that beareth fruit, he purgeth it, that it may bring forth more fruit.

Now ye are clean through the word which I have spoken unto you.

Abide in me, and I in you. As the branch cannot bear fruit of itself, except it abide in the vine; no more can ye, except ye abide in me.

I am the vine, ye are the branches: He that abideth in me, and I in him, the same bringeth forth much fruit: for without me ye can do nothing.

If a man abide not in me, he is cast forth as a branch, and is withered; and men gather them, and cast them into the fire, and they are burned.

If ye abide in me, and my words abide in you, ye shall ask what ye will, and it shall be done unto you.

Herein is my Father glorified, that ye bear much fruit; so shall ye be my disciples.

These things have I spoken unto you, that my joy might remain in you, and that your joy might be full.

Ye are my friends, if ye do whatsoever I command you.

Henceforth I call you not servants; for the servant knoweth not what his lord doeth: but I have called you friends; for all things that I have heard of my Father I have made known unto you.

Ye have not chosen me, but I have chosen you, and ordained you, that ye should go and bring forth fruit, and that your fruit should re- main: **that whatsoever ye shall ask of the Father in my name, he may give it you.**   —John 15:1-8, 11, 14-16.

540   COMFORT FROM CHRIST

Let not your heart be troubled: ye believe in God, believe also in me.

In my Father's house are many mansions: if it were not so, I would have told you. I go to prepare a place for you.

And if I go and prepare a place for you, I will come again, and receive you unto myself; that where I am, there ye may be also.

And whither I go ye know, and the way ye know.

Thomas saith unto him, Lord, we know not whither thou goest; and how can we know the way?

Jesus saith unto him, I am the way, the truth, and the life: no man cometh unto the Father, but by me.

Philip saith unto him, Lord, shew us the Father, and it sufficeth us.

Jesus saith unto him, Have I been so long time with you, and yet hast thou not known me, Philip? he that hath seen me hath seen the Father; and how sayest thou then, Shew us the Father?

Believest thou not that I am in the Father, and the Father in me? the words that I speak unto you I speak not of myself: but the Father that dwelleth in me, he doeth the works.

Believe me that I am in the Father, and the Father in me: or else believe me for the very works' sake.

Verily, verily, I say unto you, He that believeth on me, the works that I do shall he do also; and greater works than these shall he do; because I go unto my Father.

Peace I leave with you, my peace I give unto you: not as the world giveth, give I unto you. Let not your heart be troubled, neither let it be afraid. —John 14:1-6, 8-12, 27.

541 THE HOLY SPIRIT

I will pray the Father, and he shall give you another Comforter, that he may abide with you for ever;

Even the Spirit of truth; whom the world cannot receive, because it seeth him not, neither knoweth him:

But ye know him; for he dwelleth with you, and shall be in you. I will not leave you comfortless: I will come to you.

Yet a little while, and the world seeth me no more; but ye see me: because I live, ye shall live also. —John 14:16-19.

But because I have said these things unto you, sorrow hath filled your heart.

Nevertheless I tell you the truth; It is expedient for you that I go away:

For if I go not away, the Comforter will not come unto you; but if I depart, I will send him unto you.

And when he is come, he will reprove the world of sin, and of righteousness, and of judgment:

Of sin, because they believe not on me;

Of righteousness, because I go to my Father, and ye see me no more;

Of judgment, because the prince of this world is judged.

I have yet many things to say unto you, but ye cannot bear them now.

Howbeit when he, the Spirit of truth, is come, he will guide you into all truth:

For he shall not speak of himself; but whatsoever he shall hear, that shall he speak: and he will shew you things to come.

He shall glorify me: for he shall receive of mine, and shall shew it unto you.

These things I have spoken unto you, that in me ye might have peace. In the world ye shall have tribulation: but be of good cheer; I have overcome the world. —John 16:6-14, 33.

542 THE HOLY SCRIPTURES

Knowing this first, that no prophecy of the scripture is of any private interpretation.

For the prophecy came not in old time by the will of man: but holy men of God spake as they were moved by the Holy Ghost. —2 Peter 1:20, 21.

All scripture is given by inspiration of God, and is profitable for doctrine, for reproof, for correction, for instruction in righteousness:

That the man of God may be perfect, throughly furnished unto all good works. —2 Timothy 3:16, 17.

Study to shew thyself approved unto God, a workman that needeth not to be ashamed, rightly dividing the word of truth. —2 Timothy 2:15.

For whatsoever things were written aforetime were written for our learning, that we through patience and comfort of the scriptures might have hope. —Romans 15:4.

For ever, O Lord, thy word is settled in heaven.

Thy word is a lamp unto my feet, and a light unto my path.

The entrance of thy words giveth light; it giveth understanding unto the simple.

Great peace have they which love thy law: and nothing shall offend them. —Psalm 119:89, 105, 130, 165.

543   TRUE WISDOM

Happy is the man that findeth wisdom, and the man that getteth understanding.

For the merchandise of it is better than the merchandise of silver, and the gain thereof than fine gold.

She is more precious than rubies: and all the things thou canst desire are not to be compared unto her.

Length of days is in her right hand; and in her left hand riches and honour.

Her ways are ways of pleasantness, and all her paths are peace.

She is a tree of life to them that lay hold upon her: and happy is every one that retaineth her.

The Lord by wisdom hath founded the earth; by understanding hath he established the heavens.

By his knowledge the depths are broken up, and the clouds drop down the dew.

My son, let not them depart from thine eyes: keep sound wisdom and discretion:

So shall they be life unto thy soul, and grace to thy neck.

Then shalt thou walk in thy way safely, and thy foot shall not stumble.

When thou liest down, thou shalt not be afraid: yea, thou shalt lie down, and thy sleep shall be sweet.

Be not afraid of sudden fear, neither of the desolation of the wicked, when it cometh.

For the Lord shall be thy confidence, and shall keep thy foot from being taken.

Trust in the Lord with all thine heart; and lean not unto thine own understanding.

In all thy ways acknowledge him, and he shall direct thy paths.
—Proverbs 3:13-26, 5, 6.

544   THE CHURCH

When Jesus came into the coasts of Caesarea Philippi, he asked his disciples, saying, Whom do men say that I the Son of man am?

And they said, Some say that thou art John the Baptist: some, Elias; and others, Jeremias, or one of the prophets.

He saith unto them, But whom say ye that I am?

And Simon Peter answered and said, Thou art the Christ, the Son of the living God.

And Jesus answered and said unto him, Blessed art thou, Simon Bar-jona: for flesh and blood hath not revealed it unto thee, but my Father which is in heaven.

And I say also unto thee, That thou art Peter, and upon this rock I will build my church; and the gates of hell shall not prevail against it.   —Matthew 16:13-18.

Now therefore ye are no more strangers and foreigners, but fellowcitizens with the saints, and of the household of God;

And are built upon the foundation of the apostles and prophets, Jesus Christ himself being the chief corner stone;

In whom all the building fitly framed together groweth unto an holy temple in the Lord:

In whom ye also are builded together for an habitation of God through the Spirit.   —Ephesians 2:19-22.

There is one body, and one Spirit, even as ye are called in one hope of your calling;

One Lord, one faith, one baptism, one God and Father of all, who is above all, and through all, and in you all.   —Ephesians 4:4-6.

545 CHRISTIAN MINISTRY

Whosoever shall call upon the name of the Lord shall be saved. How then shall they call on him in whom they have not believed?

And how shall they believe in him of whom they have not heard?

And how shall they hear without a preacher?

And how shall they preach, except they be sent? —Romans 10:13-15.

For as we have many members in one body, and all members have not the same office: so we, being many, are one body in Christ, and every one members one of another.

Having then gifts differing according to the grace that is given to us, whether prophecy, let us prophesy according to the proportion of faith;

Or ministry, let us wait on our ministering:

Or he that teacheth, on teaching; or he that exhorteth, on exhortation. —Romans 12:4-8.

As every man hath received the gift, even so minister the same one to another, as good stewards of the manifold grace of God. If any man speak, let him speak as the oracles of God;

If any man minister, let him do it as of the ability which God giveth: that God in all things may be glorified through Jesus Christ. —1 Peter 4:10, 11.

546 CHRISTIAN UNITY

These words spake Jesus, and lifted up his eyes to heaven, and said, Father, the hour is come; glorify thy Son, that thy Son also may glorify thee:

I have manifested thy name unto the men which thou gavest me out of the world: thine they were, and thou gavest them me; and they have kept thy word.

I pray for them: I pray not for the world, but for them which thou hast given me; for they are thine.

And all mine are thine, and thine are mine; and I am glorified in them.

Neither pray I for these alone, but for them also which shall believe on me through their word; that they all may be one; as thou, Father, art in me, and I in thee,

That they also may be one in us: that the world may believe that thou hast sent me. —John 17:1, 6, 9, 10, 20, 21.

Now I beseech you, brethren, by the name of our Lord Jesus Christ, that ye all speak the same thing, and that there be no divisions among you;

But that ye be perfectly joined together in the same mind and in the same judgment. — 1 Corinthians 1:10.

With all lowliness and meekness, with longsuffering, forbearing one another in love;

Endeavouring to keep the unity of the Spirit in the bond of peace.

There is one body, and one Spirit, even as ye are called in one hope of your calling;

One Lord, one faith, one baptism, one God and Father of all, who is above all, and through all, and in you all. —Ephesians 4:2-6.

547 SIN AND FORGIVENESS

Blessed is the man that endureth temptation: for when he is tried, he shall receive the crown of life, which the Lord hath promised to them that love him.

Let no man say when he is

tempted, I am tempted of God: for God cannot be tempted with evil, neither tempteth he any man:

But every man is tempted, when he is drawn away of his own lust, and enticed.

Then when lust hath conceived, it bringeth forth sin: and sin, when it is finished, bringeth forth death.
—James 1:12-15.

But if we walk in the light, as he is in the light, we have fellowship one with another, and the blood of Jesus Christ his Son cleanseth us from all sin.

If we say that we have no sin, we deceive ourselves, and the truth is not in us.

If we confess our sins, he is faithful and just to forgive us our sins, and to cleanse us from all unrighteousness. —1 John 1:7-9.

Blessed is he whose transgression is forgiven, whose sin is covered.

Blessed is the man unto whom the Lord imputeth not iniquity, and in whose spirit there is no guile.

I acknowledged my sin unto thee, and mine iniquity have I not hid. I said, I will confess my transgressions unto the Lord; and thou forgavest the iniquity of my sin.

Many sorrows shall be to the wicked: but he that trusteth in the Lord, mercy shall compass him about.

Be glad in the Lord, and rejoice, ye righteous: and shout for joy, all ye that are upright in heart.
—Psalm 32:1, 2, 5, 10, 11.

548   LAW AND GOSPEL

Now we know that what things soever the law saith, it saith to them who are under the law:

That every mouth may be
stopped, and all the world may become guilty before God.

Therefore by the deeds of the law there shall no flesh be justified in his sight: for by the law is the knowledge of sin.

But now the righteousness of God without the law is manifested, being witnessed by the law and the prophets;

Even the righteousness of God which is by faith of Jesus Christ unto all and upon all them that believe: for there is no difference:

For all have sinned, and come short of the glory of God;

Being justified freely by his grace through the redemption that is in Christ Jesus. —Romans 3:19-24.

But before faith came, we were kept under the law, shut up unto the faith which should afterwards be revealed.

Wherefore the law was our schoolmaster to bring us unto Christ, that we might be justified by faith.

But after that faith is come, we are no longer under a schoolmaster.

For ye are all the children of God by faith in Christ Jesus.

For as many of you as have been baptized into Christ have put on Christ. —Galatians 3:23-27.

Therefore being justified by faith, we have peace with God through our Lord Jesus Christ:

By whom also we have access by faith into this grace wherein we stand, and rejoice in hope of the glory of God. —Romans 5:1, 2.

549   GOD'S INVITATION

Ho, every one that thirsteth, come ye to the waters, and he that hath no money; come ye, buy, and eat;

yea, come, buy wine and milk without money and without price.

Wherefore do ye spend money for that which is not bread? and your labour for that which satisfieth not? hearken diligently unto me, and eat ye that which is good, and let your soul delight itself in fatness.

Incline your ear, and come unto me: hear, and your soul shall live; and I will make an everlasting covenant with you, even the sure mercies of David.

Seek ye the Lord while he may be found, call ye upon him while he is near:

Let the wicked forsake his way, and the unrighteous man his thoughts: and let him return unto the Lord, and he will have mercy upon him; and to our God, for he will abundantly pardon.

For my thoughts are not your thoughts, neither are your ways my ways, saith the Lord.

So shall my word be that goeth forth out of my mouth: it shall not return unto me void, but it shall accomplish that which I please, and it shall prosper in the thing whereto I sent it.

For ye shall go out with joy, and be led forth with peace: the mountains and the hills shall break forth before you into singing, and all the trees of the field shall clap their hands.

Instead of the thorn shall come up the fir tree, and instead of the brier shall come up the myrtle tree:

And it shall be to the Lord for a name, for an everlasting sign that shall not be cut off.

—Isaiah 55:1-3, 6-8, 11-13.

550 THE WAY OF LIFE

Blessed is the man that walketh not in the counsel of the ungodly,

nor standeth in the way of sinners, nor sitteth in the seat of the scornful.

But his delight is in the law of the Lord; and in his law doth he meditate day and night.

And he shall be like a tree planted by the rivers of water, that bringeth forth his fruit in his season; his leaf also shall not wither; and whatsoever he doeth shall prosper.

The ungodly are not so: but are like the chaff which the wind driveth away.

Therefore the ungodly shall not stand in the judgment, nor sinners in the congregation of the righteous.

For the Lord knoweth the way of the righteous: but the way of the ungodly shall perish. —Psalm 1.

There is a way which seemeth right unto a man, but the end thereof are the ways of death.—Proverbs 14:12.

Trust in the Lord with all thine heart; and lean not unto thine own understanding.

In all thy ways acknowledge him, and he shall direct thy paths.
—Proverbs 3:5, 6.

Enter ye in at the strait gate: for wide is the gate, and broad is the way, that leadeth to destruction, and many there be which go in thereat:

Because strait is the gate, and narrow is the way, which leadeth unto life, and few there be that find it.
—Matthew 7:13, 14.

Jesus saith . . . I am the way, the truth, and the life: no man cometh unto the Father, but by me.
—John 14:6.

551 FAITH IN CHRIST

Now faith is the substance of things hoped for, the evidence of things not seen.

But without faith it is impossible to please him: for he that cometh

to God must believe that he is, and that he is a rewarder of them that diligently seek him. —Hebrews 11:1, 6.

And this is the will of him that sent me, that every one which seeth the Son, and believeth on him, may have everlasting life: and I will raise him up at the last day.
—John 6:40.

For whatsoever is born of God overcometh the world: and this is the victory that overcometh the world, even our faith.

Who is he that overcometh the world, but he that believeth that Jesus is the Son of God?

And this is the record, that God hath given to us eternal life, and this life is in his Son.

These things have I written unto you that believe on the name of the Son of God; that ye may know that ye have eternal life, and that ye may believe on the name of the Son of God.

And we know that the Son of God is come, and hath given us an understanding, that we may know him that is true, and we are in him that is true, even in his Son Jesus Christ. This is the true God, and eternal life. —1 John 5:4, 5, 11, 13, 20.

552 PRAYER OF PENITENCE

Have mercy upon me, O God, according to thy lovingkindness:

According unto the multitude of thy tender mercies blot out my transgressions.

Wash me throughly from mine iniquity, and cleanse me from my sin.

For I acknowledge my transgressions: and my sin is ever before me.

Against thee, thee only, have I sinned, and done this evil in thy sight: that thou mightest be justified when thou speakest, and be clear when thou judgest.

Behold, I was shapen in iniquity; and in sin did my mother conceive me.

Behold, thou desirest truth in the inward parts: and in the hidden part thou shalt make me to know wisdom.

Purge me with hyssop, and I shall be clean: wash me, and I shall be whiter than snow.

Make me to hear joy and gladness; that the bones which thou hast broken may rejoice.

Hide thy face from my sins, and blot out all mine iniquities.

Create in me a clean heart, O God; and renew a right spirit within me.

Cast me not away from thy presence; and take not thy holy spirit from me.

Restore unto me the joy of thy salvation; and uphold me with thy free spirit.

Then will I teach transgressors thy ways; and sinners shall be converted unto thee.

O Lord, open thou my lips; and my mouth shall shew forth thy praise. For thou desirest not sacrifice; else would I give it: thou delightest not in burnt offering.

The sacrifices of God are a broken spirit: a broken and a contrite heart, O God, thou wilt not despise. —Psalm 51:1-13, 15-17.

553 CONFESSION OF CHRIST

Whosoever shall confess that Jesus is the Son of God, God dwelleth in him, and he in God.
—1 John 4:15.

The word is nigh thee, even in thy

mouth, and in thy heart: that is, the word of faith, which we preach;

That if thou shalt confess with thy mouth the Lord Jesus, and shalt believe in thine heart that God hath raised him from the dead, thou shalt be saved.

For with the heart man believeth unto righteousness; and with the mouth confession is made unto salvation. —Romans 10:8-10.

Wherefore God also hath highly exalted him, and given him a name which is above every name: that at the name of Jesus every knee should bow, of things in heaven, and things in earth, and things under the earth;

And that every tongue should confess that Jesus Christ is Lord, to the glory of God the Father. —Philippians 2:9-11.

Whosoever shall confess me before men, him shall the Son of man also confess before the angels of God:

But he that denieth me before men shall be denied before the angels of God. —Luke 12:8, 9.

554 CHRISTIAN BAPTISM

And Jesus came and spake unto them, saying, All power is given unto me in heaven and in earth. Go ye therefore, and teach all nations,

Baptizing them in the name of the Father, and of the Son, and of the Holy Ghost: teaching them to observe all things whatsoever I have commanded you: and, lo, I am with you alway, even unto the end of the world. —Matthew 28:18-20.

Therefore we are buried with him by baptism into death: that like as Christ was raised up from the dead by the glory of the Father, even so we also should walk in newness of life.

For if we have been planted together in the likeness of his death, we shall be also in the likeness of his resurrection:

Knowing this, that our old man is crucified with him, that the body of sin might be destroyed, that henceforth we should not serve sin.

For he that is dead is freed from sin. Now if we be dead with Christ, we believe that we shall also live with him:

Knowing that Christ being raised from the dead dieth no more; death hath no more dominion over him. For in that he died, he died unto sin once: but in that he liveth, he liveth unto God.

Likewise reckon ye also yourselves to be dead indeed unto sin, but alive unto God through Jesus Christ our Lord. —Romans 6:4-11.

555 THE MIND OF CHRIST

If there be therefore any consolation in Christ, if any comfort of love, if any fellowship of the Spirit, if any bowels and mercies,

Fulfil ye my joy, that ye be likeminded, having the same love, being of one accord, of one mind.

Let nothing be done through strife or vainglory; but in lowliness of mind let each esteem other better than themselves.

Look not every man on his own things, but every man also on the things of others.

Let this mind be in you, which was also in Christ Jesus:

Who, being in the form of God, thought it not robbery to be equal with God:

But made himself of no reputation, and took upon him the form of a servant, and was made in the likeness of men:

(over)

And being found in fashion as a man, he humbled himself, and became obedient unto death, even the death of the cross.

Wherefore God also hath highly exalted him, and given him a name which is above every name:

That at the name of Jesus every knee should bow, of things in heaven, and things in earth, and things under the earth;

And that every tongue should confess that Jesus Christ is Lord, to the glory of God the Father.

For it is God which worketh in you both to will and to do of his good pleasure.

Do all things without murmurings and disputings: that ye may be blameless and harmless, the sons of God, without rebuke, in the midst of a crooked and perverse nation,

Among whom ye shine as lights in the world; holding forth the word of life. —Philippians 2:1-11, 13-16.

556 GROWTH IN GRACE

Grace and peace be multiplied unto you through the knowledge of God, and of Jesus our Lord,

According as his divine power hath given unto us all things that pertain unto life and godliness, through the knowledge of him that hath called us to glory and virtue:

Whereby are given unto us exceeding great and precious promises: that by these ye might be partakers of the divine nature, having escaped the corruption that is in the world through lust.

And beside this, giving all diligence, add to your faith virtue; and to virtue knowledge;

And to knowledge temperance; and to temperance patience; and to patience godliness;

And to godliness brotherly kindness; and to brotherly kindness charity.

For if these things be in you, and abound, they make you that ye shall neither be barren nor unfruitful in the knowledge of our Lord Jesus Christ.

But he that lacketh these things is blind, and cannot see afar off, and hath forgotten that he was purged from his old sins.

Wherefore the rather, brethren, give diligence to make your calling and election sure: for if ye do these things, ye shall never fall:

For so an entrance shall be ministered unto you abundantly into the everlasting kingdom of our Lord and Saviour Jesus Christ.
—2 Peter 1:2-11.

557 PRACTICAL CHRISTIANITY

I beseech you therefore, brethren, by the mercies of God, that ye present your bodies a living sacrifice, holy, acceptable unto God, which is your reasonable service.

And be not conformed to this world: but be ye transformed by the renewing of your mind, that ye may prove what is that good, and acceptable, and perfect, will of God.

For I say, through the grace given unto me, to every man that is among you, not to think of himself more highly than he ought to think; but to think soberly, according as God hath dealt to every man the measure of faith.

Let love be without dissimulation. Abhor that which is evil; cleave to that which is good.

Be kindly affectioned one to another with brotherly love; in honour preferring one another;

Not slothful in business; fervent in spirit; serving the Lord;

Rejoicing in hope; patient in tribulation; continuing instant in prayer;

Distributing to the necessity of saints; given to hospitality.

Bless them which persecute you: bless, and curse not.

Rejoice with them that do rejoice, and weep with them that weep.

Be of the same mind one toward another. Mind not high things, but condescend to men of low estate. Be not wise in your own conceits.

Recompense to no man evil for evil. Provide things honest in the sight of all men. If it be possible, as much as lieth in you, live peaceably with all men.

Dearly beloved, avenge not yourselves, but rather give place unto wrath: for it is written, Vengeance is mine; I will repay, saith the Lord.

Therefore if thine enemy hunger, feed him; if he thirst, give him drink: for in so doing thou shalt heap coals of fire on his head. Be not overcome of evil, but overcome evil with good. —Romans 12:1-3, 9-21.

558   TEMPERANCE

Wine is a mocker, strong drink is raging: and whosoever is deceived thereby is not wise. —Proverbs 20:1.

Who hath woe? who hath sorrow? who hath contentions? who hath babbling? who hath wounds without cause? who hath redness of eyes?

They that tarry long at the wine; they that go to seek mixed wine. —Proverbs 23:29, 30.

For the flesh lusteth against the Spirit, and the Spirit against the flesh: and these are contrary the one to the other: so that ye cannot do the things that ye would.

But if ye be led of the Spirit, ye are not under the law.

Now the works of the flesh are manifest, which are these; Adultery, fornication, uncleanness, lasciviousness,

Idolatry, witchcraft, hatred, variance, emulations, wrath, strife, seditions, heresies, envyings, murders, drunkenness, revellings, and such like:

Of the which I tell you before, as I have also told you in time past, that they which do such things shall not inherit the kingdom of God.

But the fruit of the Spirit is love, joy, peace, longsuffering, gentleness, goodness, faith, meekness, temperance: against such there is no law. —Galatians 5:17-23.

And whatsoever ye do in word or deed, do all in the name of the Lord Jesus, giving thanks to God and the Father by him. —Colossians 3:17.

559   CHRISTIAN GIVING

Lay not up for yourselves treasures upon earth, where moth and rust doth corrupt, and where thieves break through and steal:

But lay up for yourselves treasures in heaven, where neither moth nor rust doth corrupt, and where thieves do not break through nor steal: for where your treasure is, there will your heart be also. —Matthew 6:19-21.

Upon the first day of the week let every one of you lay by him in store, as God hath prospered him. —1 Corinthians 16:2.

Therefore, as ye abound in every thing, in faith, and utterance, and knowledge, and in all diligence, and in your love to us, see that ye abound in this grace also.

I speak not by commandment, but by occasion of the forwardness of others, and to prove the sincerity of your love.

For ye know the grace of our Lord Jesus Christ, that, that, though he was rich, yet for your sakes he became poor, that ye through his poverty might be rich. —2 Corinthians 8:7-9.

But this I say, He which soweth sparingly shall reap also sparingly; and he which soweth bountifully shall reap also bountifully.

Every man according as he purposeth in his heart, so let him give; not grudgingly, or of necessity: for God loveth a cheerful giver.
—2 Corinthians 9:6, 7.

560   CHRISTIAN ASSURANCE

As many as are led by the Spirit of God, they are the sons of God.

For ye have not received the spirit of bondage again to fear; but ye have received the Spirit of adoption, whereby we cry, Abba, Father.

The Spirit itself beareth witness with our spirit, that we are the children of God:

And if children, then heirs; heirs of God, and joint-heirs with Christ; if so be that we suffer with him, that we may be also glorified together.

For I reckon that the sufferings of this present time are not worthy to be compared with the glory which shall be revealed in us.

And we know that all things work together for good to them that love God, to them who are the called according to his purpose.

What shall we then say to these things? If God be for us, who can be against us?

He that spared not his own Son, but delivered him up for us all, how shall he not with him also freely give us all things?

Who shall separate us from the love of Christ? shall tribulation, or distress, or persecution, or famine, or nakedness, or peril, or sword?

Nay, in all these things we are more than conquerors through him that loved us.

For I am persuaded, that neither death, nor life, nor angels, nor principalities, nor powers, nor things present, nor things to come,

Nor height, nor depth, nor any other creature, shall be able to separate us from the love of God, which is in Christ Jesus our Lord.
—Romans 8:14-18, 28, 31, 32, 35, 37-39.

561   LOVE

Though I speak with the tongues of men and of angels, and have not love, I am become as sounding brass, or a tinkling cymbal.

And though I have the gift of prophecy, and understand all mysteries, and all knowledge;

And though I have all faith, so that I could remove mountains, and have not love, I am nothing.

And though I bestow all my goods to feed the poor, and though I give my body to be burned, and have not love, it profiteth me nothing.

Love suffereth long, and is kind; love envieth not; love vaunteth not itself, is not puffed up,

Doth not behave itself unseemly, seeketh not her own, is not easily provoked, thinketh no evil;

Rejoiceth not in iniquity, but rejoiceth in the truth;

Beareth all things, believeth all things, hopeth all things, endureth all things.

Love never faileth: but whether there be prophecies, they shall fail; whether there be tongues, they shall cease; whether there be knowledge, it shall vanish away.

For we know in part, and we prophesy in part.

But when that which is perfect is come, then that which is in part shall be done away.

When I was a child, I spake as a child, I understood as a child, I thought as a child: but when I became a man, I put away childish things.

For now we see through a glass, darkly; but then face to face: now I know in part; but then shall I know even as also I am known.

And now abideth faith, hope, love, these three; but the greatest of these is love. —1 Corinthians 13.

562 PRAYER

When ye pray, use not vain repetitions, as the heathen do: for they think that they shall be heard for their much speaking.

Be not ye therefore like unto them: for your Father knoweth what things ye have need of, before ye ask him.

After this manner therefore pray ye:

Our Father which art in heaven, Hallowed be thy name.

Thy kingdom come. Thy will be done in earth, as it is in heaven.

Give us this day our daily bread. And forgive us our debts, as we forgive our debtors.

And lead us not into temptation, but deliver us from evil:

For thine is the kingdom, and the power, and the glory, for ever. Amen. —Matthew 6:7-13.

Continue in prayer, and watch in the same with thanksgiving.
—Colossians 4:2.

Confess your faults one to another, and pray one for another, that ye may be healed. The effectual fervent prayer of a righteous man availeth much. —James 5:16.

Be careful for nothing; but in every thing by prayer and supplication with thanksgiving let your requests be made known unto God.

And the peace of God, which passeth all understanding, shall keep your hearts and minds through Christ Jesus. —Philippians 4:6, 7.

563 CIVIL POWER

Let every soul be subject unto the higher powers. For there is no power but of God: the powers that be are ordained of God.

Whosoever therefore resisteth the power, resisteth the ordinance of God: and they that resist shall receive to themselves damnation.

For rulers are not a terror to good works, but to the evil. Wilt thou then not be afraid of the power? do that which is good, and thou shalt have praise of the same:

For he is the minister of God to thee for good. But if thou do that which is evil, be afraid; for he beareth not the sword in vain: for he is the minister of God, a revenger to execute wrath upon him that doeth evil.

Wherefore ye must needs be subject, not only for wrath, but also for conscience sake.

For for this cause pay ye tribute also: for they are God's ministers, attending continually upon this very thing.

Render therefore to all their dues: tribute to whom tribute is

 (over)

due; custom to whom custom; fear to whom fear; honour to whom honour.

Owe no man any thing, but to love one another: for he that loveth another hath fulfilled the law.
—Romans 13:1-8.

564 SPIRITUAL WARFARE

Finally, my brethren, be strong in the Lord, and in the power of his might.

Put on the whole armour of God, that ye may be able to stand against the wiles of the devil.

For we wrestle not against flesh and blood, but against principalities, against powers, against the rulers of the darkness of this world, against spiritual wickedness in high places.

Wherefore take unto you the whole armour of God, that ye may be able to withstand in the evil day, and having done all, to stand.

Stand therefore, having your loins girt about with truth, and having on the breastplate of righteousness;

And your feet shod with the preparation of the gospel of peace;

Above all, taking the shield of faith, wherewith ye shall be able to quench all the fiery darts of the wicked.

And take the helmet of salvation, and the sword of the Spirit, which is the word of God:

Praying always with all prayer and supplication in the Spirit, and watching thereunto with all perseverance and supplication for all saints. —Ephesians 6:10-18.

The night is far spent, the day is at hand: let us therefore cast off the works of darkness, and let us put on the armour of light.

Let us walk honestly, as in the

day; not in rioting and drunkenness, not in chambering and wantonness, not in strife and envying.

But put ye on the Lord Jesus Christ, and make not provision for the flesh, to fulfil the lusts thereof.
—Romans 13:12-14.

565 THE RETURN OF CHRIST

But I would not have you to be ignorant, brethren, concerning them which are asleep, that ye sorrow not, even as others which have no hope.

For if we believe that Jesus died and rose again, even so them also which sleep in Jesus will God bring with him.

For this we say unto you by the word of the Lord, that we which are alive and remain unto the coming of the Lord shall not prevent them which are asleep.

For the Lord himself shall descend from heaven with a shout, with the voice of the archangel, and with the trump of God: and the dead in Christ shall rise first:

Then we which are alive and remain shall be caught up together with them in the clouds, to meet the Lord in the air: and so shall we ever be with the Lord.

Wherefore comfort one another with these words.

But of the times and the seasons, brethren, ye have no need that I write unto you. For yourselves know perfectly that the day of the Lord so cometh as a thief in the night.

Therefore let us not sleep, as do others; but let us watch and be sober.

For they that sleep sleep in the night; and they that be drunken are drunken in the night.

But let us, who are of the day, be

sober, putting on the breastplate of faith and love; and for an helmet, the hope of salvation.

For God hath not appointed us to wrath, but to obtain salvation by our Lord Jesus Christ,

Who died for us, that, whether we wake or sleep, we should live together with him.

—1 Thessalonians 4:13—5:2, 6-10.

566 CHRIST AND IMMORTALITY

Now is Christ risen from the dead, and become the firstfruits of them that slept.

For since by man came death, by man came also the resurrection of the dead.

For as in Adam all die, even so in Christ shall all be made alive.

And so it is written, The first man Adam was made a living soul; the last Adam was made a quickening spirit.

The first man is of the earth, earthy: the second man is the Lord from heaven.

As is the earthy, such are they also that are earthy: and as is the heavenly, such are they also that are heavenly.

And as we have borne the image of the earthy, we shall also bear the image of the heavenly.

For this corruptible must put on incorruption, and this mortal must put on immortality.

So when this corruptible shall have put on incorruption, and this mortal shall have put on immortality, then shall be brought to pass the saying that is written, Death is swallowed up in victory.

O death, where is thy sting? O grave, where is thy victory?

The sting of death is sin; and the strength of sin is the law.

But thanks be to God, which giveth us the victory through our Lord Jesus Christ.

—1 Corinthians 15:20-22, 45, 47-49, 53-57.

567 THE JUDGMENT

And I saw a great white throne, and him that sat on it, from whose face the earth and the heaven fled away; and there was found no place for them.

And I saw the dead, small and great, stand before God; and the books were opened: and another book was opened, which is the book of life: and the dead were judged out of those things which were written in the books, according to their works.

And the sea gave up the dead which were in it; and death and hell delivered up the dead which were in them: and they were judged every man according to their works.

And death and hell were cast into the lake of fire. This is the second death.

And whosoever was not found written in the book of life was cast into the lake of fire.

—Revelation 20:11-15.

As therefore the tares are gathered and burned in the fire; so shall it be in the end of this world.

The Son of man shall send forth his angels, and they shall gather out of his kingdom all things that offend, and them which do iniquity;

And shall cast them into a furnace of fire: there shall be wailing and gnashing of teeth.

Then shall the righteous shine forth as the sun in the kingdom of their Father. Who hath ears to hear, let him hear.

—Matthew 13:40-43.

568 THE NEW CREATION

And I saw a new heaven and a new earth: for the first heaven and the first earth were passed away; and there was no more sea.

And I John saw the holy city, new Jerusalem, coming down from God out of heaven, prepared as a bride adorned for her husband.

And I heard a great voice out of heaven saying, Behold, the tabernacle of God is with men, and he will dwell with them, and they shall be his people, and God himself shall be with them, and be their God.

And God shall wipe away all tears from their eyes; and there shall be no more death, neither sorrow, nor crying, neither shall there be any more pain: for the former things are passed away.

And he that sat upon the throne said, Behold, I make all things new. And he said unto me, Write: for these words are true and faithful.

And he said unto me, It is done. I am Alpha and Omega, the beginning and the end. I will give unto him that is athirst of the fountain of the water of life freely.

He that overcometh shall inherit all things; and I will be his God, and he shall be my son.

And he carried me away in the spirit to a great and high mountain, and shewed me that great city, the holy Jerusalem, descending out of heaven from God,

Having the glory of God: and her light was like unto a stone most precious, even like a jasper stone, clear as crystal;

And I saw no temple therein: for the Lord God Almighty and the Lamb are the temple of it.

And the city had no need of the sun, neither of the moon, to shine in it: for the glory of God did lighten it, and the Lamb is the light thereof.

And the nations of them which are saved shall walk in the light of it: and the kings of the earth do bring their glory and honour into it.

And the gates of it shall not be shut at all by day: for there shall be no night there.

And they shall bring the glory and honour of the nations into it.

And there shall in no wise enter into it any thing that defileth,

Neither whatsoever worketh abomination, or maketh a lie: but they which are written in the Lamb's book of life.
—Revelation 21:1-7, 10, 11, 22-27.

569 THE IDEAL MOTHER

Who can find a virtuous woman? for her price is far above rubies.

The heart of her husband doth safely trust in her, so that he shall have no need of spoil.

She will do him good and not evil all the days of her life.

She seeketh wool, and flax, and worketh willingly with her hands.

She is like the merchants' ships; she bringeth her food from afar.

She riseth also while it is yet night, and giveth meat to her household, and a portion to her maidens.

She considereth a field, and buyeth it: with the fruit of her hands she planteth a vineyard.

She girdeth her loins with strength, and strengtheneth her arms.

She perceiveth that her merchandise is good: her candle goeth not out by night.

She layeth her hands to the spindle, and her hands hold the distaff.

She stretcheth out her hand to the poor; yea, she reacheth forth her hands to the needy.

She is not afraid of the snow for her household: for all her household are clothed with scarlet.

She maketh herself coverings of tapestry; her clothing is silk and purple.

Her husband is known in the gates, when he sitteth among the elders of the land.

She maketh fine linen, and selleth it; and delivereth girdles unto the merchant.

Strength and honour are her clothing; and she shall rejoice in time to come.

She openeth her mouth with wisdom; and in her tongue is the law of kindness.

She looketh well to the ways of her household, and eateth not the bread of idleness.

Her children arise up, and call her blessed; her husband also, and he praiseth her.

Many daughters have done virtuously, but thou excellest them all.

Favour is deceitful, and beauty is vain: but a woman that feareth the Lord, she shall be praised.
—Proverbs 31:10-30.

570 CHRIST AND CHILDREN

At the same time came the disciples unto Jesus, saying, Who is the greatest in the kingdom of heaven? And Jesus called a little child unto him, and set him in the midst of them, and said,

Verily I say unto you, Except ye be converted, and become as little children, ye shall not enter into the kingdom of heaven.

Whosoever therefore shall humble himself as this little child, the same is greatest in the kingdom of heaven. And whoso shall receive one such little child in my name receiveth me.

But whoso shall offend one of these little ones which believe in me, it were better for him that a millstone were hanged about his neck, and that he were drowned in the depth of the sea.

Take heed that ye despise not one of these little ones; for I say unto you, That in heaven their angels do always behold the face of my Father which is in heaven.—Matthew 18:1-6, 10.

Whosoever shall receive one of such children in my name, receiveth me: and whosoever shall receive me, receiveth not me, but him that sent me. —Mark 9:37.

And they brought young children to him, that he should touch them: and his disciples rebuked those that brought them.

But when Jesus saw it, he was much displeased, and said unto them, Suffer the little children to come unto me, and forbid them not: for of such is the kingdom of God.

Verily I say unto you, Whosoever shall not receive the kingdom of God as a little child, he shall not enter therein.

And he took them up in his arms, put his hands upon them, and blessed them. —Mark 10:13-16.

Topical Index of Scripture Readings

Armor, Christian.............. 564
Assurance, Christian.......... 560
Baptism
    Christ's 531
    Christian 554
Beatitudes 538
Bible 542
Children 570
Christ
    Baptism 531
    Birth 529, 530
    Children 570
    Comforter 540
    Confession of............ 553
    Crucifixion 532, 535
    Faith in................ 551
    Immortality, and........ 566
    Incarnation 528
    Judge 567
    Last Supper............. 533
    Mind of................ 555
    Resurrection 536
    Return 565
    Teachings of..... 538, 539, 562
    Triumphal entry......... 534
Christian, The
    Activity 550
    Assurance 521, 560, 566
    Baptism 554
    Comfort 540
    Confession 553
    Eternal Life..... 566, 567, 568
    Discipleship 539
    Faith 551
    Gospel armor............ 564
    Growth 556
    Love 561
    Ministry 537, 545
    Obedience 527
    Practical Christianity. 557, 564
    Prayer 552, 562
    Repentance 552
    Sin and forgiveness....... 547
    Stewardship 559
    Vine and branches....... 539
Christian Unity.............. 546
Church, The
    Mission 537, 545
    Nature 544
    Unity 546
Civil power.................. 563
Comfort, from Christ......... 540
Communion 533

Confession of Christ......... 553
Death 566
Eternal Life........ 566, 567, 568
Evangelism 537
Faith 551
Giving 559
God
    Adoration and praise...... 525
    Care 521, 522
    Commandments 524
    Creator 519
    Invitation 549
    Omniscience 520
    Obedience 527
    Prayer 552, 562
    Providence 523
    Thanksgiving 526
    Worship 525
Great commission............ 537
Holy Spirit.................. 541
Immortality 566
Incarnation 528
Invitation 549
Judgment 565, 567
Last supper.................. 533
Law and gospel.............. 548
Love 561
Ministry, Christian........... 545
Missions 537, 553, 554
Mother, the ideal............ 569
New Creation................ 568
Obedience 527
Patriotism 563
Prayer 552, 562
Providence, divine........... 523
Repentance 552
Return, Christ's............. 565
Resurrection
    Christ's 536
    Final 565, 566, 568
Scriptures, Holy............. 542
Shepherd Psalm, the......... 522
Sin 547, 552
Stewardship 559
Temperance 558
Ten Commandments.......... 524
Thanksgiving 525, 526
Unity, Christian.............. 546
Warfare, spiritual............ 564
Way of life................. 550
Wisdom 543
Word of God................ 542
Worship 525

TOPICAL INDEX

ADMONITION

Did you think to....119
Fight the good fight.346
Give of your best to.348
Have you any room.174
Help somebody to-..196
I am praying for you.109
In times like these..352
Leave it there......383
Let Him in......... 68
Let Jesus come into. 55
Let the lower lights.181
My soul, be on thy..350
Take the name of..378
Take time to be holy.342
The heavenly vision.155
The nail-scarred....316
Though your sins be.142
Throw out the life-..198
To the work!.......363
Why do you wait?.. 61
Will Jesus find us..187
Work, for the night.120
Yield not to temp-..333
You may have the.. 69
(See Challenge)

ADORATION

All glory, laud and.415
All hail, Immanuel!.518
All people that on.. 12
Blessed be the name. 16
Bread of heaven....433
Crown Him with.... 77
Glory to His name.188
Here, O my Lord..436
Holy, holy, holy.... 2
I love Him because.214
Jesus, the very.....463
Majestic sweetness..130
More love to Thee..282
My Jesus, I love....297
O perfect love.....461
O sacred Head, now.338
O Thou in whose...105
Oh, how I love Jesus.226
Praise ye the Lord.. 14
Since the fullness..233
Spirit of God, de-.. 50
Still, still with...... 11
The sands of time..255
Ye servants of God 67
(See Praise, Worship)

ADVENT

(See Christ: Advent)

ASPIRATION

A passion for souls.195
Breathe on me...... 3
Close to Thee......298
Come, Thou Fount.. 17
Dear Lord and.....414
Draw me nearer....265
Follow on 431
Higher ground......262
I long to glorify....167
I need Jesus........266
I shall be like Him..488
I would be like Jesus.270
I would be true.....260
Jesus, and shall it...111
Jesus, revealed in me 240
Jesus, Rose of......381
Just a closer walk...485

Lead, kindly Light..277
Lord, I hear of.....284
Make me a blessing.184
More about Jesus...275
More holiness give..269
More like the Master 280
More love to Thee..282
Must Jesus bear the.189
My faith looks up..344
Nearer, my God, to.272
Nearer, still nearer..267
Nearer the cross....409
O for a closer walk.276
O for a faith that.... 6
O Jesus, I have.....274
O Love that wilt not. 74
O Master, let me....429
O to be like Thee!.. 18
Others 185
Revive Thy work....114
Savior, like a.......480
Savior, more than..176
Stepping in the.....459
Sweet will of God..125
Teach me Thy will..124
Teach me to pray...115
The way of the cross.402
There shall be show-.279
We would see Jesus.412
Whiter than snow...145
(See Consecration)

ASSURANCE

A shelter in the.....211
Anywhere with Jesus 286
Arise, my soul......129
Art thou weary, art. 57
Be still, my soul.... 98
Blessed assurance...289
Come, ye discon-...201
Constantly abiding.. 42
Dwelling in Beulah.206
Glorious things of...335
God leads us along.473
God will take care..293
Great is Thy.......148
He hideth my soul..247
He is able to....... 35
He leadeth me.....219
He lives............164
He will answer every 223
He's a friend of....199
Heavenly sunlight... 27
His eye is on the....248
His mighty hand....314
How firm a founda-. 38
I belong to the King.212
I know that my......419
I know who holds to-250
I know whom I have.213
I never walk alone..315
I've found a Friend.370
It is well with my... 73
Jesus never fails....165
Jesus, Thy blood....169
Just when I need...285
Leaning on the.....292
Like a river glori-...103
Moment by moment. 40
My anchor holds....291
My sins are blotted.136
Never alone!.......312
No, not one!.......224
No other plea......193
Now I belong to....230
O God, our help....467
Once for all........139

Precious hiding place 41
Safe in the arms of. 44
Some time we'll un-.496
Standing on the.....323
Surely goodness and.339
Tell it to Jesus.....116
The Bible stands....322
The haven of rest...244
The lily of the......157
The Lord is my shep-374
The Lord's my shep-.373
The Rock that is....294
The solid Rock.....310
Under His wings....311
Unto the hills......122
We have an anchor..287
We shall see the....498
What a Friend......517
What God hath.....474
Wonderful peace....101
(See Trust)

BAPTISM

Buried with Christ..318
Follow on..........431
Jesus, I my cross...271
Jesus paid it all....131
O happy day.......227
O Master, let me....429
Take my life, and...388
'Tis so sweet to....241
Trust and obey.....365
Where He leads I'll.401

BIBLE

Beautiful words of..325
Break Thou the.....320
Holy Bible, book....253
In times like these..352
O Word of God.....319
Open my eyes, that I.278
Standing on the.....323
The Bible stands....322
Thy Word have I hid 324
Thy Word is like a..327
Wonderful words of.326

BURDENS

Burdens are lifted..203
I must tell Jesus....113
Leave it there......383
Tell it to Jesus.....116
(See Trials)

CHALLENGE

A charge to keep...362
As a volunteer......341
Fight the good fight.346
Give of your best to.348
Hold the fort.......345
I am resolved.......349
I gave my life for... 58
Jesus, and shall it...111
Jesus calls us.......343
O Zion, haste.......446
Rescue the perishing.194
Rise up, O men.....351
Soldiers of Christ...356
Sound the battle cry.359
Stand up, stand up..357
Stand up, stand up..358
The banner of the...360
The Son of God....179
Who is on the......366

Will Jesus find us...187
Yield not to temp-..333
(See Admonition)

CHILDREN'S HYMNS

Come to the Savior.307
Dare to be a Daniel.512
I'll be a sunbeam...515
Jesus bids us shine..347
Jesus loves even me.234
Jesus loves me......513
Jewels 511
Praise Him, all ye..514
Tell me the stories..191
The children's 510

CHOIR

All hail, Immanuel!.518
And can it be that I.107
Bring your vessels..263
Christ is King.......163
Fairest Lord Jesus.. 5
God of our fathers..454
Hallelujah for the...132
Hallelujah, what a..158
Heaven came down. 96
I heard the voice of. 54
I've discovered the..239
Jesus is coming.....173
Jesus, Savior.......192
Joyful, joyful, we... 23
Just a closer walk...485
Living for Jesus.....259
Make me a blessing.184
Master, the tempest.102
Praise ye the Father.121
Rejoice, ye pure in.. 7
Savior, my heart is..392
Seeking the lost.....306
Surely goodness and.339
The spacious firma-. 25
The unveiled Christ.161
Though your sins be.142
Unto the hills......122
When I see my Sav-.288
Wonderful grace of.470

CHRIST

Advent and Birth:

Angels, from the.... 92
Away in a manger.. 93
Hark! the herald.... 81
I heard the bells.... 91
If Jesus had not....368
It came upon the.... 84
Joy to the world!... 88
O come, all ye..... 83
O little town of..... 82
Silent night! holy... 87
The first noel...... 90
There's a song in the 85
Thou didst leave Thy 89
We three kings of... 80
While shepherds.... 86

Blood:

Are you washed in..328
Jesus, Thy blood....169
Nor silver nor gold..137
Nothing but the....138
Redeemed 140
Saved by the blood.329
There is a fountain.141
There is power in...330

TOPICAL INDEX

'Twas Jesus' blood..332
When I see the blood 331

Character:
All that thrills my.. 65
Fairest Lord Jesus.. 5
He is so precious...208
Jesus is the sweetest. 36
Jesus, Rose of.....381
Jesus, the very.....463
Majestic sweetness..130
My Savior first of...256
O could I speak.... 20
O that will be glory.494
The heavenly vision.155
The lily of the.....157
When we see Christ.504
Why do I sing about.149

Comforter:
All things in Jesus..202
Beautiful words of..325
Burdens are lifted...203
Does Jesus care?...384
I must tell Jesus....113
It's just like His....218
Just a closer walk..485
Just when I need...285
Leave it there......383
Look to the Lamb of 53
Moment by moment. 40
No one understands.404
Only Jesus 153
Our great Savior...154
Peace, perfect peace.489
Precious hiding place 41
The Lord is my shep-374
The Lord's my shep-.373
The touch of His...427
Under His wings...311
Wonderful, wonder-.151

Example:
I shall be like Him.488
I would be like Jesus 270
Jesus only, let me...411
More like the Master 280
O to be like Thee!.. 18
Stepping in the.....459
Where He leads I'll.401

Friend:
He's a friend of....199
I need Jesus.......266
I never walk alone.. 315
I've found a Friend.370
Jesus is all the.....220
Jesus never fails....165
No, not one!......224
No one understands.404
The children's.....510
The Lily of the.....157
What a Friend.....517

Guide:
All the way my.....472
Each step I take....290
Follow on.........431
Footprints of Jesus.505
I will follow Thee..395
If Jesus goes with..397
Jesus only, let me...411
Jesus, Savior, pilot.477
Lead, kindly Light..277
Our great Savior....154
Precious Lord, take.249
Stepping in the.....459
Where He leads I'll.401

Intercessor:
Accepted in the Be-.499

Arise, my soul.....129
In the hour of......281
Jesus, Thy blood...169
My hope is in the.. 37
Something for Thee.264

Kingship and Reign:
All hail, Immanuel!.518
All hail the power.. 8
All hail the power.. 10
Blessed be the name 16
Christ is King......163
Crown Him with... 77
From Greenland's ..443
I've heard the......216
Jesus Christ is......379
Jesus is coming....173
Jesus only, let me..411
Jesus shall reign... 75
Lead on, O King... 76
Praise Him! praise.. 19
The unveiled Christ.161
True-hearted, whole-364
We shall see the....498
We've a story to...449
What if it were to-.175
Ye servants of God. 67

Life and Ministry:
If Jesus had not....368
One day!.........377
Sweeter as the years.235
Tell me the stories..191
Tell me the story...237
The great Physician.159
The Stranger of....162

Light:
Heavenly sunlight... 27
I heard the voice of. 54
Lead, kindly Light..277
O Love that wilt not. 74
O Word of God....319
Sunlight 30
Sunshine in the soul. 31
The light of the....156

Lord:
Have Thine own way 387
Jesus Christ is.....379
Living for Jesus....259
My hope is in the.. 37
(See Christ: Kingship)

Love:
He the pearly gates.483
I love Him because.214
I love to tell the...215
It's just like His....218
Ivory palaces......375
Jesus loves even me.234
Love divine, all.... 45
Love led Him to....134
Love lifted me.....221
My Savior's love...182
O Love that wilt not. 74
Precious hiding place 41
Since the fullness...233
Sunlight 30
Sweeter as the years 235
Tell me the old, old. 79
There is a green....340

Name:
All hail the power.. 8
All hail the power.. 10
Blessed be the name. 16
Glory to His name..188
He keeps me singing 296
How sweet the name 435

Jesus is the sweetest. 36
Oh, how I love Jesus 226
Take the name of...378
The name of Jesus.160
Ye servants of God. 67

Refuge:
A shelter in the.....211
He hideth my soul..247
Hiding in Thee.....389
His mighty hand...314
I heard the voice of. 54
Jesus, lover of my..152
Jesus never fails....165
Jesus, Savior, pilot.477
Just when I need...285
Leaning on the.....292
Master, the tempest.102
Nearer, still nearer.267
Only Jesus.........153
Precious hiding place 41
Rock of ages.......243
Safe in the arms of. 44
The haven of rest...244
The Rock that is....294
Under His wings...311
Unto the hills.....122
Whom have I but...380

Resurrection:
Christ arose!......416
Christ the Lord is..417
Come, ye faithful..418
He lives..........164
I know that my.....419
In the garden......428
Wounded for me...369

Return:
Christ is King......163
Christ returneth....170
Come, ye thankful..509
He is coming again.171
How great Thou art! 34
I know that my....419
Jesus is coming...173
One day!.........377
Some day!........ 71
Sooner or later.....482
We'll work till......228
What if it were to-..175
When the roll is....500
Will Jesus find us...187
Wounded for me...369

Rock:
A shelter in the.....211
He hideth my soul..247
Hiding in Thee.....389
In times like these..352
My anchor holds...291
Rock of ages.......243
The Rock that is...294
The solid Rock.....310
We have an anchor.287

Sacrifice:
According to Thy...432
Art thou weary, art. 57
Hallelujah, what a..158
He died for me....334
I love Him because.214
I will sing the won-.133
In tenderness He...371
Ivory palaces......375
Jesus paid it all....131
Lead me to Calvary.337
Love led Him to....134
My Savior's love....182
Nailed to the cross. 33

O Jesus, Thou art.. 56
O sacred Head, now 338
One day!..........377
Praise Him! praise.. 19
Tell me the story...237
Ten thousand angels.410
The ninety and nine.197
The unveiled Christ.161
There is a green....340
'Tis midnight; and..321
What will you do...304
When I see my Sav-.288
Wounded for me...369
(See Christ: Suffering)

Savior:
Accepted in the Be-.499
Blessed Redeemer..128
Hallelujah, what a..158
He died for me....334
He hideth my soul..247
I am not skilled....479
Jesus has lifted me..217
Jesus saves.........445
Jesus, Thy blood...169
Majestic sweetness. 130
My hope is in the.. 37
My Redeemer......222
My Savior first of...256
Now I belong to....230
O could I speak.... 20
O for a thousand....456
O Thou God of my. 15
Once for all.......139
Our great Savior...154
Pass me not, O.... 51
Redeemed 140
Saved, saved!.....231
The great Physician.159
The heavenly vision.155
There is a fountain.141
What a wonderful..376
Why do I sing about.149

Shepherd:
Bring them in...... 22
In tenderness He...371
O Thou in whose...105
Praise Him! praise. 19
Savior, like a......480
Seeking the lost.....306
Surely goodness and.339
The King of love...372
The Lord is my shep-374
The Lord's my shep-373
The ninety and nine.197

Suffering:
Alas! and did my... 94
And can it be that I.107
At the cross....... 95
Beneath the cross of.426
Blessed Redeemer..128
Crown Him with... 77
He wore a crown of.403
I gave my life for... 58
'Tis midnight; and..321
When I survey the.413
(See Christ: Sacrifice)

Teacher:
Break Thou the.....320
Lord, speak to me..273
More about Jesus...275
O Word of God....319
Spirit of God, de-..124
Teach me Thy will..124
Teach me to pray..115

Triumphal Entry:
All glory, laud and..415

TOPICAL INDEX

CHRISTMAS
(See Christ: Advent)

CHURCH
Faith:
Faith of our fathers.423
O Word of God....319

Fellowship:
Blest be the tie....430
For the beauty of..457
Glorious things of..335
I love Thy kingdom.313
Rise up, O men....351
The church's one...336

Militant and Triumphant:
A mighty fortress...466
Faith is the victory!.425
Fling out the banner.437
Hail to the bright-..438
I love Thy kingdom.313
Jerusalem the golden 507
O Zion, haste......446
Onward, Christian..353
The banner of the..360
The church's one...336

CLEANSING
Are you washed in..328
Channels only......398
Cleanse me........252
Grace greater than..469
I am coming, Lord.. 52
Jesus paid it all....131
Nothing but the....138
O happy day......227
Savior, more than..176
Whiter than snow..145
(See Holiness of Life)

COMFORT
A shelter in the....211
Beyond the sunset..486
Come, ye discon-...201
Count your blessings 516
Face to face......493
God leads us along.473
God will take care..293
He leadeth me....219
He'll understand and 484
Holy Spirit, faith-.. 46
I won't have to....506
It is well with my... 73
Near to the heart..464
No night there....492
On Jordan's stormy.490
Precious Lord, take.249
Some golden day-...495
Some time we'll un-.496
Sweet hour of prayer 110
Tell it to Jesus.....116
The beautiful garden 117
The Rock that is...294
'Tis the blessed....118
Trust in the Lord..246
We shall see the...498
When love shines in.143
When we see Christ.504
Where the gates....502
(See Christ: Comforter)

COMMUNION
(See Fellowship,
Lord's Supper)

CONFESSION OF SIN
Beneath the cross of 426
I am coming to the.. 21
Into my heart......354

Is my name written.. 60
Jesus, I come.....295
Jesus, lover of my..152
Lead, kindly Light..277
Lord, I'm coming... 63
Nearer, still nearer.267

CONFLICT
(See Warfare, Christian)

CONSECRATION
Alas! and did my... 94
All for Jesus.......394
At the cross....... 95
Beneath the cross of.426
Channels only......398
Cleanse me........252
Come, Holy Spirit..406
Fill me now....... 48
Footprints of Jesus.505
Have Thine own way 387
His way with the..385
Holy Ghost, with.. 47
I am coming to the. 21
I am resolved......349
I need Thee every..478
I will praise Him... 32
I'd rather have....106
I'll go where you..399
I'll live for Him...283
I've found a Friend.370
Is your all on the..390
Jesus, I my cross..271
Jesus, Savior......192
Lead me to Calvary.337
Living for Jesus...259
Love lifted me....221
Make me a blessing.184
Make me a channel.186
Moment by moment. 40
My Jesus, as Thou. 43
Now I belong to...230
O for a closer walk.276
O to be like Thee!.. 18
Open my eyes, that I.278
Others 185
Savior, like a......480
Savior, my heart is.392
So send I you.....442
Something for Thee.264
Take my life, and..388
Trust and obey....365
When I survey the..413
Where He leads me.393
Who is on the.....366
(See Aspiration)

CONVERSION
A new name in....200
Amazing grace.....487
At Calvary........400
He took my sins...150
I need Thee every..478
I surrender all.....391
I'll live for Him...283
I've discovered the.239
Jesus, I come.....295
Lord, I'm coming.. 63
O happy day......227
Ye must be born...147
(See Invitation,
Salvation)

COURAGE
Am I a soldier of..361
Anywhere with Jesus 286
"Are ye able," said.261
Count your blessings 516
Dare to be a Daniel.512
Sound the battle cry.359
Stand up, stand up.357

CROSS
of Believer:
"Are ye able," said.261
Jesus, I my cross...271
Lead me to Calvary.337
Must Jesus bear the.189
Nearer, my God, to.272
O Love that wilt not. 74
Where He leads me.393
Where the gates....502

of Christ:
Alas! and did my... 94
At Calvary........400
At the cross....... 95
Beneath the cross of.426
Burdens are lifted...203
Crown Him with.... 77
Glory to His name.188
Hallelujah for the..132
He died for me....334
I am coming to the. 21
I love Him because.214
In the cross of.....408
Kneel at the cross..405
Lead me to Calvary.337
Nailed to the cross. 33
Near the cross.....407
Nearer the cross....409
Room at the cross..460
The banner of the..360
The old rugged cross 317
The way of the cross 402
There is a green....340
When I survey the..413

DEVOTIONAL
Abide with me.....462
Alas! and did my... 94
All for Jesus......394
At the cross....... 95
Beneath the cross of.426
Day is dying in the.420
He died for me....334
In the hour of.....281
Jesus, revealed in...240
Jesus, Savior......192
My faith looks up..344
Near the cross.....407
Near to the heart..464
O Love that wilt not. 74
O Master, let me...429
O sacred Head, now.338
Savior, like a......480
Still, still with..... 11
Sun of my soul....422
(See Meditation)

DISCIPLESHIP
All for Jesus.......394
"Are ye able," said.261
Close to Thee......298
Follow on.........431
Footprints of Jesus.505
Give me thy heart 300
I will follow Thee 395
I'll go where you..399
I'll live for Him...283
I'll put Jesus first..396
Jesus calls us......343
Jesus, I my cross..271
Lead me to Calvary.337
Lord, speak to me..273
Must Jesus bear the.189
O Jesus, I have....274
Trust and obey....365
Where He leads me.393

EASTER
(See Christ:
Resurrection)

CROSS
of Believer:

ETERNAL LIFE
I know that my....419
I shall be like Him..488
Jerusalem the golden 507
No night there.....492
Peace, perfect peace.489
Some time we'll un-.496
Songs of praises....476
Still, still with..... 11
We're marching to..126
Where the gates....502
(See Heaven)

EVENING HYMNS
Abide with me.....462
Day is dying in the.420
Now the day is over.421
Savior, breathe an..190
Sun of my soul.....422

FAITH
Faith is the victory!.425
Faith of our fathers.423
Faith of our mothers 424
His eye is on the...248
My faith looks up..344
O for a faith that... 6
(See Trust)

FAITHFULNESS
of Believer:
Bringing in the.....444
Faith of our fathers.423
I will follow Thee..395
I would be true....260
It pays to serve...183
Jesus, and shall it..111
Jesus calls us......343
True-hearted, whole-364
We have an anchor.287
We'll work till.....228
When we all get to.501
Will Jesus find us...187

of God:
(See God: Faithfulness)

FELLOWSHIP
of Believers:
Blest be the tie.....430
(See Church:
Fellowship)

with God:
Follow on.........431
He lives..........164
I am His, and He..465
I never walk alone.315
In the garden......428
Just a closer walk..485
Leaning on the.....292
Near to the heart..464
O for a closer walk.276
O Master, let me...429
The nail-scarred....316

FORGIVENESS
Christ receiveth....204
Gone, yes, gone for-.257
Grace greater than..469
He the pearly gates.483
He took my sins....150
Jesus, Thy blood...169
My sins are blotted.136
Nothing but the....138
Ring the bells of.... 28
Saved! 229
Saved by the blood.329

TOPICAL INDEX

There is power in...330
There's a new song. 70
Though your sins be 142
Whiter than snow....145
Wonderful grace of.470

GOD

Creator:
All creatures of our. 24
For the beauty of..457
Great is thy........148
How great Thou art! 34
It took a miracle....135
Joyful, joyful, we... 23
Praise ye the Lord.. 14
The spacious firma-. 25

Faithfulness:
Abide with me.....462
Be still, my soul... 98
Great is Thy.......148
Jesus never fails....165
Leave it there......383
Like a river glori-..103
Never alone!.......312
O God, our help....467
This is my Father's.458

Holiness:
Day is dying in the.420
Holy, holy, holy.... 2

Love and Mercy:
Come, Thou Fount.. 17
Depth of mercy!...168
Great is thy.......148
He is able to...... 35
Surely goodness and.339
Sweet peace, the.... 99
The love of God....166
There's a wideness..468

Majesty and Power:
A mighty fortress...466
Battle hymn of the..453
Come, Thou Al-.... 4
Holy, holy, holy.... 2
It took a miracle...135
O worship the King. 13

Providence:
All people that on.. 12
God be with you...177
God will take care..293
Guide me, O Thou.475
I know who holds to-250
In the hollow of His.251
Like a river glori-..103
Now thank we all...508
O God, our help....467
O worship the King. 14
Praise ye the Lord.. 14
Songs of praises....476
The King of love...372
Trust in the Lord..246
Unto the hills......122
What God hath.....474

Trinity:
All creatures of our. 24
Come, Thou Al-.... 4
Holy, holy, holy.... 2
In tenderness He...371
Praise ye the Father.121

GRACE

Accepted in the Be-.499
Amazing grace 487
Grace greater than..469

Jesus is the sweetest. 36
Only a sinner.......225
Saved by grace.....471
Wonderful grace of.470

GUIDANCE

God leads us along..473
Guide me, O Thou..475
He leadeth me.....219
Holy Spirit, faith-... 46
Songs of praises....476
Thy Word have I hid 324
Where He leads I'll.401
(See Christ. Guide)

HEAVEN

Beulah land 481
Beyond the sunset..486
Come to the Savior.307
Come, we that love.123
Face to face.......493
Guide me, O Thou..475
He the pearly gates.483
He'll understand and 484
I won't have to....506
In my heart there... 26
My Savior first of..256
O could I speak.... 20
O that will be glory.494
On Jordan's stormy.490
Saved by grace.....471
Shall we gather at...491
Some day!......... 71
Some golden day-...495
Sooner or later.....482
Sweet by and by....497
The sands of time...255
The way of the cross 402
We shall see the....498
We'll work till....228
When the roll is....500
When we all get to..501
When we see Christ.504
Will there be any...503
(See Eternal Life)

HOLINESS OF LIFE

Breathe on me..... 3
Bring your vessels..263
Come, Holy Spirit..406
Fill me now........ 48
Have Thine own way 387
Higher ground......262
Holy Ghost, with... 47
I am coming to the.. 21
I will praise Him... 32
Is thy heart right...172
Just a closer walk...485
Let Jesus come into. 55
Love divine, all..... 45
More holiness give..269
More like the Master 280
Take time to be.....342
There is power in...330
Thy Holy Spirit.... 97
Thy Word have I...324
(See Cleansing)

HOLY SPIRIT

Blessed quietness...108
Break Thou the....320
Breathe on me..... 3
Bring your vessels..263
Channels only 398
Cleanse me........252
Come, Holy Spirit..406
Fill me now........ 48
Have Thine own way 387
Holy Ghost, with... 47
Holy Spirit, faith-... 46

Is your all on the..390
Open my eyes, that I 278
Spirit of God, de-.. 50
The Comforter has.. 49
Thy Holy Spirit.... 97

HOME

Faith of our mothers 424
For the beauty of...457
The church in the..367

HOPE

Heaven came down. 96
My hope is in the... 37
O God, our help....467
Since Jesus came... 29
Take the name of...378
(See Faith, Trust)

HUMILITY

Beneath the cross of.426
Give me thy heart..300
His way with thee..385
I surrender all......391
If Jesus goes with...397
Into my heart......354
Nothing between...386
O Love that wilt not. 74
O sacred Head, now.338
O to be like Thee!.. 18
Others 185
(See Submission)

INVITATION

for Consecration:
Bring your vessels..263
Give me thy heart..300
Give of your best..348
I gave my life for... 58
I surrender all......391
Is thy heart right...172
(See Consecration,
Discipleship)

for Salvation:
Almost persuaded...299
Are you washed in..328
Art thou weary, art. 57
Christ receiveth....204
Come to the feast...305
Come to the Savior.307
Don't turn the......309
Give me thy heart..300
Have you any room.174
He is able to...... 35
I am coming, Lord.. 52
I heard the voice of. 54
Into my heart......354
Is my name written. 60
Jesus, I come......295
Jesus is calling..... 59
Just as I am....... 62
Kneel at the cross..405
Let Him in......... 68
Let Jesus come into. 55
Look to the Lamb of 53
Lord, I'm coming... 63
O Jesus, Thou art... 56
Once for all........139
Only trust Him....144
Pass me not, O..... 51
Room at the cross..460
Softly and tenderly.303
Springs of living... 64
The light of the.....156
The Savior is.......308
The Stranger of....162
What will you do...304
Who at my door is..258

"Whosoever" mean-.238
"Whosoever will"...302
Why do you wait?... 61
Why not now?......301
Ye must be born....147

JOY

A new name in.....200
Beulah land........481
Blessed assurance ..289
Bringing in the.....444
Come, we that love.123
Dwelling in Beulah.206
Gone, yes, gone for-.257
He included me.....205
He keeps me singing 296
He lives 164
He took my sins...150
Heaven came down. 96
Heavenly sunlight... 27
His eye is on the...248
I am His, and He...465
I've discovered the.239
In my heart there... 26
In the service of....178
Jesus loves even me.234
Joy to the world!... 88
Joyful, joyful, we... 23
O day of rest and... 78
O happy day.......227
Rejoice, ye pure in.. 7
Ring the bells of... 28
Since Jesus came... 29
Springs of living... 64
Sunshine in the soul. 31
There's a new song. 70
To God be the.....127
Trust and obey.....365
'Twas a glad day... 66
We're marching to. 126
What if it were to-..175
When love shines in 143
When we all get to..501
Wonderful grace of.470
Wonderful, wonder-.151
You may have the... 69

JUDGMENT

Battle hymn of the..453
Come, ye thankful..509
Since Jesus came.... 29
When I see the blood 331

KINGDOM

(See Christ: Kingship)

LORD'S DAY

O day of rest and... 78
Safely through...... 72

LORD'S SUPPER

According to Thy...432
Beneath the cross of.426
Bread of heaven....433
Communion hymn ..434
Dear Lord and.....414
Here, O my Lord...436
In the cross of.....408
Jesus, the very.....463
Majestic sweetness.130
My Jesus, I love....297
Near the cross......407
There is a fountain.141
This do in re-.......439
'Tis midnight; and..321
When I survey the..413

LOVE

I love Him because.214
In my heart there... 26

TOPICAL INDEX

It's just like His....218
Love divine, all.... 45
Love led Him to....134
Love lifted me.....221
More love to Thee. 282
My Jesus, I love....297
O perfect love......461
Oh, how I love Jesus 226
Since the fullness...233
There's a wideness. 468
When love shines in.143
Wonderful story of.146

LOYALTY

Dare to be a Daniel.512
Follow on.........431
I would be true.....260
In the hour of.....281
Jesus calls us.......343
Jesus, I my cross....271
Loyalty to Christ...355
O Jesus, I have.....274
True-hearted, whole- 364
What will you do...304

MEDITATION

Dear Lord and.....414
Draw me nearer...265
From every stormy.104
I need Thee every...478
I'll live for Him....283
I'll put Jesus first...396
Jesus, lover of my..152
Jesus, the very......463
Lord, I hear of.....284
More love to Thee. 282
My Jesus, I love....297
Nearer, still nearer.267
Nearer the cross....409
Open my eyes, that I 278
Savior, more than...176
Something for Thee. 264
Sun of my soul.....422
Sweet hour of prayer 110
(See Devotional)

MERCY

At Calvary........400
Depth of mercy!....168
Softly and tenderly.303
Surely goodness and.339
There's a wideness..468
(See Forgiveness)

MISSIONARY

Bring them in...... 22
Faith of our fathers.423
Fling out the banner.437
From Greenland's .443
Go ye into all the...441
Hail to the bright-..438
I'll go where you...399
If Jesus goes with...397
Jesus saves........445
Jesus shall reign.... 75
Let the lower lights.181
Macedonia 440
O Zion, haste......446
Send the light.....447
So send I you......442
The banner of the...360
The ninety and nine.197
The regions beyond.448
The Son of God....179
To the work!......363
We've a story to....449
Where cross the....180
Work, for the night.120

MORNING HYMNS

Holy, holy, holy.... 2
Still, still with..... 11
When morning gilds. 1

MOTHER'S DAY

Faith of our mothers 424

NATIONAL

Battle hymn of the..453
God of our fathers. 454
My country, 'tis....455
O beautiful for....450
The star-spangled..451
We gather together. 382
Where cross the....180

NATURE

Come, ye thankful..509
Fairest Lord Jesus.. 5
For the beauty of...457
Still, still with...... 11
This is my Father's.458
(See God: Creator)

PALM SUNDAY

(See Christ:
Triumphal Entry)

PEACE

Be still, my soul.... 98
Blessed quietness...108
Constantly abiding.. 42
Dear Lord and.....414
From every stormy..104
I heard the bells.... 91
In the hollow of His.251
It is well with my... 73
Jesus, Savior, pilot..477
Leaning on the.....292
Like a river glori-..103
Lord, I have shut...112
Master, the tempest.102
Peace, perfect peace.489
Sweet peace, the.... 99
The haven of rest...244
Wonderful peace...100
Wonderful peace....101

PRAISE

of Christ:

All glory, laud and..415
All hail, Immanuel!.518
All that thrills my... 65
All things in Jesus..202
Blessed be the name. 16
Blessed Redeemer...128
Christ is King......163
Crown Him with... 77
Face to face........493
Fairest Lord Jesus.. 5
Glory to His name..188
Hallelujah, what a..158
He is so precious...208
How sweet the name.435
I will praise Him... 32
I will sing the......133
It's just like His....218
Jesus is all the......220
Jesus, Rose of......381
My Redeemer.....222
My Savior first of...256
O could I speak.... 20
O for a thousand...456
O Thou God of my.. 15
O Word of God.....319
Oh, how I love Jesus 226
Our great Savior....154
Praise Him! praise.. 19

Revive us again.....268
Since the fullness...233
The great Physician.159
The lily of the......157
The name of Jesus..160
The unveiled Christ.161
We would see Jesus.412
What a wonderful...376
When morning gilds. 1
Whom have I but...380
Why do I sing about.149
Wonderful grace of..470
Wonderful, wonder-.151
Wounded for me....369

of God:

All creatures of our. 24
All people that on... 12
Come, Thou Fount.. 17
Come, we that love.123
Great is Thy.......148
How great Thou art! 34
Joyful, joyful, we... 23
O worship the King. 13
Praise ye the Father.121
To God be the.....127
We gather together.382
We're marching to..126
(See Adoration,
Worship)

PRAYER

Hymns about:

Did you think to....119
From every stormy.104
He will answer prayer 223
Lord, I have shut...112
Sweet hour of prayer 110
Teach me to pray...115
Tell it to Jesus......116
The beautiful garden 117
'Tis the blessed......118
What a Friend......517

Hymns of:

Abide with me......462
Break Thou the.....320
Breathe on me..... 3
Come, ye discon-....201
Dear Lord and.....414
Draw me nearer....265
Guide me, O Thou..475
Have Thine own way 387
Here, O my Lord...436
I am coming, Lord. 52
I am praying for you 109
I am trusting Thee..242
I must tell Jesus....113
I need Thee every...478
Jesus, lover of my..152
Jesus, Savior, pilot..477
Jesus, the very......463
Just a closer walk...485
Lead, kindly Light..277
Lead me to Calvary.337
Lord, I'm coming... 63
Lord, speak to me.273
Love divine, all..... 45
More holiness give..269
More love to Thee. 282
My faith looks up...344
My Jesus, as Thou.. 43
My Jesus, I love....297
Near the cross......407
Nearer, my God, to.272
Nearer, still nearer..267
O Jesus, I have.....274
O Jesus, Thou art... 56
O Master, let me...119
O perfect love......461
O sacred Head, now.338

Open my eyes, that I 278
Pass me not, O..... 51
Precious Lord, take.249
Savior, breathe in..190
Savior, like a......480
Savior, more than...176
Sun of my soul.....422
Take my life, and...388
Take time to be.....342

PROMISES

Beautiful words of..325
Go ye into all the...441
His mighty hand....314
How firm a founda-. 38
Standing on the.....323
What God hath.....474
Where He leads I'll..441
"Whosoever will"...302

PSALMS

A mighty fortress...466
All people that on... 12
Be still, my soul.... 98
Jesus shall reign.... 75
Joy to the world!... 88
O God, our help....467
O worship the King. 13
Surely goodness and.339
The King of love...372
The Lord is my shep-374
The Lord's my shep-.373
The spacious firma-. 25
Thy Word have I...324
Unto the hills......122

PURITY

(See Cleansing,
Holiness of Life)

REDEMPTION

A new name in.....200
Alas! and did my... 94
All glory, laud and.415
Amazing grace.....487
At Calvary........400
At the cross....... 95
Blessed Redeemer..128
My Redeemer.....222
Nor silver nor gold..137
O Thou God of my. 15
Once for all........139
Praise Him! praise.. 19
Redeemed 140
Since I have been..232
There is a green-...340
'Twas Jesus' blood.332
(See Salvation)

REPENTANCE

At Calvary........400
Depth of mercy!....168
(See Confession of Sin)

REVIVAL

Lord, I hear of.....284
O for a closer walk.276
Revive Thy work....114
Revive us again....268
There shall be show-.279

SALVATION

All that thrills my... 65
And can it be that I.107
Arise, my soul......129
Blessed assurance...289
Blessed Redeemer...128
Buried with Christ..318
Christ liveth in me..207

page 503

Depth of mercy!....168
Glory to His name..188
Gone, yes, gone for-.257
He included me.....205
He is able to.......35
He lifted me........209
Heaven came down. 96
How great Thou art! 34
I am His, and He...465
I am not skilled....479
I will sing the won-.133
I've heard the......216
In my heart there... 26
Into my heart.......354
Is my name written.. 60
It took a miracle...135
Jesus saves.........445
My sins are blotted.136
No other plea......193
Nothing but the.....138
O Thou God of my.. 15
Only a sinner.......225
Praise Him! praise.. 19
Rock of ages.......243
Room at the cross...460
Saved! 229
Saved by grace.....471
Saved by the blood.329
Saved, saved!......231
Since I have been...232
Since Jesus came... 29
Springs of living.... 64
Tell me the old, old. 79
The love of the....166
The old rugged cross 317
The solid Rock.....310
There is a fountain. 141
To God be the......127
'Twas a glad day.... 66
When I see the blood 331
"Whosoever" mean-.238
"Whosoever will"..302
Wonderful story of.146
Wonderful words of.326

SANCTIFICATION

Bring your vessels...263
Love divine, all..... 45
(See Holiness of Life)

SECOND COMING
(See Christ: Return)

SECURITY
(See Assurance)

SERVICE

All for Jesus.......394
Anywhere with Jesus 286
Bringing in the.....444
Channels only......398
He'll understand and 484
Help somebody to-..196
His way with thee..385
I'll go where you....399
In the service of....178
It pays to serve.....183
Let the lower lights.181
Lord, speak to me..273
Love lifted me......221
Make me a blessing.184
O Master, let me...429
Open my eyes, that I 278
Others 185
Rescue the perishing.194
Rise up, O men.....351
Seeking the lost....306
So send I you......442
Something for Thee.264
Take my life, and...388
To the work!.......363

We'll work till.....228
Will there be any...503
Work, for the night.120
(See Discipleship,
Missionary)

SERVICE MUSIC

Benedictions:
Amens......Back cover
Father, give Thy
.........Back cover
God be with you....177
Lord, dismiss us....254

Call to Worship:
The Lord is in His
.........Front cover

Doxologies:
All creatures of our. 24
Praise God (Bourgeois)
.........Front cover
Praise God from whom
(Keswick) 24

Gloria Patri:
Glory be to (Greatorex)
.........Front cover
Glory be to (Meineke)
.........Front cover

Offertory Responses:
All things come of Thee
.........Front cover
We give Thee but
(Barnby)..Back cover
We give Thee but
(Schumann) 452

Processionals:
Joyful, joyful, we... 23
O day of rest and... 78
Praise ye the Father.121

SOCIAL RIGHTEOUSNESS

God of our fathers..454
Hail to the bright-..438
I would be true.....260
O beautiful for.....450
We've a story to....449
Where cross the....180

SOLOS

Be still, my soul.... 98
Each step I take....290
God leads us along..473
He died for me.....334
His eye is on the...248
How great Thou art! 34
I love Him because..214
I would be true.....260
I'd rather have.....106
Just a closer walk..485
Near to the heart..464
Precious Lord, take.249
Surely goodness and.339
Sweet will of God...125
Teach me Thy will..124
The love of God....166
The name of Jesus..160
The ninety and nine.197
The Savior is.......308
The Stranger of....162
Trust in the Lord...246
Who at my door is..258
Why do I sing about.149

SORROW
(See Comfort, Trials)

SOUL WINNING

A passion for souls..195
Bring them in....... 22
Bringing in the.....444
I am praying for you 109
Let the lower lights.181
Make me a blessing.184
Make me a channel.186
Must I go, and.....236
Rescue the perishing 194
Ring the bells of.... 28
Seeking the lost.....306
Send the light......447
Throw out the life-.198
Will there be any....503
(See Missionary)

STEWARDSHIP

A charge to keep....362
He'll understand and 484
In the service of....178
Make me a channel.186
Must I go, and.....236
So send I you......442
Take my life, and..388
We give Thee but..452
(See Service)

SUBMISSION

I surrender all......391
My Jesus, as Thou.. 43
O Love that wilt not. 74
Sweet will of God...125
Teach me Thy will..124
Trust and obey.....365
(See Humility)

TEMPTATION

Did you think to....119
Each step I take....290
Hiding in Thee.....389
Higher ground......262
I need Thee every...478
In the hour of......281
My anchor holds....291
My soul, be on thy..350
Never alone!.......312
Yield not to temp-..333

TESTIMONY

A child of the......210
A new name in.....200
All things in Jesus..202
Amazing grace......487
At Calvary.........400
Beulah land........481
Blessed assurance..289
Blessed quietness....108
Christ liveth in me..207
Christ receiveth....204
Constantly abiding.. 42
Glory to His name..188
He included me.....205
He is so precious...208
He lifted me.......209
He lives............164
He wore a crown of.403
He's a Friend of...199
Heavenly sunlight... 27
I am His, and He...465
I belong to the King.212
I heard the voice of. 54
I know whom I have 213
I love Him because.214
I will sing the won-..133
I'd rather have.....106
I've discovered the.239
In tenderness He...371
It is well with my.. 73
Jesus has lifted me!.217

Jesus is all the.....220
Jesus loves even me.234
Jesus paid it all.....131
Love lifted me......221
My anchor holds....291
My Redeemer.......222
My Savior's love....182
My sins are blotted..136
Nailed to the cross.. 33
No other plea......193
Now I belong to....230
O happy day........227
Oh, how I love Jesus 226
Only a sinner.......225
Only Jesus.........153
Saved!.............229
Saved by grace.....471
Saved, saved!......231
Since Jesus came... 29
Springs of living.... 64
Sweeter as the years.235
The haven of rest...244
'Tis so sweet to....241
Trusting Jesus.....245
'Twas a glad day.... 66
'Twas Jesus' blood..332
We have an anchor..287
When the roll is....500
"Whosoever" mean-.238
Wonderful peace....100
(See Witnessing)

THANKFULNESS

Come, ye thankful..509
Count your blessings 516
For the beauty of...457
Now thank we all..508
Rejoice, ye pure in.. 7
We gather together.382

TRIALS

A shelter in the....211
Did you think to...119
Does Jesus care?...384
He keeps me singing 296
Hiding in Thee.....389
How firm a founda-. 38
I must tell Jesus....113
I need Jesus........266
In the hour of......281
Leave it there......383
More love to Thee..282
My anchor holds....291
Never alone!.......312
O, for a faith that.. 6
Our great Savior...154
Tell it to Jesus.....116
The Rock that is...294
The touch of His...427
What a Friend.....517
What God hath....474
Where He leads me.393
(See Burdens)

TRINITY
(See God: Trinity)

TRUST

His eye is on the...248
I am trusting Thee..242
In the hollow of His.251
Jesus is all the.....220
Leaning on the.....292
My Jesus, as Thou.. 43
Only trust Him.....144
Some time we'll un-.496
Surely goodness and.339
The haven of rest...244
The Lord is my shep-374
The Lord's my shep-.373

TOPICAL INDEX

The nail-scarred 316
The solid Rock.....310
'Tis so sweet to.....241
Trust and obey.....365
Trust in the Lord...246
Trusting Jesus......245
(See Assurance)

VICTORY

A mighty fortress...466
Christ arose!.......416
Faith is the victory!.425
God leads us along..473
Hallelujah for the...132
Lead on, O King.... 76
Loyalty to Christ...355
Onward, Christian ..353
Stand up, stand up..358
This is my Father's.458
We gather together..382
(See Warfare,
Christian)

WARFARE, CHRISTIAN

Am I a soldier of...361
As a volunteer......341
Fight the good fight.346
Hold the fort.......345

My soul, be on thy..350
O Jesus, I have.....274
Soldiers of Christ...356
Sound the battle cry.359
Stand up, stand up..357
The banner of the...360
The Son of God....179
True-hearted, whole-364
Who is on the......366
(See Victory)

WEDDING

Channels only......398
Great is Thy........148
Jesus calls us.......343
More love to Thee..282
O Jesus, I have.....274
O Love that wilt not. 74
O perfect love......461
Savior, my heart is..392
Something for Thee.264
Spirit of God, de-... 50
Take my life, and...388

WITNESSING

Accepted in the Be-.499
And can it be that I.107
Heaven came down. 96

I am praying for you 109
I long to glorify....167
I love to tell the....215
I've heard the......216
In my heart there... 26
Jesus saves.........445
My hope is in the... 37
Nor silver nor gold.137
Redeemed 140
Since I have been...232
Sunlight 30
Sunshine in the soul. 31
Sweet peace, the.... 99
The Comforter has.. 49
The light of the.....156
There's a new song. 70
We're marching to..126
When love shines in.143
(See Testimony)

WORSHIP

All hail the power.. 8
All hail the power.. 10
Be still, my soul.... 98
Come, Thou Al-.... 4
Come, we that love.123
Day is dying in the..420
For the beauty of...457
Glorious things of..335

Joyful, joyful, we... 23
Love divine, all..... 45
Now thank we all...508
O day of rest and... 78
O worship the King. 13
Praise ye the Father.121
Rejoice, ye pure in.. 7
Safely through...... 72
The church's one....336
The spacious firma-. 25
We're marching to..126
(See Adoration, Praise)

YOUTH

"Are ye able," said.261
Dare to be a Daniel.512
Give of your best...348
I need Jesus........266
I would be true.....260
I've discovered the..239
Into my heart.......354
Living for Jesus....259
Loyalty to Christ...355
Make me a blessing.184
More like the Master 280
Open my eyes, that I.278
Savior, my heart is..392
Springs of living.... 64
Surely goodness and.339

GENERAL INDEX

A call for loyal soldiers................ 341
A CHARGE TO KEEP I HAVE............. 362
A CHILD OF THE KING.................. 210
A Friend I have called Jesus.......... 218
A MIGHTY FORTRESS IS OUR GOD........ 466
A NEW NAME IN GLORY................. 200
A PASSION FOR SOULS.................. 195
A pilgrim was I and a-wandering...... 339
A ruler once came to Jesus by night.... 147
A SHELTER IN THE TIME OF STORM...... 211
A sinner, lost, condemned was I........ 332
A wonderful Savior is Jesus my Lord.... 247
ABIDE WITH ME....................... 462
ACCEPTED IN THE BELOVED............. 499
ACCORDING TO THY GRACIOUS WORD..... 432
ALAS! AND DID MY SAVIOR BLEED?...... 94
Alas, and did my (AT THE CROSS) 95
ALL CREATURES OF OUR GOD AND KING... 24
ALL FOR JESUS 394
ALL GLORY, LAUD AND HONOR......... 415
ALL HAIL, IMMANUEL!................. 518
ALL HAIL THE POWER OF JESUS' NAME
   (Coronation) 8
ALL HAIL THE POWER OF JESUS' NAME
   (Diadem) 10
ALL HAIL THE POWER OF JESUS' NAME
   (Miles Lane) 9
All hail to Thee, Immanuel........... 518
ALL PEOPLE THAT ON EARTH DO DWELL. 12
All praise to Him who reigns above.... 16
ALL THAT THRILLS MY SOUL........... 65
ALL THE WAY MY SAVIOR LEADS ME..... 472
"All things are ready," come to the feast 305
ALL THINGS COME OF THEE..... Front Cover
ALL THINGS IN JESUS.................. 202
All to Jesus I surrender............... 391
ALMOST PERSUADED.................... 299
AM I A SOLDIER OF THE CROSS?........ 361
AMAZING GRACE...................... 487
AMENS....................... Back Cover
AMERICA (MY COUNTRY, 'TIS OF THEE) . 455
AMERICA THE BEAUTIFUL
   (O BEAUTIFUL FOR SPACIOUS SKIES) 450
AND CAN IT BE THAT I SHOULD GAIN?... 107
ANGELS, FROM THE REALMS OF GLORY... 92
ANYWHERE WITH JESUS................ 286
"ARE YE ABLE," SAID THE MASTER...... 261
Are you looking for the fullness....... 263
ARE YOU WASHED IN THE BLOOD?.. 328
Are you weary, are you heavy-hearted?.. 116
ARISE, MY SOUL, ARISE!.............. 129
ART THOU WEARY, ART THOU LANGUID?. 57
AS A VOLUNTEER...................... 341
AT CALVARY......................... 400
AT THE CROSS....................... 95
AWAY IN A MANGER.................. 93

BATTLE HYMN OF THE REPUBLIC........ 453
Be not dismayed whate'er betide....... 293

BE STILL, MY SOUL...`.................. 98
BEAUTIFUL ISLE OF SOMEWHERE
   (SOME DAY!) 71
BEAUTIFUL WORDS OF JESUS............. 325
BENEATH THE CROSS OF JESUS........... 426
BENEDICTION.................. Back Cover
BEULAH LAND........................ 481
BEYOND THE SUNSET................... 486
BLESSED ASSURANCE..................... 289
BLESSED BE THE NAME.................. 16
BLESSED QUIETNESS.................... 108
BLESSED REDEEMER.................... 128
BLEST BE THE TIE THAT BINDS.......... 430
BREAD OF HEAVEN.................... 433
BREAK THOU THE BREAD OF LIFE........ 320
BREATHE ON ME, BREATH OF GOD........ 3
Brightly beams our Father's mercy..... 181
BRING THEM IN...................... 22
BRING YOUR VESSELS, NOT A FEW....... 263
BRINGING IN THE SHEAVES.............. 444
BURDENS ARE LIFTED AT CALVARY....... 203
BURIED WITH CHRIST.................. 318

CHANNELS ONLY...................... 398
CHRIST AROSE!....................... 416
Christ has for sin atonement made...... 376
CHRIST IS KING...................... 163
Christ Jesus my Lord from heaven came. 214
CHRIST LIVETH IN ME................. 207
Christ my Lord gave all for me........ 167
Christ our Redeemer died on the cross.. 331
CHRIST RECEIVETH SINFUL MEN......... 204
CHRIST RETURNETH................... 170
CHRIST THE LORD IS RISEN TODAY...... 417
Christ, the transforming light.......... 240
CLEANSE ME......................... 252
CLOSE TO THEE....................... 298
Come, every soul by sin oppressed...... 144
Come, friends, sing of the faith....... 163
COME, HOLY SPIRIT................... 406
Come into my heart, blessed Jesus...... 354
COME, THOU ALMIGHTY KING........... 4
COME, THOU FOUNT................... 17
COME TO THE FEAST.................. 305
COME TO THE SAVIOR................. 307
COME, WE THAT LOVE THE LORD....... 123
Come, we that love the Lord
   (WE'RE MARCHING TO ZION) 126
COME, YE DISCONSOLATE.............. 201
COME, YE FAITHFUL, RAISE THE STRAIN... 418
COME, YE THANKFUL PEOPLE, COME..... 509
Coming to Jesus, my Savior........... 101
COMMUNION HYMN.................... 434
CONSTANTLY ABIDING................. 42
COUNT YOUR BLESSINGS............... 516
CROWN HIM WITH MANY CROWNS........ 77

DARE TO BE A DANIEL................. 512
DAY IS DYING IN THE WEST............ 420

Days are filled with sorrow and care.... 203
DEAR LORD AND FATHER OF MANKIND.... 414
Deep in my heart there's a gladness..... 149
DEPTH OF MERCY! CAN THERE BE...... 168
DID YOU THINK TO PRAY?............. 119
DOES JESUS CARE?..................... 384
DON'T TURN THE SAVIOR AWAY......... 309
Down at the cross where my Savior died 188
Down in the valley with my Savior...... 431
DOXOLOGY.................... Front Cover
DRAW ME NEARER..................... 265
DWELLING IN BEULAH LAND............. 206
Dying with Jesus, by death reckoned.... 40

EACH STEP I TAKE.................... 290
Earthly friends may prove untrue...... 165
Earthly pleasures vainly call me........ 270
Encamped along the hills of light....... 425
Ere you left your room this morning... 119
EVEN ME
    (LORD, I HEAR OF SHOWERS OF BLESSING) 284

FACE TO FACE........................ 493
FAIREST LORD JESUS.................. 5
FAITH IS THE VICTORY!............... 425
FAITH OF OUR FATHERS................ 423
FAITH OF OUR MOTHERS............... 424
Far away in the depths of my spirit.... 100
Far away the noise of strife........... 206
Far, far away in heathen darkness...... 441
Father, give Thy benediction.... Back cover
FIGHT THE GOOD FIGHT................ 346
FILL ME NOW........................ 48
FLING OUT THE BANNER! LET IT FLOAT... 437
FOLLOW ON.......................... 431
FOOTPRINTS OF JESUS................. 505
For salvation full and free............ 411
FOR THE BEAUTY OF THE EARTH........ 457
Free from the law, O happy condition.. 139
Friends all around me are trying....... 202
FROM EVERY STORMY WIND............. 104
FROM GREENLAND'S ICY MOUNTAINS...... 443
From over hill and plain.............. 355

Give me a passion for souls, dear Lord.. 195
GIVE ME THY HEART.................. 300
GIVE OF YOUR BEST TO THE MASTER..... 348
GLORIA PATRI.................. Front Cover
GLORIOUS THINGS OF THEE ARE SPOKEN.. 335
GLORY BE TO THE FATHER....... Front Cover
GLORY TO HIS NAME.................. 188
GO YE INTO ALL THE WORLD........... 441
GOD BE WITH YOU.................... 177
God has given you His promise........ 223
God hath not promised skies always blue 474
GOD LEADS US ALONG................ 473
GOD OF OUR FATHERS, WHOSE ALMIGHTY
    HAND............................ 454
GOD WILL TAKE CARE OF YOU......... 293
GONE, YES, GONE FOREVERMORE!....... 257
GRACE GREATER THAN OUR SIN........ 469
GREAT IS THY FAITHFULNESS........... 148

GUIDE ME, O THOU GREAT JEHOVAH.... 475
Guide me, O Thou great Jehovah
    (SONGS OF PRAISES)................. 476

HAIL TO THE BRIGHTNESS............. 438
HALLELUJAH FOR THE CROSS!.......... 132
HALLELUJAH, WHAT A SAVIOR!......... 158
HARK! THE HERALD ANGELS SING....... 81
Hark! 'tis the Shepherd's voice I hear... 22
HAVE THINE OWN WAY, LORD!........ 387
Have thy affections been nailed........ 172
HAVE YOU ANY ROOM FOR JESUS?....... 174
Have you been to Jesus for the........ 328
Have you failed in your plan.......... 316
HE DIED FOR ME.................... 334
HE HIDETH MY SOUL................. 247
HE INCLUDED ME................... 205
HE IS ABLE TO DELIVER THEE.......... 35
HE IS COMING AGAIN................ 171
HE IS SO PRECIOUS TO ME............ 208
HE KEEPS ME SINGING............... 296
HE LEADETH ME.................... 219
HE LIFTED ME..................... 209
HE LIVES.......................... 164
HE THE PEARLY GATES WILL OPEN...... 483
HE TOOK MY SINS AWAY............. 150
HE WILL ANSWER EVERY PRAYER....... 223
HE WORE A CROWN OF THORNS........ 403
HE'LL UNDERSTAND AND SAY "WELL
    DONE"........................... 484
HE'S A FRIEND OF MINE.............. 199
HEAVEN CAME DOWN AND GLORY FILLED
    MY SOUL......................... 96
HEAVENLY SUNLIGHT................. 27
Heav'n and earth proclaim............ 379
HELP SOMEBODY TODAY.............. 196
HERE, O MY LORD, I SEE THEE FACE TO
    FACE............................ 436
HIDING IN THEE.................... 389
HIGHER GROUND.................... 262
HIS EYE IS ON THE SPARROW.......... 248
HIS MIGHTY HAND.................. 314
HIS WAY WITH THEE................. 385
Ho, my comrades! see the signal........ 345
HOLD THE FORT.................... 345
HOLY BIBLE, BOOK DIVINE............ 253
HOLY GHOST, WITH LIGHT DIVINE....... 47
HOLY, HOLY, HOLY.................. 2
HOLY SPIRIT, FAITHFUL GUIDE.......... 46
Hover o'er me, Holy Spirit........... 48
How FIRM A FOUNDATION
    (Foundation) 38
HOW FIRM A FOUNDATION
    (Portuguese Hymn) 39
HOW GREAT THOU ART!.............. 34
How I praise Thee, precious Savior..... 398
HOW SWEET THE NAME OF JESUS SOUNDS. 435

I AM COMING, LORD.................. 52
I AM COMING TO THE CROSS.......... 21
I am happy in the service of the King.. 178
I am happy today and the sun shines... 238

I Am His, and He Is Mine.............. 465
I Am Not Skilled to Understand...... 479
I Am Praying for You................ 109
I Am Resolved....................... 349
I am saved from sin, I have peace..... 314
I am so glad that our Father in heav'n.. 234
I am so happy in Christ today.......... 205
I am Thine, O Lord.................. 265
I am thinking today of that beautiful.. 503
I Am Trusting Thee, Lord Jesus...... 242
I am weak but Thou art strong........ 485
I Belong to the King................. 212
I came to Jesus, weary, worn and sad... 150
I can hear my Savior calling.......... 393
I come to the garden alone........... 428
I don't know about tomorrow.......... 250
I Gave My Life for Thee............. 58
I have a Savior, He's pleading in....... 109
I have a song I love to sing........... 232
I have a song that Jesus gave me....... 26
I have found a friend in Jesus......... 157
I hear the Savior say................. 131
I hear Thy welcome voice............. 52
I Heard the Bells on Christmas Day.. 91
I Heard the Voice of Jesus Say...... 54
I know not why God's wondrous grace.. 213
I Know That My Redeemer Liveth.... 419
I Know Who Holds Tomorrow....... 250
I Know Whom I Have Believed...... 213
I Long to Glorify Thee.............. 167
I Love Him Because He First Loved Me 214
I Love Thy Kingdom, Lord........... 313
I Love to Tell the Story........... 215
I must needs go home by the way of the 402
I Must Tell Jesus................... 113
I Need Jesus......................... 266
I Need Thee Every Hour............. 478
I Never Walk Alone................. 315
I saw One hanging on a tree.......... 334
I serve a risen Savior................ 164
I Shall Be Like Him................ 488
I stand amazed in the presence........ 182
I Surrender All..................... 391
I thirsted in the barren land.......... 64
I wandered in the shades of night...... 30
I was lost in sin when Jesus found me.. 66
I was once a sinner.................. 200
I was sinking deep in sin............. 221
I was straying when Christ found me... 41
I Will Follow Thee.................. 395
I Will Praise Him................... 32
I will sing of my Redeemer.......... 222
I Will Sing the Wondrous Story...... 133
I Won't Have to Cross Jordan Alone.. 506
I Would Be Like Jesus.............. 270
I Would Be True.................... 260
I'd Rather Have Jesus.............. 106
I'll Be a Sunbeam.................. 515
I'll Go Where You Want Me to Go.... 399
I'll Live for Him................... 283
I'll Put Jesus First in My Life....... 396
I'm pressing on the upward way....... 262

I've Discovered the Way of Gladness.. 239
I've Found a Friend.................. 370
I've found a friend who is all to me.... 231
I've found a refuge.................. 153
I've Heard the King................. 216
I've reached the land of corn and wine.. 481
I've seen the lightning flashing........ 312
I've wandered far away from God...... 63
If Jesus Goes with Me................ 397
If Jesus Had Not Come!............. 368
If the world from you withhold........ 383
If, when you give the best of your..... 484
If you are tired of the load of your..... 55
If you from sin are longing to be free.. 53
In fancy I stood by the shore.......... 162
In loving kindness Jesus came......... 209
In My Heart There Rings a Melody.. 26
In shady, green pastures, so rich....... 473
In Tenderness He Sought Me.......... 371
"In the Beloved" accepted am I........ 499
In the Cross of Christ................ 408
In the Garden...................... 428
In the Hollow of His Hand.......... 251
In the Hour of Trial................ 281
In the land of fadeless day........... 492
In the Service of the King........... 178
In Times Like These................. 352
Into My Heart....................... 354
Is My Name Written There?......... 60
Is Thy Heart Right with God?........ 172
Is Your All on the Altar?.......... 390
Is your life a channel of blessing...... 186
It Came Upon the Midnight Clear..... 84
It Is Well with My Soul.............. 73
It may be at morn, when the day...... 170
It may be in the valley............... 397
It may not be on the mountain's height. 399
It Pays to Serve Jesus.............. 183
It Took a Miracle................... 135
It's Just Like His Great Love........ 218
Ivory Palaces....................... 375

Jerusalem the Golden................ 507
Jesus, and Shall It Ever Be?......... 111
Jesus Bids Us Shine.................. 347
Jesus Calls Us....................... 343
Jesus Christ Is Lord of All........... 379
Jesus comes with pow'r to gladden..... 143
Jesus Has Lifted Me!................. 217
Jesus, I Come....................... 295
Jesus, I My Cross Have Taken........ 271
Jesus Is All the World to Me........ 220
Jesus Is Calling...................... 59
Jesus Is Coming Again................ 173
Jesus is coming to earth again.......... 175
Jesus is standing in Pilate's hall....... 304
Jesus is tenderly calling thee home..... 59
Jesus Is the Sweetest Name I Know.... 36
Jesus, keep me near the cross.......... 407
Jesus, Lover of My Soul............. 152
Jesus Loves Even Me................. 234
Jesus Loves Me...................... 513

Jesus my Lord will love me forever.... 230
JESUS NEVER FAILS..................... 165
JESUS ONLY, LET ME SEE.............. 411
JESUS PAID IT ALL.................. 131
JESUS, REVEALED IN ME.............. 240
JESUS, ROSE OF SHARON................ 381
JESUS SAVES......................... 445
JESUS, SAVIOR....................... 192
JESUS, SAVIOR, PILOT ME.............. 477
JESUS SHALL REIGN................... 75
JESUS, THE VERY THOUGHT OF THEE..... 463
JESUS, THY BLOOD AND RIGHTEOUSNESS... 169
Jesus wants me for a sunbeam......... 515
Jesus! what a Friend for sinners!....... 154
JEWELS............................. 511
JOY TO THE WORLD!................... 88
JOYFUL, JOYFUL, WE ADORE THEE...... 23
Joys are flowing like a river............ 108
JUST A CLOSER WALK WITH THEE....... 485
Just a few more days to be filled with... 502
JUST AS I AM....................... 62
JUST WHEN I NEED HIM MOST.......... 285

King of my life, I crown Thee now..... 337
KNEEL AT THE CROSS................. 405

LEAD, KINDLY LIGHT.................. 277
LEAD ME TO CALVARY................ 337
LEAD ON, O KING ETERNAL........... 76
LEANING ON THE EVERLASTING ARMS...... 292
LEAVE IT THERE..................... 383
LET HIM IN......................... 68
LET JESUS COME INTO YOUR HEART...... 55
LET THE LOWER LIGHTS BE BURNING..... 181
Lift up your heads, pilgrims aweary... 171
LIKE A RIVER GLORIOUS.............. 103
LIVING FOR JESUS.................... 259
Look all around you, find someone in.. 196
LOOK TO THE LAMB OF GOD........... 53
LORD, DISMISS US WITH THY BLESSING.... 254
Lord, help me live from day to day..... 185
Lord, I care not for riches............. 60
LORD, I HAVE SHUT THE DOOR........ 112
LORD, I HEAR OF SHOWERS OF BLESSING.. 284
LORD, I'M COMING HOME............. 63
Lord Jesus, I long to be perfectly...... 145
LORD, SPEAK TO ME.................. 273
LOVE DIVINE, ALL LOVES EXCELLING.... 45
Love divine, so great and wondrous.... 483
LOVE LED HIM TO CALVARY........... 134
Love led the Savior in days long ago.... 134
LOVE LIFTED ME..................... 221
Loved with everlasting love............ 465
Low in the grave He lay.............. 416
LOYALTY TO CHRIST.................. 355

MACEDONIA......................... 440
MAJESTIC SWEETNESS SITS ENTHRONED.... 130
MAKE ME A BLESSING................ 184
MAKE ME A CHANNEL OF BLESSING...... 186
"Man of Sorrows," what a name....... 158
Mankind is searching every day....... 239

Marvelous grace of our loving Lord.... 469
Marvelous message we bring.......... 173
MASTER, THE TEMPEST IS RAGING....... 102
Mine eyes have seen the glory......... 453
MOMENT BY MOMENT................. 40
MORE ABOUT JESUS.................. 275
MORE HOLINESS GIVE ME............. 269
MORE LIKE THE MASTER.............. 280
MORE LOVE TO THEE................. 282
MUST I GO, AND EMPTY-HANDED?...... 236
MUST JESUS BEAR THE CROSS ALONE?.... 189
MY ANCHOR HOLDS.................. 291
MY COUNTRY, 'TIS OF THEE........... 455
My faith has found a resting place...... 193
MY FAITH LOOKS UP TO THEE.......... 344
My Father is omnipotent............. 135
My Father is rich in houses and lands.. 210
My hope is built on nothing less....... 310
MY HOPE IS IN THE LORD............. 37
MY JESUS, AS THOU WILT!............ 43
MY JESUS, I LOVE THEE.............. 297
My life, my love, I give to Thee....... 283
My Lord has garments so wondrous fine 375
MY REDEEMER....................... 222
MY SAVIOR FIRST OF ALL............. 256
MY SAVIOR'S LOVE.................. 182
MY SINS ARE BLOTTED OUT, I KNOW!.... 136
MY SOUL, BE ON THY GUARD.......... 350
My soul in sad exile was out on life's... 244
My stubborn will at last hath yielded... 125

NAILED TO THE CROSS................ 33
Naught have I gotten but what I....... 225
NEAR THE CROSS.................... 407
NEAR TO THE HEART OF GOD.......... 464
NEARER, MY GOD, TO THEE........... 272
NEARER, STILL NEARER............... 267
NEARER THE CROSS.................. 409
NEVER ALONE!...................... 312
NO NIGHT THERE.................... 492
NO, NOT ONE!...................... 224
NO ONE UNDERSTANDS LIKE JESUS...... 404
NO OTHER PLEA.................... 193
NOR SILVER NOR GOLD.............. 137
Not now, but in the coming years...... 496
NOTHING BETWEEN................... 386
NOTHING BUT THE BLOOD............. 138
NOW I BELONG TO JESUS............. 230
Now let songs of triumph swell loud.... 257
NOW THANK WE ALL OUR GOD........ 508
NOW THE DAY IS OVER.............. 421

O BEAUTIFUL FOR SPACIOUS SKIES...... 450
O COME, ALL YE FAITHFUL........... 83
O COULD I SPEAK................... 20
O DAY OF REST AND GLADNESS........ 78
O FOR A CLOSER WALK WITH GOD...... 276
O, FOR A FAITH THAT WILL NOT SHRINK.. 6
O FOR A THOUSAND TONGUES TO SING.... 456
O GOD, OUR HELP IN AGES PAST....... 467
O HAPPY DAY....................... 227
O JESUS, I HAVE PROMISED.......... 274

O Jesus, Thou Art Standing........... 56
O land of rest, for thee I sigh!........ 228
O Little Town of Bethlehem........ 82
O Lord my God! when I in awesome.... 34
O Love That Wilt Not Let Me Go... 74
O Master, Let Me Walk with Thee... 429
O Perfect Love.................... 461
O Sacred Head, Now Wounded....... 338
O safe to the Rock that is higher...... 389
O sometimes the shadows are deep..... 294
O soul, are you weary and troubled?.... 155
O spread the tidings 'round.......... 49
O That Will Be Glory.............. 494
O Thou God of My Salvation........ 15
O Thou, in Whose Presence.......... 105
O to Be Like Thee!................. 18
O what a wonderful, wonderful day.... 96
O Word of God Incarnate........... 319
O Worship the King................ 13
O Zion, Haste..................... 446
Of Jesus' love that sought me......... 235
Ofttimes the day seems long.......... 504
Oh, How I Love Jesus............... 226
Oh, say, can you see, by the dawn's.... 451
On a hill far away.................. 317
On Jordan's Stormy Banks........... 490
On this holy Lord's day morning...... 434
Once far from God and dead in sin.... 207
Once for All...................... 139
Once my life was filled with discord.... 70
Once my way was dark and dreary.... 233
Once our blessed Christ of beauty...... 161
One Day!......................... 377
Only a Sinner..................... 225
Only Jesus....................... 153
Only Trust Him................... 144
Onward, Christian Soldiers.......... 353
Open My Eyes, That I May See..... 278
Others........................... 185
Our God hath given promise......... 251
Our Great Savior.................. 154
Out in the highways and byways of life 184
Out of my bondage, sorrow and night.. 295
Out of the depths to the glory above.... 217

Pass Me Not, O Gentle Savior........ 51
Peace, Perfect Peace................ 489
Praise God, from whom....... Front Cover
Praise Him, All Ye Little Children... 514
Praise Him! praise Him!............ 19
Praise Him, praise Him, all ye little.... 514
Praise Ye the Father............... 121
Praise Ye the Lord, the Almighty..... 14
Precious Hiding Place.............. 41
Precious Lord, Take My Hand....... 249

Redeemed......................... 140
Rejoice, Ye Pure in Heart........... 7
Rescue the Perishing............... 194
Revive Thy Work.................. 114
Revive Us Again................... 268
Ring the Bells of Heaven........... 28

Rise Up, O Men of God.............. 351
Rock of Ages...................... 243
Room at the Cross for You.......... 460

Safe in the Arms of Jesus........... 44
Safely Through Another Week....... 72
Saved!........................... 229
Saved by Grace................... 471
Saved by the Blood................ 329
Saved, Saved!..................... 231
Savior, Breathe an Evening Blessing... 190
Savior, I will follow Thee........... 395
Savior, Like a Shepherd Lead Us...... 480
Savior, More Than Life to Me....... 176
Savior, My Heart Is Thine.......... 392
Savior, Thy dying love.............. 264
Search me, O God.................. 252
Seeking the Lost.................. 306
Send the Light.................... 447
Shall We Gather at the River?....... 491
Silent Night! Holy Night!........... 87
Simply trusting ev'ry day............ 245
Since I Have Been Redeemed......... 232
Since Jesus Came into My Heart..... 29
Since the Fullness of His Love Came In 233
Sing the wondrous love of Jesus........ 501
Sing them over again to me.......... 326
Sinners Jesus will receive........... 204
So precious is Jesus, my Savior......... 208
So Send I You..................... 442
Softly and Tenderly Jesus Is Calling.. 303
Soldiers of Christ, Arise!............ 356
Some Day!........................ 71
Some day the silver cord will break.... 471
Some glorious morning sorrow will.... 495
Some Golden Daybreak............. 495
Some Time We'll Understand........ 496
Something for Thee................ 264
Somewhere the sun is shining......... 71
Songs of Praises................... 476
Sooner or Later................... 482
Sound the Battle Cry.............. 359
Sowing in the morning.............. 444
Spirit of God, Descend upon My Heart 50
Springs of Living Water............. 64
Stand Up, Stand Up for Jesus (Geibel) 357
Stand Up, Stand Up for Jesus (Webb) 358
Standing by a purpose true.......... 512
Standing on the Promises.......... 323
Stepping in the Light.............. 459
Still, Still with Thee.............. 11
Sun of My Soul.................... 422
Sunlight......................... 30
Sunshine in the Soul.............. 31
Surely Goodness and Mercy......... 339
Sweet are the promises.............. 401
Sweet By and By................... 497
Sweet Hour of Prayer.............. 110
Sweet Peace, the Gift of God's Love.. 99
Sweet Will of God................. 125
Sweeter as the Years Go By......... 235
Sweetly, Lord, have we heard Thee..... 505

GENERAL INDEX

'AKE MY LIFE, AND LET IT BE......... 388
'AKE THE NAME OF JESUS WITH YOU..... 378
'AKE TIME TO BE HOLY.............. 342
'EACH ME THY WILL, O LORD......... 124
'EACH ME TO PRAY.................. 115
'ELL IT TO JESUS..................... 116
'ELL ME THE OLD, OLD STORY.......... 79
'ELL ME THE STORIES OF JESUS........ 191
'ELL ME THE STORY OF JESUS.......... 237
'EN THOUSAND ANGELS................ 410
'HE BANNER OF THE CROSS............. 360
'HE BEAUTIFUL GARDEN OF PRAYER..... 117
'HE BIBLE STANDS.................... 322
'HE CHILDREN'S FRIEND IS JESUS........ 510
'HE CHURCH IN THE WILDWOOD......... 367
'HE CHURCH'S ONE FOUNDATION........ 336
'HE COMFORTER HAS COME........... 49
'he cross it standeth fast.............. 132
'he cross upon which Jesus died....... 460
'HE FIRST NOEL..................... 90
'HE GREAT PHYSICIAN................ 159
'HE HAVEN OF REST................. 244
'HE HEAVENLY VISION................ 155
'HE KING OF LOVE MY SHEPHERD IS... 372
'HE LIGHT OF THE WORLD IS JESUS...... 156
'HE LILY OF THE VALLEY............. 157
'HE LORD IS IN HIS HOLY...... Front Cover
'HE LORD IS MY SHEPHERD........... 374
'HE LORD'S MY SHEPHERD............ 373
'he Lord's our Rock, in Him we hide.. 211
'HE LOVE OF GOD.................. 166
'HE NAIL-SCARRED HAND............. 316
'HE NAME OF JESUS................. 160
'HE NINETY AND NINE............... 197
'HE OLD RUGGED CROSS.............. 317
'HE REGIONS BEYOND................ 448
'HE ROCK THAT IS HIGHER THAN I.... 294
'HE SANDS OF TIME................. 255
'he Savior is calling, is calling........ 309
'HE SAVIOR IS WAITING.............. 308
'he service of Jesus true pleasure...... 183
'HE SOLID ROCK.................... 310
'HE SON OF GOD GOES FORTH TO WAR... 179
'HE SPACIOUS FIRMAMENT ON HIGH...... 25
'HE STAR-SPANGLED BANNER........... 451
'HE STRANGER OF GALILEE............ 162
'HE TOUCH OF HIS HAND ON MINE..... 427
'he trial of the cross was approaching.. 439
'HE UNVEILED CHRIST................ 161
'he vision of a dying world.......... 440
'HE WAY OF THE CROSS LEADS HOME.... 402
'he whole world was lost in the...... 156
'he world all about me has now...... 396
'here are days so dark that I seek..... 427
'here comes to my heart one sweet.... 99
'here have been names that I have.... 36
'HERE IS A FOUNTAIN................. 141
'HERE IS A GREEN HILL FAR AWAY...... 340
'here is a name I love to hear........ 226
'here is a place of quiet rest......... 464
'here is never a day so dreary......... 151
'HERE IS POWER IN THE BLOOD......... 330

THERE SHALL BE SHOWERS OF BLESSING.. 279
There was One who was willing to die.. 33
There were ninety and nine........... 197
There's a call comes ringing.......... 447
There's a church in the valley........ 367
There's a garden where Jesus is waiting 117
There's a land that is fairer than day.. 497
THERE'S A NEW SONG IN MY HEART...... 70
There's a peace in my heart.......... 42
There's a royal banner given.......... 360
THERE'S A SONG IN THE AIR........... 85
There's a Stranger at the door........ 68
THERE'S A WIDENESS IN GOD'S MERCY.... 468
There's not a friend like the lowly.... 224
There's sunshine in my soul today..... 31
There's within my heart a melody...... 296
They bound the hands of Jesus........ 410
THIS DO IN REMEMBRANCE OF ME...... 439
THIS IS MY FATHER'S WORLD........... 458
Tho' the angry surges roll........... 291
Tho' the way we journey may be...... 498
THOU DIDST LEAVE THY THRONE........ 89
Thou, my everlasting portion.......... 298
THOUGH YOUR SINS BE AS SCARLET..... 142
THROW OUT THE LIFE-LINE............. 198
THY HOLY SPIRIT, LORD, ALONE........ 97
THY WORD HAVE I HID IN MY HEART.. 324
Thy Word is a lamp to my feet....... 324
THY WORD IS LIKE A GARDEN, LORD.... 327
'TIS MIDNIGHT; AND ON OLIVE'S BROW... 321
'TIS SO SWEET TO TRUST IN JESUS...... 241
'TIS THE BLESSED HOUR OF PRAYER..... 118
'Tis the grandest theme thro' the ages.. 35
TO GOD BE THE GLORY.............. 127
To the regions beyond I must go....... 448
TO THE WORK!.................... 363
TRUE-HEARTED, WHOLE-HEARTED........ 364
TRUST AND OBEY.................... 365
TRUST IN THE LORD................. 246
TRUSTING JESUS.................... 245
Trying to walk in the steps of the..... 459
'TWAS A GLAD DAY WHEN JESUS FOUND
ME............................. 66
'Twas God's own Son who came to earth 403
'TWAS JESUS' BLOOD................. 332

UNDER HIS WINGS................... 311
UNTO THE HILLS.................... 122
Up Calvary's mountain one dreadful.... 128

Walking in sunlight, all of my journey. 27
WE GATHER TOGETHER................ 382
WE GIVE THEE BUT THINE OWN
(Barnby)....................Back Cover
WE GIVE THEE BUT THINE OWN
(Schumann)...................... 452
WE HAVE AN ANCHOR............... 287
We have heard the joyful sound........ 445
We praise Thee, O God, for the Son.... 268
WE SHALL SEE THE KING SOME DAY..... 498
WE THREE KINGS OF ORIENT ARE........ 80

GENERAL INDEX

We Would See Jesus................ 412
We'll Work till Jesus Comes......... 228
We're Marching to Zion............. 126
We've a Story to Tell to the Nations 449
What a fellowship, what a joy divine... 292
What a Friend We Have in Jesus...... 517
What a wonderful change in my life.... 29
What a Wonderful Savior!.......... 376
What a wondrous message in God's.... 136
What can wash away my sin?........ 138
What God Hath Promised........... 474
What If It Were Today?............ 175
What Will You Do with Jesus?...... 304
When all my labors and trials........ 494
When He cometh, when He cometh.... 511
When I come to the river at ending.... 506
When I saw the cleansing fountain..... 32
When I See My Savior............. 288
When I See the Blood.............. 331
When I shall reach the more excellent.. 488
When I Survey the Wondrous Cross... 413
When Jesus comes to reward His....... 187
When Love Shines In................ 143
When Morning Gilds the Skies........ 1
When my lifework is ended........... 256
When peace, like a river............. 73
When the Roll Is Called Up Yonder.. 500
When the trumpet of the Lord shall.... 500
When upon life's billows you are..... 516
When We All Get to Heaven....... 501
When We See Christ................. 504
When we walk with the Lord......... 365
Where Cross the Crowded Ways of Life................................. 180
Where He Leads I'll Follow.......... 401
Where He Leads Me................. 393
Where the Gates Swing Outward Never 502

While Shepherds Watched Their Flocks 8
While we pray and while we plead..... 30
Whiter Than Snow.................. 14
Who at My Door Is Standing?........ 25
Who can cheer the heart like Jesus.... 6
Who Is on the Lord's Side?.......... 36
Whom Have I But Thee?............. 38
Whom have I on earth, Lord Jesus..... 38
"Whosoever heareth," shout........... 30
"Whosoever" Meaneth Me............ 23
"Whosoever Will"................... 30
Why Do I Sing About Jesus?......... 14
Why Do You Wait?.................. 6
Why Not Now?..................... 30
Why should I charge my soul with care 19
Why should I feel discouraged........ 24
Will Jesus Find Us Watching?........ 18
Will There Be Any Stars?........... 50
Will your anchor hold in the storms.... 28
Wonderful Grace of Jesus........... 47
Wonderful Peace (Cornell) 10
Wonderful Peace (Lillenas) 10
Wonderful Story of Love............. 14
Wonderful, Wonderful Jesus.......... 15
Wonderful Words of Life............. 32
Work, for the Night Is Coming....... 12
Would you be free from the burden.... 33
Would you live for Jesus............. 38
Wounded for Me.................... 36

Ye Must Be Born Again............. 14
Ye Servants of God, Your Master Proclaim.......................... 6
Years I spent in vanity and pride...... 40
Yield Not to Temptation............ 33
You have longed for sweet peace....... 39
You May Have the Joy-Bells......... 6